ECONOMICS OF RESEARCH AND DEVELOPMENT

*A Publication of the Mershon Center
For Education in National Security*

ECONOMICS of RESEARCH and DEVELOPMENT

Edited by Richard A. Tybout

Ohio State University Press

"The Process of Technical Change," by Edwin Mansfield,
was first published in "Economic Analysis and Policy,"
edited by Myron Joseph, Norton Seeber, and G. L. Bach.
Copyright © 1963 by Prentice-Hall, Inc. Used by
permission of the publisher.

A somewhat shortened version of "The Allocation of
Research and Development Resources: Some Problems of
Public Policy," by Richard R. Nelson, was first
published in German under the title "Forschungsmittel
und öffentliches Interesse" in "Atomzeitalter."

"Policy Issues Involved in the Conduct of Military
Development Programs," by Burton H. Klein, was first
published by the Rand Corporation.

ACKNOWLEDGMENTS

IT IS WITH PLEASURE that I reflect on the genesis of this collection of essays. The papers which constitute the present volume were first presented at the Ohio State University Conference on Economics of Research and Development, October, 1962. The conference had been organized to bring together my friends from Germany and the United States for an exchange of views and information on the economics of research and development.

Dr. Helmut Krauch was organizing, in early 1962, a group of German scholars, physical and social scientists, to make an itinerant study of social aspects of research and development in the United States. I simultaneously proposed a series of conference topics to him and to a number of friends in this country. The response was encouraging. The program grew with the evident interest of scholars working in the area. The U.S. National Science Foundation and the Ohio State University Mershon Committee on Education in National Security provided financial assistance. Additional funds came from the registration fees paid by the group of academic and industrial participants in the conference who constituted an interested, active audience.

Foremost among those to give interest and encouragement were, of course, the contributors whose names and works appear in the succeeding pages of this volume. Special acknowledgment is also due several persons who helped conduct the conference: Professor Dr.-Ing. Siegfried Balke, Minister of Atomic Energy, Federal Republic of Germany, who served as chairman in Part VI and as an interested participant throughout; Dr. J. Herbert Hollomon, Assistant Secretary of Commerce for Science and Technology, for a most interesting banquet address (published herein) and ensuing discussion; Dr. Frederic W. Heimberger, for his kind offices on several occasions and his challenging introductory remarks; Dean Robert J. Nordstrom, who chaired Part V and implemented the conduct of the conference in other ways; and Dean James R. McCoy, who chaired the evening session. Persons serving as chairmen of other sessions are represented among the contributors. Their help above and beyond the call of duty was crucial for the success of the conference. Professor Edison L. Bowers and the Battelle group, represented by John S. Crout, vice-president, Battelle Memorial Institute, gave the project special interest and support.

Assistance of a very tangible sort was rendered by my friend Harold B. Pepinsky, professor of psychology, in the editing of the Part III papers. For extensive help with mechanical and clerical matters, the undersigned thanks Dean William E. Schlender and his staff and Mrs. Martha Mounts and her staff.

RICHARD A. TYBOUT

CONTENTS

INTRODUCTION   *Richard A. Tybout*   3

PART I: HISTORY OF SCIENCE

CATASTROPHE AND UTILITARIANISM IN THE DEVELOPMENT
OF BASIC SCIENCE   *Jacob Schmookler*   19

HISTORIC CHANGES IN THE DIVISION OF LABOR IN
EUROPEAN RESEARCH   *Hans P. Bahrdt*   34

    Comment on Bahrdt and Schmookler
      Everett Mendelsohn   51

    Comment on Bahrdt and Schmookler
      Melvin Kranzberg   59

PART II: INDUSTRIAL RESEARCH AND DEVELOPMENT

ECONOMIC ANALYSIS AND THE RESEARCH AND DEVELOPMENT
DECISION   *Jesse W. Markham*   67

    Comment on Markham
      W. Eric Gustafson   81

R&D DIFFERENCES AMONG INDUSTRIES   *Yale Brozen*   83

ENGINEERING AND PRODUCTIVITY CHANGE: SUSPENSION-
BRIDGE STIFFENING TRUSSES   *Robert S. Merrill*   101

Comment on Brozen and Merrill
  Frederic M. Scherer   128

Comment on Merrill and Brozen
  Edward Ames   132

THE PROCESS OF TECHNICAL CHANGE   Edwin Mansfield   136

Comment on Mansfield
  Zvi Griliches   148

PART III: INTERNAL ORGANIZATION

THE PERSONALITY FACTOR IN RESEARCH PLANNING
  Paul Matussek   153

HIERARCHY OR TEAM? CONSIDERATIONS ON THE ORGANI-
ZATION OF R&D CO-OPERATIVES   Horst Rittel   174

IDEA FLOW AND PROJECT SELECTION IN SEVERAL INDUS-
TRIAL RESEARCH AND DEVELOPMENT LABORATORIES
  Albert H. Rubenstein and Richard C. Hannenberg   219

Comment on Part III Papers
  Harold B. Pepinsky   245

PART IV: PUBLIC POLICY

Special Address: SCIENCE AND INNOVATION
  The Honorable J. Herbert Hollomon,
  Assistant Secretary of Commerce
    for Science and Technology   251

CLASSIFICATION OF SOCIAL COSTS AND SOCIAL BENEFITS
IN RESEARCH AND DEVELOPMENT
  Bruno Fritsch, Helmut Krauch, and Richard A. Tybout 258

APPROPRIATE GOVERNMENT AND PRIVATE RESEARCH ROLES
IN A MIXED ECONOMY   *Irving H. Siegel*   268

THE ALLOCATION OF RESEARCH AND DEVELOPMENT
RESOURCES: SOME PROBLEMS OF PUBLIC POLICY
   Richard R. Nelson   288

PART V: MILITARY RESEARCH
AND DEVELOPMENT

POLICY ISSUES INVOLVED IN THE CONDUCT OF MILITARY
DEVELOPMENT PROGRAMS   *Burton H. Klein*   309

THE INTERACTION OF GOVERNMENT AND CONTRACTOR
ORGANIZATIONS IN WEAPONS ACQUISITION
   Paul W. Cherington   327

      Comment on Part V Papers
         J. Stefan Dupré   344

PART VI: INTERNATIONAL
COLLABORATION

U.S.–EURATOM COLLABORATION: AN EXPERIMENT IN
INTERNATIONAL RESEARCH AND DEVELOPMENT
   Philip Mullenbach   353

SYSTEM AND FUNCTIONS OF EURATOM   *Hans K. Sauer*   368

      Comment on Mullenbach and Sauer
         Jaroslav G. Polach   381

THE MUTUAL WEAPONS DEVELOPMENT PROGRAM
   Richard U. Sherman, Jr.   386

      Comment on Sherman, Mullenbach, and Sauer
         Foster Lee Smith   401

PART VII: THE EMERGENT NATIONS

ECONOMICS OF TECHNOLOGY FOR LESS-DEVELOPED AREAS
  Richard A. Tybout   409

RESEARCH AND DEVELOPMENT FOR THE EMERGENT NATIONS
  Kenneth E. Boulding   422

  Comment on Boulding
    Bruno Fritsch   438

  Comment on Part VII Papers
    Harold J. Barnett   443

INDEX TO AUTHORS CITED   451

SUBJECT INDEX   454

FIGURES

Fig. 1.—Graph presentation of the relationships in "hierarchy" and "team."   182

Fig. 2a.—Systematic search.   2b.—Comparison of duration of search.   198

Fig. 3.—Probability of success for group problem-solving.   3a.—Influence of number of participants upon probability of group success.   3b.—Influence of number of steps upon probability of group success.   3c.—Dependence of probability of group success on the probability of success for the individual.   202

Fig. 4.—Flow-graph representation of a problem-solving procedure.   4a.—Explanation of symbols. 4b.—Transfer function of a trial-and-error procedure.   4c.—Example of the flow in a problem-solving procedure.   206

Fig. 5.—Representation of a system-design co-operative.   5a.—Composition of a matrix representing the co-operative.   5b.—Example of a system-design co-operative.   5c.—Example of a system-design co-operative.   213

Fig. 6.—Idea-flow model.   220

Fig. 7.—Idea-flow questionnaire.   224

Fig. 8.—Idea-flow: results from pretest. Number of projects in each classification and estimated number of man months to complete each project.   234

Fig. 9.—Estimated time required to complete R&D
projects, by company name and idea-classification
code.   235

Fig. 10.—Estimated time to complete projects—summary for twelve managers representing companies
1, 2, 3, 5, 6, 7, 8, 9, 10, 12, 13, and 14.   237

Fig. 11.—Number of ideas received and estimated
number of man months required to complete projects—summary for twelve managers. Companies
1, 2, 3, 5, 6, 7, 8, 9, 10, 12, 13, and 14.   238

TABLES

1. Structure of Six Industries Accounting for Three-quarters of All Industrial Research in 1951   68

2. Research and Development in Relation to GNP, 1930 and 1945-59 (Selected Years)   76

3. Research Performed and Financed, 1951-60 (Dollar Amounts, Percentage of Sales and of Investments)   85

4. Research Expenditures as a Percentage of Sales, by Industry, 1927-60   93

5. Basic Research Performance, by Industry, 1953, 1956, and 1960   98

6. Company 20: Active Projects, February 28, 1962, Classified by Idea Type and Distributed to the Period in Which Work Started   229

7. Company 20: Distribution of Projects by Estimated Time for Completion and Period in Which Work Started   230

8. Managerial Positions of Twelve Men Who Pre-tested the Modified Questionnaire (by Company Number)   232

9. Consultation Patterns in Two Departments of a Company   240

CONTRIBUTORS

EDWARD AMES, professor of economics, Purdue University. Author: *Soviet Economic Processes* (Homewood, Illinois, 1965); articles on Soviet economics, economic theory, and technological change.

HANS P. BAHRDT, professor of sociology, University of Göttingen. Author: (with others) *Technik und Industriearbeit* (Tübingen, 1957); (with others) *Das Gesellschaftsbild des Arbeiters* (Tübingen, 1957); *Industriebürokratie* (Stuttgart, 1958); articles on technology and industrial labor.

HAROLD J. BARNETT, professor of economics, Washington University. Author: *Energy Uses and Supplies* (Washington, D. C., 1950); (with Chandler Morse) *Scarcity and Growth* (Baltimore, Maryland, 1963); articles on energy economics, technological change, and economic development.

KENNETH E. BOULDING, professor of economics and research director, Center for Research on Conflict Resolution, University of Michigan. John Bates Clark Medal, American Economic Association, 1949; fellow, Center for Advanced Study in Behavioral Sciences, 1954–55; fellow, American Academy of Sciences; fellow, American Philosophical Society; American Council of Learned Societies Prize for Distinguished Scholarship in the Humanities, 1962. Author: *Economic Analysis* (4th ed.; New York, 1965); *A Reconstruction of Economics* (New York, 1950); *The Organizational Revolution* (New York, 1953); *Principles of Economic Policy* (Englewood Cliffs, 1959); *Conflict and Defense* (New York, 1962); *The Meaning of the Twentieth Century* (New York, 1964); other books, pamphlets, and articles on religion, human values, economic theory, conflict resolution, collective decision-making, and other topics.

YALE BROZEN, professor of business economics, director, Research Management Program, and director, Summer Program in Applied Economics for College Teachers of Economics, Graduate School of Business, University of Chicago. Author of articles on industrial research and development, productivity, and economic theory.

PAUL W. CHERINGTON, James J. Hill Professor of Transportation and research director, Weapons Acquisition Research Project, Graduate School of Business Administration, Harvard University. Author: *Airline Price Policy* (Boston, 1958); (with R. Gilbeu) *The Business Representative in Washington* (Washington, D. C., 1958); articles on public regulation and national security.

J. STEFAN DUPRÉ, associate professor of political economy, University of Toronto. Author: (with S. A. Lakoff) *Science and the Nation: Policy and Politics* (Englewood Cliffs, 1962); articles on defense contracting.

ZVI GRILICHES, professor of economics, University of Chicago. Phi Beta Kappa; Jesse D. Carr Fellow in Agriculture; research training fellow, Social Science Research Council; Award of Merit, American Farm Economics Association, 1957, 1959, 1960; faculty research fellow, Ford Foundation, 1963–64; fellow, Econometric Society. Author of articles on statistical measurement of productivity, technological change, and related subjects.

BRUNO FRITSCH, professor of political economy, Heidelberg University. Author: *Die Geld und Kredittheorie von Karl Marx* (Zurich, 1954); *Geschichte und Theorie der Amerikanischen Stabilisierungspolitik 1933–39 und 1946–53* (Zurich, 1959); articles on economic policy, planning, and development.

W. ERIC GUSTAFSON, research adviser, Institute of Development Economics, Karachi, Pakistan. Author of articles on the economics of research and development.

RICHARD HANNENBERG, research assistant, Department of Industrial Engineering and Management Sciences, Northwestern University.

J. HERBERT HOLLOMON, assistant secretary of commerce for science and technology. Sigma Xi; Rossiter W. Raymond Award, American Institute of Mining Engineers, 1946; Alfred Nobel Prize, 1947; Rosenheim Medal, British Institute of Metals, 1958; fellow, American Academy of Arts and Sciences, and American Physical Society. Author: *Problem of Fracture: A Report to the Welding Research Council* (New York, 1946); (with Leonard Jaffe) *Ferrous Metallurgical Design* (New York, 1947); articles on topics in metallurgy and on science policy.

BURTON H. KLEIN, head, Economics Department, RAND Corporation. David A. Wells Prize, Harvard, 1952–53. Author: *Germany's Economic Preparations for War* (Cambridge, Massachusetts, 1959); other works on economics of national security and research and development.

MELVIN KRANZBERG, professor of history and director of the Graduate Program in Science, Technology, and Society, Case Institute of Technology; secretary, Society for the History of Technology; editor-in-chief, *Technology and Culture.* Author of *The Siege of Paris, 1870–1871* (Ithaca, New York, 1950); *1848—A Turning Point?* (Boston, 1959); and articles on European history, the Industrial Revolution, and other aspects of the history of science and technology.

HELMUT KRAUCH, director, Studiengruppe für Systemforschung, Heidelberg; and director, Institut für Automation, Berlin. Author: (with W. Kunz) *Namenreaktionen der orgnischen Chemie* (Heidelberg, 1961), (translated edition, New York, 1964); articles on topics in chemistry and systems analysis.

EDWIN MANSFIELD, professor of economics, University of Pennsylvania; associate editor, *Journal of the American Statistical Association.* Faculty research fellow, Ford Foundation, 1960–61. Author of articles on technological change, industrial organization, operations research, and related topics.

JESSE W. MARKHAM, professor of economics, Princeton University. Ford Foundation research professor, 1958–59. Author:

Competition in the Rayon Industry (Cambridge, Massachusetts, 1952); *The Fertilizer Industry: Study of an Imperfect Market* (Nashville, Tennessee, 1958); *The Common Market: Friend or Competitor?* (New York, 1964); articles on industrial concentration, patent policy, research and development, and related topics.

PAUL MATUSSEK, professor of psychology and neurology, University of Munich and head, Department for Psychopathology and Psychotherapy, German Research Institute for Psychiatry, Munich. Author: *Metaphysische Probleme der Medizin* (Berlin, 1950); articles on psychoanalysis and psychotherapeutics.

EVERETT MENDELSOHN, assistant professor of history of science, and research associate in science and public policy, Graduate School of Public Administration, Harvard University. Society of Fellows, Harvard University, 1957–60. Author: *Heat and Life* (Cambridge, Massachusetts, 1964); and articles on topics in the history of science.

ROBERT S. MERRILL, associate professor and associate chairman, Department of Anthropology, University of Rochester. Senior research fellow, Ford Foundation, 1961–62. Author of articles on motivation for and diffusion of technological change.

PHILIP MULLENBACH, president, Growth Industry Shares, Inc. Author: *Civilian Nuclear Power: Economic Issues and Policy Formation* (New York, 1963); and other works on atomic energy.

RICHARD R. NELSON, Economics Department, RAND Corporation. Editor, *Rate and Direction of Inventive Activity* (Princeton, 1962). Author of articles on economic theory and technological change.

HAROLD B. PEPINSKY, professor of psychology, Ohio State University. Outstanding Research Award, Council of Guidance and Personnel Associations, 1951; fellow, John Simon Guggenheim Foundation, 1961. Author: (with Pauline Pepinsky) *Counseling Theory and Practice* (New York, 1954); other works on counseling psychology, personality, and social psychology.

JAROSLAV G. POLACH, research associate, Resources for the Future, Inc. Author: *Euratom: Its Background, Issues and Economic Implications* (New York, 1964); articles on comparative law.

HORST RITTEL, lecturer on design theory, College of Environmental Design, University of California (Berkeley), lecturer on epistemology and methodology, Hochschule für Gestaltung, Ulm, and research associate, Studiengruppe für Systemforschung, Heidelberg.

ALBERT H. RUBENSTEIN, professor of industrial engineering and management sciences, Northwestern University; editor, *Transactions on Engineering Management*, Institute of Radio Engineers; and director of studies, College of Research and Development, Institute of Management Sciences. Author of articles on research management, organization theory, and communications.

HANS SAUER, special scientific assistant, Federal German Ministry of Atomic Energy.

FREDERIC M. SCHERER, assistant professor of economics, Princeton University. Author: (with others) *Patents and the Corporation* (Boston, 1958); (with M. J. Peck) *The Weapons Acquisition Process: An Economic Analysis* (Boston, 1962); *The Weapons Acquisition Process: Economic Incentives* (Boston, 1964); articles on economics of research and development.

JACOB SCHMOOKLER, professor of economics, University of Minnesota. Fellow, John Simon Guggenheim Foundation, 1956–57; faculty research fellow, Ford Foundation, 1959–60. Author of articles on the use of patent statistics, determinants of inventive activity, and other topics in the economics of research and development.

RICHARD U. SHERMAN, JR., Mershon Professor of Economics, Ohio State University; and professor of foreign affairs, National War College. Author: (with Herbert Striner) *Defense Spending and the U.S. Economy* (Chevy Chase, 1958); other works on defense economics.

IRVING H. SIEGEL, member, Research Council, Research Analysis Corporation. Phi Beta Kappa; fellow, American Statistical Association, New York Academy of Sciences, and American Association for the Advancement of Science. Author: (with H. Magdoff and M. B. Davis) *Production, Employment and Productivity in 59 Manufacturing Industries, 1919–36* (Philadelphia, 1940); *Concepts and Measurement of Production and Productivity* (Washington, D. C., 1952); *Soviet Labor Productivity* (Chevy Chase, 1952); *Strengthening Washington's Technical-Resource Base* (Chevy Chase, 1963); and articles on productivity, patents, technology, and wage policy.

FOSTER LEE SMITH, colonel, United States Air Force and chief, War Plans, Headquarters, United States Air Forces in Europe.

RICHARD A. TYBOUT, professor of economics, Ohio State University. Tau Beta Pi; Phi Kappa Phi; faculty study fellow, Ford Foundation, 1959–60. Author: *Government Contracting in Atomic Energy* (Ann Arbor, 1958); *Atomic Power and Energy Resource Planning* (Columbus, Ohio, 1958); *The Reactor Supply Industry* (Columbus, Ohio, 1960); articles on energy economics, highway planning, and public investments.

ECONOMICS OF RESEARCH AND DEVELOPMENT

INTRODUCTION

Richard A. Tybout

THE ESSAYS which constitute this volume were presented as papers at the Ohio State Conference on Economics of Research and Development, October, 1962. The authors are primarily economists, but a strong interdisciplinary flavor is added by the participation of contributors from other social sciences and from the physical sciences. Non-economists among contributors represent the fields of history, sociology, anthropology, political science, psychology, industrial engineering, chemistry, and mathematics. The reader will find a corresponding range in their viewpoints, though the essays deal mainly with economic phenomena.

In a second respect, the conference—and this book—afford a blend of intellectual currents. The conference was designed to take advantage of a visit to the United States by a group of German scholars who had been engaged for some years in the study of subjects covered herein. Their contributions add international content and approach. It is interesting to observe that the authors as a whole represent two leading western nations with histories of high productivity in science and technology.

The book is divided into seven parts according to a combined temporal and subject-matter progression. The subject matter progresses from descriptive (often quantitatively descriptive) analysis in the first three parts to prescriptive analysis in the last four. The temporal progression extends from a historical analysis of the past (Part I) to problems of the future (Part VII).

Comments have been prepared on most of the papers by selected peers of their authors. These comments introduce different points of view, synthesis, and often new facts. There is, of course, no presumption that the last word has been said by either the commentators or the authors.

I

The focus of this work on the economics of research and development places it in a changing intellectual environment. Economists have been concerned from the time of Adam Smith, and before, with the causes of increased productivity. For the half to three-quarters of a century preceding the 1950's, however, they typically eschewed the subject of technological change as a variable endogenous to economic reasoning. (An outstanding exception was the late Joseph A. Schumpeter, whose name is often associated with the current renaissance in the study of economics of technological change). The traditional concern of modern economics, insofar as it bore on productivity, was with allocative efficiency and full employment at given states of technology.

Now, a change is in progress, of which the present work, and more than a few predecessors, are harbingers. In less than a decade, the subject of economics of technological change has come into its own as a research area, though hardly as an established component of university economics curricula.[1] Increased interest in the subject has resulted from the confluence of policy demands on the subject matter of economics and the development of a broader-based economic science itself. Included especially among policy issues has been the prominence of science in cold-war tactics and armaments. Other sources of policy concern include technological unemployment resulting from automation and the effects of tech-

---

[1] Even on this point, scattered exceptions appear. The Ohio State University, for example, offered in academic year 1962-63 a course entitled Economics of Research and Development. For an early survey of the literature, see Richard R. Nelson, "The Economics of Invention: A Survey of the Literature," *Journal of Business* (April, 1959). The most recent definitive compendium is National Bureau of Economic Research, *The Rate and Direction of Inventive Activity* (Princeton, N. J., 1962).

nological change on over-all economic growth. Within the field
of economics itself, deeper understanding of interfirm competition and the broadening approach that economists are
taking to their subject have worked to establish technology
as an endogenous variable. Over all of these influences lies
the fact that research and development is now accounting for
an estimated national expenditure in the range of twenty
billion dollars and has been growing at a rate of 15 to 20 per
cent a year for the last two decades.[2] An annual rate of growth
of 17.5 per cent corresponds to a doubling of research and
development expenditures every 4.3 years.

The essays in this book have most to do with the economics
of invention and not very much to do with those succeeding
stages in technological change known as innovation and diffusion. Whereas invention refers to the first knowledge of new
technological relationships, innovation refers to their first economic use and diffusion to the process by which they come
into widespread use. Invention is the least likely of the three
processes—invention, innovation, and diffusion—to admit a
precise calculus of economic decision-making. Indeed, Klein
argues, in effect, that the problems of developing military
technologies illustrate the importance of the learning process
and sequential reduction of uncertainty, neither of which are
an integral part of received economic theory. His policy suggestions based on these observations differ from the recommendations that would follow from a more traditional economic analysis of development. (See Part V.)

The very process of concentrating on allocative efficiency
in a comparative statical analysis predisposes one to a view
of the invention process that can inhibit even the asking of
the right questions for a full understanding of research-and-
development decision-making. The message is familiar to
readers of Joseph A. Schumpeter. It is also implicit in Markham's discussion of research and development as a dynamic
element in market structure, particularly of oligopoly.

---

[2] Research and development expenditures for various sectors of the
economy and unduplicated totals are given in Jesse W. Markham, "Inventive Activity: Government Controls and the Legal Environment," in *The
Rate and Direction of Inventive Activity,* for selected years, the most
recent of which is 1959. To get an estimate of research and development,
the growth trends from Markham's data were used to extrapolate his
1959 total national expenditure of twelve billion dollars.

The term "R&D" is used herein as a surrogate for organized inventive activity, broadly conceived to encompass a range of institutions from the eighteenth-century master-apprentice combination, through the modern white-coated laboratory team, to the processes of engineering design. The activities of the part-time attic inventor are not explicitly considered, though the fruits of his work are clearly a part of social response to necessity wherever over-all inventive output of society is discussed.[3] This orientation is largely a result of the lack of data on the activities of the little man and the focus of the essays on other microeconomic units: the firm, the laboratory, the team, the R&D contractor, the Department of Defense, Euratom, and so on. Macroeconomic phenomena enter to a limited extent in the generalized analysis of public policy (Part IV) and, in more important respects, in the role of R&D for the less-developed areas of the world (Part VII).

Finally, it is well to make explicit the implied tenet that economic forces have much to do with the course of events in science and technology. Economic traditionalism is founded on a contrary view and so is much of the philosophy of science. A large part of the apparent conflict with science qua science dissolves by simple reference to the widespread practice of *defining* applied research and development as directed toward economic ends. Corroborative evidence of the part played by economic incentives in both organized and unorganized invention abounds.[4] On the other hand, the converse of the foregoing is found in the companion definition of pure science as that which is directed to no "practical" ends. Here, it is best to note Schmookler's distinction between pure science and basic science. The latter has no specific application in mind (by definition) but may, nonetheless, be undertaken for the purpose of ultimate economic gain, as the first step in a strategy, as it were, for the production of commercial

---

[3] The role of the independent spare-time inventor is not be be underestimated, however. Even today, he accounts for a surprisingly large part of all patented inventions. See Jacob Schmookler, "Inventors Past and Present," *Review of Economics and Statistics,* Vol. XXXIX (August, 1957).

[4] A start in investigating this subject may be had by referring to the two works cited in footnote 1, above.

results. Thus, Shell Development undertook basic research in the oxidation of hydrocarbons. The work was clearly basic but also had obvious connections with subjects of commercial interest and did, in fact, lead to applied research on the role of hydrogen peroxide.[5] The point is that before a conclusion can be reached on the possible influence of economic variables on the course of science, it is necessary to take account of society-wide economic influences in the financing of science, in the education and recruitment of scientists, and in the control of supplementary inputs for research and development.

The issue leads also to the personal motivations and philosophies of scientists as individuals. Within the context of social values, controls, and economic consideration for his own livelihood, the scientist exercises choices, sometimes leading him to an impecunious pursuit of his scientific interests, come what may, but subject to the limitations of available supplementary inputs in the form of materials, equipment, and assistants. Largely the philosophy of science operates at a different level of discourse. Personal motivations are governed by a rationale of thought. Science as an adventure and science as a way of life introduce an autonomous element in society. No one would argue that Michael Faraday or any of his contemporaries had much of a notion of what would come of the laws of electromagnetism, nor Albert Einstein of $e = mc^2$. Both the economic and the non-economic elements of R&D are present. Insofar as the scientific *method* in itself is concerned, there is no implied incompatibility with an analysis of societal (particularly economic) influences.[6] Possible conflicts in the interpretation of history of science remain (as illustrated in Part I). But it is clear from the works published, herein and elsewhere, that research and development is in large degree a social process subject to economic analysis and interpretation.

---

[5] Reported in Robert S. Merrill, "Some Society-Wide Research and Development Institutions," in *The Rate and Direction of Inventive Activity*, p. 417. Merrill's article and Joseph J. Spengler's comments on it deal with lines of social causation and control of science, which in turn determine the importance of economic variables.

[6] The point is illustrated and amplified in Abbot P. Usher, *History of Mechanical Inventions* (Rev. ed.; Cambridge, Mass., 1954), chaps. i-iv.

II

"The past is prologue" in R&D as in other social institutions. Part I consists of two historic papers written by an economist and a sociologist, respectively, plus comments on the same by two historians.

Schmookler addresses the very issue noted above: To what extent is basic science oriented by social problems? His own prior work has done much to establish the importance of economic demand as a governor of invention. Schmookler's extension of economic causation to the citadels of science raises profound questions: Has basic science generally been considered to have utility? To what extent have public and private groups acted on any such utility? Is there a change taking place in the role of public policy for basic science, as might be adduced from the existence and programs of the U.S. National Science Foundation? Differences (and agreements) among Schmookler, Mendelsohn, and Kranzberg open new vistas in relatively unexplored terrain.

Bahrdt is concerned with the organizational functioning of science (and early counterparts of R&D) from antiquity to modern times, particularly from the standpoint of modern Western Europe. Many of today's problems of communication and co-ordination within the R&D team can be fruitfully analyzed with the perspective afforded by a review of increasing specialization (division of labor) in science over the course of its development and the relative efficacy of different social group patterns in accommodating and fostering it. In this sense, Bahrdt's paper serves as an introduction to the study of the modern R&D organization (Part III) as well as a work in its own right.

Modern industrial R&D is the subject of analysis in Part II. A principal set of issues surround the relationships of R&D to the competitive structure of industry. Markham suggests that patterns of finance for R&D not deducible from a single-firm analysis of the profit calculus can be explained by the mutual interactions of R&D rivals. Oligopoly theory is sufficiently dynamic to accommodate the R&D decision, but it is also sufficiently intractable to discourage the hope of finding a simple predictive interindustry theory of R&D expenditures.

Whether industrial concentration (as distinguished from firm size alone) fosters the suport of R&D has been a bone of contention since Schumpeter gave his famous obiter dictum to the effect that the financial surplus accruing to monopolists provides a fund from which R&D, and hence productivity increases, can result, perhaps bettering in a long-run dynamic context the allocative efficiencies that are expected of pure competition. Brozen cites numerical evidence to controvert a relationship between concentration and R&D expenditures, but Scherer is able to reinterpret the facts to give some support to the Schumpeterian dictum.

In the course of his analysis, Brozen argues on deductive grounds against the expectation that any substantial amount of R&D might be conducted by firms (perhaps firms engaged in R&D alone) which would sell knowledge to be applied by others throughout the industrial community. The issue has far-reaching implications. If R&D contracting is a viable practice, possible economies of scale in large laboratories need not work against the smaller business firms (though other effects might—consider, for example, the Schumpeterian financial surplus argument).[7]

Differences in R&D expenditures among industries have been found to vary significantly from differences in value added.[8] Brozen provides an explanation of the observed fact by reference to the "science base," a measure of the extent to which received technologies are subject to extension by systematic inquiry. Where a good science base does not exist, R&D must revert to a try-every-bottle-on-the-shelf approach,

---

[7] R&D employment tends to be more concentrated than total manufacturing when concentration of the latter is measured in value added. James S. Worley, "The Changing Direction of Research and Development among Firms," in *The Rate and Direction of Inventive Activity*. The association of size of firm with industrial concentration need only exist in industries with high R&D expenditures to justify the application of the Schumpeterian argument. See Worley, *ibid.,* for identification of these industries.

[8] *Ibid.*

in Brozen's analysis. Ames raises conceptual questions on the use of the science base and Scherer cites empirical findings that cast doubt on its applicability in selected cases. A general formulation of the interindustry determinants of R&D expenditures continues to elude the economic analyst, but evidence is accumulating through the compilation of information in specific cases.

A considerable broadening of the subject matter is suggested by Merrill's empirical study of routine engineering design, an unexpected source of productivity gain. His careful work disabuses the reader of any sharp distinctions between the laboratory and the drawing board as sources of new production functions. It also contributes insights to the socioeconomic process of diffusion.

Mansfield summarizes the strands in his own empirical work over the last several years. These include: (1) R&D budgeting; (2) the innovation process, firm size, and growth; and (3) diffusion. The topics thus extend over a wide range of subject matter relevant for technological change treated from the standpoint of the single firm. Working almost alone in these areas, as noted by Griliches, Mansfield has produced significant results. Mansfield's work is largely complementary to the other papers in Part II inasmuch as it deals primarily with the firm (as opposed to the industry) and to an important degree with processes (innovation and diffusion) subsequent to invention.

Part III pursues the subject of R&D decision-making to the level of group dynamics internal to the organization. The subject is approached from three widely different viewpoints: the individual psyche (Matussek), the mathematical model (Rittel), and empirical observation of communication and control processes (Rubenstein and Hannenberg). Pepinsky's reconciliation indicates various ways in which the three papers pursue different issues and complementary subjects. In combination, they bode well for progress in organizational strategy for R&D.

Organizational problems are susceptible to systematic treatment where probability concepts (subjective or objective) can be employed. The point is illustrated in Rittel's analysis. The practicability of a probabilistic approach is the greater where minor improvements in products and processes constitute the main grist of the industrial R&D mill. That such improvements are, in fact, the object of most industrial R&D projects is implied by Rubenstein and Hannenberg's survey. It is interesting to note that problems of communication and co-ordination also revealed by the Rubenstein-Hannenberg analysis can be traced to increased specialization discussed by Bahrdt, but qualified in particular cases, of course, by the psychological considerations indicated by Matussek.

Part IV is pivotal in the sense that it provides a general framework for the understanding and evaluation of public policy, a subject explicitly involved in each of the three succeeding parts. Commensurate with the importance of the subject, Part IV is introduced by a special address by the Honorable J. Herbert Hollomon, Assistant Secretary of Commerce for Science and Technology.

The special characteristics of knowledge as a commodity have recently been comprehensively stated by Arrow.[9] The Fritsch-Krauch-Tybout essay, written in the same tradition, relates the economic characteristics of knowledge (output of R&D activity) to a general classification scheme for market and non-market society-wide cost and benefit effects. The result is to offer a framework for systematic identification of the possible consequences of alternative public policies.

Nelson and Siegel draw on a wealth of experience in public decision-making for R&D, especially for military projects. Any attempt to fill the empty boxes labeled in the Fritsch-Krauch-Tybout article must take account of the large number of institutional influences poignantly described by Siegel. Nelson offers specific guidance and thoughtful judgments of the contemporary scene, emphasizing the role of economic analysis in choosing among alternative public investments (and policies) in R&D. There are bounds to the relevance of R&D output, however collective knowledge may be in principle, and important short-term scarcities in R&D personnel, both of which work to define the costs and benefits from particular public policies. More specifically, Nelson discusses the significance of these facts for choices among our national programs

[9] Kenneth J. Arrow, "Economic Welfare and the Allocation of Resources for Invention," in *The Rate and Direction of Inventive Activity.*

for defense, atomic energy, space, and, too often forgotten, civil R&D goals.

Special problems and issues arise in defining the "mix" of public and private enterprise for government-financed military R&D. These problems are the major focus of Part V.

The business firm with its private cybernetics of R&D, explored empirically by Mansfield and Rubenstein-Hannenberg, is brought into the arena of public considerations discussed in Part IV to become a partner in (often ambitious) technological change. Nowhere else in society is new technology exploited with the intensity characterizing defense (defined broadly to include the cold-war–motivated space program). And nowhere else is there as complex a fusion of public and private enterprise.

The authors of the essays in Part V represent two principal loci of economic research on military R&D: The Rand Corporation, of which Klein is economics department head, and the Harvard Weapons Acquisition Group, of which Cherington is director. The issues separating them—which are summarized by Dupré (who is not connected with either group)— revolve around the question of whether central control or decentralized parallel R&D efforts will result in the more rapid advance in over-all military effectiveness from R&D, given that financial (budgetary) resources continue at roughly the current levels. Different conclusions follow where different levels of technological novelty are involved.

The implications of the alternatives are considerable. From the standpoint of the economic science of R&D, a better understanding of the technological learning process will point the direction for incorporation of dynamic variables in allocational processes (whether market or non-market). At stake in public policy is not only efficiency in defense R&D—which could conceivably be important enough to determine national survival—but also the relative influence of private business concerns in the determination of defense policy. The cold war is being fought in the laboratories (public and private). More broadly, and perhaps without too much overstatement, a large part of international policy *and* the business future of the affected private firms are being simultaneously determined in the same laboratories. The possibility of conflict of interest has occurred to men of such dissimilar views and attainments as C. Wright Mills and Dwight D. Eisenhower. Whether such a conflict of interest is serious depends on how centralized weapons development must be, and hence how much it need limit the Department of Defense to dependence on a small number of futuristic weapons suppliers.

Part VI explores the problems and prospects of two international programs for R&D: Euratom and the Mutual Weapons Development Program. Supranational co-operation in R&D was crucial to the World War II Manhattan Project for the development of the atomic bomb. Whether it can achieve viable economic status short of hot-war pressures is the major issue in Part VI. Economic considerations (especially as result from energy costs) were important in spawning Euratom, but so also were international prestige and training in technologies of possible military significance. Mullenbach interprets Euratom in the context of European Common Market aspirations, in full bloom at the time of his writing. Despite the sober view now taken (June, 1963) of the Common Market, the extent of supranational collaboration in Euratom is still impressive, as made clear in Sauer's paper. Sherman discovers the seeds of continuing R&D collaboration in the Mutual Weapons Development Program. A number of cogent observations on the evaluation of the program appear in Smith's comments.

Science is traditionally an international community and many have considered it an entering wedge for international-ism.[10] Now, the programs described in Part VI introduce international collaboration in applied technology. Economic considerations leading to international R&D may well lead to other sorts of collaboration. The use of common concepts in equipment design and perhaps even the development of common replacement parts and practices can go far, within the limits of the affected industrial community, to implement the same political objectives as a common market and a common currency.

---

[10] Samples of this view abound in the issues of the *Bulletin of the Atomic Scientists,* particularly in early post–World War II years when the United States proposals for international control of atomic energy occupied a prominent place in the proceedings of the United Nations and in public discussion.

The same observations can be made of the relationships between the advanced and the less-developed nations, though science has not generally played an important part in aid programs. With the exception of atomic energy, the rather extensive programs that have been undertaken in aid of economic development (on both sides of the iron curtain) tend to focus on non-R&D problems. To a certain extent, the United Nations has provided a clearing house for technologies suitable for the new nations.[11] But the technologies are those already in existence in the advanced nations. The question of whether other, heretofore unknown, technologies might be more suitable for the emergent nations is given primary attention in Part VII.

Most notably, *neither* of the papers presented in Part VII takes the position that the menu of technologies developed by the Western world from its beginnings to date is adequate for the new nations (or, indeed, adequate for the long-term survival of the human race). Tybout explores the implications for technology of the resource position in which the less-developed countries find themselves today and the prospective changes in this position that can be expected to accompany economic development. There is some reason to hold that economic development in the new nations might well result in the long-term co-existence of cottage industry and automated process manufacture, omitting in the middle Western-style skilled labor manufacturing.

Boulding conducts a far-ranging analysis of the research, education, and development needs of the emergent nations. He is concerned with research extending beyond technological problems to problems of peace, social organization, and value systems. He concludes by pleading for

> . . . a massive intellectual effort of at least the magnitude we are devoting to space research devoted to solving the intellectual and organizational problems which surround this great transition to the developed world society.

On the physical and technological side, as Boulding notes, the problems of a high-level technology are still unsolved.

---

[11] A major survey was conducted in the recent United Nations Conference on the Application of Science and Technology for the Benefit of the Less-Developed Areas (Geneva, 1963).

Present technologies depend largely on entropic processes which dissipate accumulated energy and material resources. A permanent high-level technology is conceivable, based on the sea and atmosphere as ultimate resources and on nuclear fusion and the sun for energy. How large a population the world could permanently support from such technologies is a further question, the answer to which depends on social organization and Boulding's other considerations, to say nothing of the problems of actually restraining world population to optimal size.

III

The seven parts into which the essays are divided extend from a long view of the past to contemporary industrial R&D, to internal organization, to public policy, to military R&D, to international collaboration, to a long view of the future. Science and technology serve as a basis for socioeconomic analysis. The precedent is Schumpeterian. But the context belongs to the world of the 1960's with its quantitatively oriented social science, big government, international rivalries, and rapidly growing expenditures on research and development.

POSTSCRIPT
(June 29, 1965)

It will be clear to the reader that some changes could have been made in a few of the essays appearing in Part VI and perhaps also in Part V to reflect up-to-the-minute institutional context. No effort was made to do this, however, on the ground that the value of what the authors have to say is scarcely affected by the difference in time from the original date of presentation to the present.

I

HISTORY OF SCIENCE

CATASTROPHE AND UTILITARIANISM IN THE DEVELOPMENT OF BASIC SCIENCE

Jacob Schmookler

RECENT FINDINGS lead to the conclusion that inventors respond far more to demand conditions than had customarily been assumed.[1] This result raises once again the question of whether a more or less similar relation exists between demand and the development of basic science. The present paper represents a preliminary approach to some aspects of the question.

Since the origins of basic science have been the subject of lengthy debate among historians and sociologists of science, it would appear that an economist dabbling in the area must be guilty of hunting without a license. There are, however, extenuating circumstances. On the one hand, economists share with other social scientists a concern with the nature of the interconnections between economic development and other aspects of social change such as the growth of science. On the other hand, the tools of the economist's trade may enable us to come more effectively into contact with some phases of this question in which several disciplines share an interest. In any case, if the advance of science is man's noblest enterprise, it is nonetheless a part of the seamless web of history. It is therefore proper for an economist to examine some of its economic aspects.

Before coming to the body of my paper, I should like to make a few, perhaps unnecessary, parenthetical remarks about motives. In the first place, let me record the impression I have

---

[1] Cf. the author's "Changes in Industry and in the State of Knowledge as Determinants of Industrial Invention," *The Rate and Direction of Inventive Activity,* ed. Richard R. Nelson (Princeton, N.J., 1962); "Economic Sources of Inventive Activity," *Journal of Economic History* (March, 1962); "Invention, Innovation, and Business Cycles," in Joint Economic Committee, *Variability of Private Investment in Plant Equipment* (Washington, D.C., 1962), Pt. II; and, with Oswald Brownlee, "Determinants of Inventive Activity," *American Economic Review* (May, 1962).

that some previous discussions of the subject are either naïve or out of focus. Labor economists and sociologists have long known that the supply of labor in any market is influenced by many factors, only some of which are economic. This is no less true of scientists. Any given scientist may pursue a particular project mainly to make a living, to please his dean, to spite a colleague, to build a research empire, or to isolate himself from or stand out above his peers. Such more or less conscious motivations may themselves reflect deeper and darker reaches of the human spirit, which are the special province of psychology. Viewed in this perspective, the common dichotomy drawn between "the disinterested pursuit of truth" and research devoted to the advancement of the general welfare obviously does not exhaust the range of influences to which scientists are subject. What sets these two objectives in a class by themselves is that, for a scientist, other more personal motives can be reached only through them. The reason for this is simply that the rewards to scientists in terms of income, prestige, position, honors, etc., are rationed by his colleagues and the outside world only on grounds of these two criteria. These, the "public goals" of scientific endeavor, have constituted the exclusive focus of earlier discussions of our subject. I propose here to continue the precedent, but this may mean that important parts of the subject will be neglected.

Secondly, I believe considerable controversy can be eliminated by recognizing two things. In the first place, a scientist may pursue a project because of its prospective contribution to knowledge, and his colleagues may applaud his results for the same reason, at the same time that his financiers, private or public, expect and perhaps receive "useful" knowledge. This suggests that whatever the motives of academic scientists were during the last century or two, the external support of science may have had a primarily utilitarian animus, with great consequences for the growth of science. Secondly, research without a *specific* utilitarian objective may nonetheless be broadly utilitarian in intent. By this I do not wish to suggest, as some Marxist writers have, that scientists who thought they sought knowledge only for its own sake were in fact responding to broad socioeconomic forces.[2] Rather, I am suggesting the much more obvious point that society has become increasingly appreciative both of the cornucopia that is science and of the unpredictable character of its results. In consequence, over the generations society has become increasingly willing to provide support for general non-mission–oriented research for reasons as utilitarian as those which largely motivated the spread of popular education or, before that, geographic exploration.

This paper is concerned primarily, then, with the question of whether science has been *supported* during the past century or two primarily for humanistic or for utilitarian reasons. To a lesser extent, it is concerned with the motives of the scientists themselves. Since our focus is on basic science, this means that, as a matter of course, we are concerned primarily with academic science, for it is mainly in the institutions of higher learning that the leading scientific discoveries of the modern age have been made.

I

We may take as our paradigm the course of support of basic research in the United States in the last two decades, and inquire whether or not the pattern so clearly etched there is exceptional or typical of the growth of basic research in the last century or two. Both government and industry in America have greatly expanded their support of basic research since the close of World War II. The lessons the war taught about the military, medical, and industrial potentialities of science were well learned. As the National Science Foundation recently expressed it, "Science supplies not only the information

---

[2] This, of course, is possible, although it behooves those who suggest the existence of such a mechanism to demonstrate its *modus operandi* in each instance.

needed to solve specific problems but, more importantly, it opens up new opportunities which usually cannot be foreseen until the new knowledge is obtained. To insure such new opportunities, research support is required for the acquisition of new fundamental knowledge." [3] The strong influence of military considerations in the promotion of basic research is reflected both in the extensive postwar support given it by the Office of Naval Research before the establishment of the National Science Foundation and by the marked increase in basic research funds following the launching of the Russian Sputnik. Many spokesmen for the scientific community have lamented the heavy weight accorded instrumental considerations in the nation's scientific program, and have yearned for a condition in which science would be supported for its own sake. I strongly share these sentiments, but it is worth asking whether American experience has been indeed as different from European in this regard as has often been assumed. A hasty survey of the progress of science since the seventeenth century suggests that it has not.

If I read the record correctly, to some extent from the beginning of modern science and certainly in the last two centuries, basic research was financed by European governments primarily to implement the traditional purposes of state policy—to promote the health and welfare of the citizenry and the military power of the state. Even the great private foundations which financed most of the basic research in America until recently were similarly motivated. The second lesson writ large by the history of modern science is that substantial changes in the level of external support are usually attributable to some specific, extrascientific, dramatic event or circumstance. In brief, I suggest that *the great propulsive force exerted by the Soviet satellite successes on American research and education is typical of the events which promoted the growth of modern science.*

Before justifying these statements, it seems in order to recall that in earlier ages, particularly in classical Greece [4]

---

[3] *National Science Foundation, Eleventh Annual Report, 1961* (NSF 62-1), p. 3.

[4] Cf. Benjamin Farrington, *Greek Science,* Vols. I and II (London, 1944, 1949).

and in post-Renaissance Europe,[5] a love of learning for its own
sake played a greater role than now. Perhaps it even dominated the scientific enterprise. Let me simply note in this
connection that (1) the capacity of science to serve utilitarian
ends varies directly with its level of development, so that
if science was to be pursued at all in an earlier age, it had
to be pursued largely for its own sake—it was less likely than
now to yield a valuable by-product; and (2) man's constant
desire to know the design of the cosmos and the place of the
earth and of man in it meant that an unusually high premium
would be paid for new knowledge for its own sake when
traditional beliefs were shattered in the early days of classical
Greece and in Renaissance and post-Renaissance Europe.

The broad humanistic animus behind early modern science
is indicated by the backgrounds of a few of the leading
scientists of the time: Copernicus was a protégé of his uncle,
the sovereign Bishop of Ermland, who arranged a canory for
his nephew to enjoy in absentia; Kepler was a mathematician
to Rudolph II of Bohemia, a post previously occupied by
Tycho Brahe, himself an aristocrat; Galileo's patron was a
Medici, the Grand Duke of Tuscany; and Newton was professor of mathematics at Cambridge.

Nonetheless, utilitarian considerations provided a powerful
stimulus to the activities of scientists themselves almost from
the beginning of the scientific revolution. Francis Bacon's
vision, foreshadowing that of eighteenth-century Enlighten-
ment, of a world from which science had banished want was
widely shared, at least from the beginning of the seventeenth
century onward, by the doctors, philosophers, mathematicians,
craftsmen, artistocrats, and dilettantes who cultivated science
then. Thus Butterfield writes of this period:

> *The passion to extend the scientific method to every branch of*
> *thought was at least equalled by the passion to make science serve*
> *the cause of industry and agriculture, and it was accompanied by a*
> *sort of technological fervor* . . . it is difficult, even in the early
> history of the Royal Society, to separate the interest shown in the
> cause of pure scientific truth from the curiosity in respect of useful
> inventions . . . It has become a debatable question how far the

---

[5] Cf. Rupert Hall, *The Scientific Revolution* (London, 1954),
chap. vii.

HISTORY OF SCIENCE

direction of scientific interest was itself affected by technical needs or preoccupations in regard to shipbuilding and other industries; but the Royal Society followed Galileo in concerning itself, for example, with the important question of the mode of discovering longitude at sea.[6]

Gillispie comments in a similar vein:

> Baconism has always held a special appeal as the way of science in societies which develop a vocation for the betterment of man's estate and which confide not in aristocracies, whether of birth or brains, but in a wisdom to be elicited from common pursuits—in seventeenth-century England, in eighteenth-century France, in nineteenth-century America, among Marxists of all countries. . . . *His (Bacon's) was the philosophy that inspired science as an activity, a movement carried on in public and of concern to the public. This aspect of science scarcely existed before the seventeenth century. Since then it has accompanied and at times enveloped intellectual effort.*[7]

Hall concurs saying, "The ideal of social progress was . . . a commonplace among seventeenth-century scientists, and with varying degrees of assurance the attainment of this ideal was linked with the application of scientific knowledge to technology." [8] Indeed, the progress of technology and science inevitably raised among educated men generally the humanitarian hope that through the development of science the prosperity of the period could somehow be spread to include all classes of society.

This hope runs like a thread through the intellectual history of the eighteenth century and, of course, formed an important and integral element in the ideology of the American and French Revolutions. Diderot's influential *Encyclopedie* was perhaps the most full-bodied expression of these aspirations.

Even in England, where the support of science with public funds was negligible, the utilitarian orientation of early scientists and the influence of the geographic and commercial revolutions on the direction of inquiry are plainly evident.

---

[6] H. Butterfield, *The Origins of Modern Science* (Rev. ed.; New York, 1959), p. 185. (Italics supplied.)

[7] Charles Coulston Gillispie, *The Edge of Objectivity, An Essay in the History of Scientific Ideas* (Princeton, N.J.: 1960), p. 75. (Italics supplied.)

[8] A. R. Hall, *The Scientific Revolution, 1500–1800,* (Boston [paperback ed.], 1956), p. 218.

Christopher Wren, professor of astronomy at Gresham College, said in 1657 in his inaugural address that "there was hardly anything more glorious to be aimed at in art than the knowledge of longitude." The solution to this problem lay in improved theory and construction of clocks; and English scientists, including Robert Hooke, the first curator of the Royal Society, devoted considerable time to these matters. Members of the Society also enlarged navigational technology by astronomical observations, geographic exploration, and meteorological studies. Similarly, an interest in solving the problems of agriculture, medicine, and industry (particularly textiles) motivated many of the chemical pursuits of the members.[9]

If the prospect of applications seriously affected the unsupported efforts of scientists, the support of science by monarchs and aristocrats hardly expressed an unalloyed love of knowledge. On the Continent the state promoted science and scientific education as an instrument of policy. In an age when the nations of modern Europe were emerging and struggling with each other for survival, science was seized upon and cultivated to accomplish military or economic ends otherwise unattainable, or attainable only at great cost under the prevailing state of the technical arts. It was the mercantilist Colbert who established the French Académie Royale des Sciences in 1666 and who "suggested problems to it in accordance with political interests." [10] A generation later the members of the Académie were engaged in developing cascades and fountains for the palace at Versailles. This may signify that science was still too immature for its cultivation to have been profitable, but it also indicates to what extent the early Académie was a creature of the state. The first scientific academy in Berlin, founded in 1700 by Frederick I under the guidance of the scientist-philosopher-statesman, Leibniz, was likewise a mercantilist creation, "aimed at furthering the interests of the German nation and raising its technological standards." [11]

The quest for national power, apparently more than any other influence, accounted for the growth of science and in-

---

[9] Cf. *The Royal Society Tercentenary* (London, 1961), compiled from a Special Supplement of the *Times* (London), July, 1960.

[10] Cf. Hall, *op. cit.*, p. 195.

[11] *Ibid.*, p. 201.

terest in scientific matters in France during the eighteenth century, an era dominated by France's struggle to displace England as the premier power in the world. The monarchy's utilitarian orientation is illustrated by the kinds of scientific institutions which it established: The Royal Academy of Surgery in 1731; the Veterinary School in 1766; the School of Bridges and Roads (founded by the physiocratic economist, Turgot) in 1775; and the Royal School of Mines in 1783.[12]

While the scientific institutions of the old regime were destroyed by the Jacobins during the Terror "in a fit of vulgar, sentimental petulance against the hauteur of abstract science, the personal tyranny of mathematics, the superiority of science over the artisan," Gillispie writes:

> Upon the *tabula rasa* left by the Jacobins, the Directory erected a new set of scientific institutions: the first *Ecole Normale*, the *Ecole Polytechnique*, new medical faculties in Paris, Strasbourg, and Montpellier, the *Conservatoire des Arts et Metiers*. Only the *Museum d'Histoire Naturelle* emerged flourishing from the Terror, favored by the romantic enthusiasm for Botany and Rousseau's Nature. Other schools were revived, the *Ecole des Mines,* the *Ecole des Ponts et Chaussées,* the *Collège de France*. Finally at the summit was created the *Institut de France*. Thus, France was endowed at one stroke with her scientific institutions, and the first generation who taught and studied in them assured the restoration of her scientific leadership and its enlargement in the early nineteenth century.
>
> It was a remarkable effort, animated by a consistent philosophy, which was nothing less than to unify the sciences through a common conception of scientific method, and in so doing to link them both institutionally and philosophically to realizing the idea of progress. So for a time, science was organized as a function of its educational mission. *Polytechnique* assembled the first scientific faculty, as distinguished a faculty, man for man, as has ever existed. For the first time, students were offered systematic technical instruction, directed toward engineering to be sure, but under the foremost men. Students,

---

[12] John T. Merz, *A History of European Thought in the Nineteenth Century* (London, 1907), I, 107 n. Merz comments, "For the growth and diffusion of the scientific spirit itself, the great schools in Paris were even of greater value than the popular writings of Voltaire and Buffon. Most of the academicians were trained in these schools, and many of them taught there for many years."—pp. 106–7. In addition to these establishments founded by the crown, independent provincial academies of science, chartered by the King, were affiliated with the Académie des Sciences. Suggestive of the link between science and social reform is that the provincial academies numbered among their members Rousseau, Robespierre, Marat, Danton, and Bonaparte (*ibid,* p. 107 n).

able and eager, chosen by competition, were immensely exhilarated
by the sense of being conducted at once to the very forefront of
scientific conquest, and at being told that the future of the Republic,
which was to say mankind, depended on how they acquitted themselves in so exposed a situation.[13]

This crucial role of state support, with its essentially utilitarian animus, in the growth of French science to pre-eminence
in the eighteenth and early nineteenth centuries is repeated
later in Germany and England. It is noteworthy that when
he conquered Prussia, Napoleon closed the University of
Halle, where *Wissenschaft,* the critical, empirical approach to
knowledge was flourishing. It is equally significant that the
creation of the University of Berlin, established in 1809 to
replace that at Halle, was part of an effort of the Prussian
rulers "to modernize their country in order to avoid a recur-
rence of another military catastrophe." [14]

Wilhelm von Humboldt, scholar and statesman, was responsible for the reorganization of Prussian education generally
and the establishment of the University of Berlin in particular.
A memorial of his published in 1810 brilliantly developed the
political benefits of academic freedom and the unfettered
pursuit of science:

> On the whole the State should not look to the Universities at all for
> anything that directly concerns its own interests, but should rather
> cherish a conviction that, *in fulfilling their real destination, they will
> not only serve its own purposes, but serve them on an infinitely
> higher plane, commanding a much wider field of operation, and
> affording room to set in motion much more efficient springs and forces
> than are at the disposal of the State itself.*[15]

At the University of Berlin, the emphasis was on professional
training, rather than on the classical, humanist tradition. In
this as in other respects the university set the pattern not only
for other German universities—Breslau (1811), Bonn (1818),

---

[13] Gillispie, *op. cit.,* p. 176.

[14] John Joseph Beer, *The Emergence of the German Dye Industry*
(Urbana, Ill., 1959), p. 58; cf. also Sir Eric Ashby, *Technology and the
Academics* (London, 1959), pp. 20–27; and Friedrich Paulsen, *The
German Universities and University Study,* trans. F. Thilly and W. W.
Elwang (New York, 1906), pp. 50–55.

[15] Cited in Friedrich Paulsen, *German Education, Past and Present,*
trans. T. Lorenz (London, 1908), pp. 185–87. (Italics supplied.)

Munich (1826) [16]—but also for universities throughout the world. By the 1820's, because the continuing drive of the German states to develop their economies pressed upon existing manpower, while the older universities displayed a characteristic reluctance to develop vocationally oriented curricula, *Technische Hochschule* were established on the pattern of the *Ecole Polytechnique* to relieve the shortage of military, civil, and mechanical engineers. At the University of Giessen, the great German chemist, Justus von Liebig, himself educated at the Polytechnique, instituted the teaching laboratory and laid the foundations for German chemical supremacy. For a considerable time, however, Germany was a net exporter of chemists, for it was not until a native textile industry had developed, under the auspices of government and foreign private investment, that a market for chemists developed in the coal-tar dye industry in the 1860's and 1870's in Germany.[17]

With the rise of the chemical industry in Germany, private enterprise moved into position beside the state itself as a source of support for German academic science. It provided such support directly by hiring its graduates, but it also provided considerable indirect support.

Beer writes:

> The chemical industrialist got the chemical students interested in dye research and, as is often the case, once these young men started certain lines of investigation, many spent the rest of their lives going in the same direction. When these boys graduated, they were frequently offered positions by the dye companies to continue their lines of investigation. Furthermore, if, in the course of their academic researches, they had come up with compounds or processes that seemed of practical value, those firms that donated the original chemicals or had perhaps cooperated with the research in other ways, were usually able to get first option on the use of these discoveries.
>
> The older chemists engaged in industry used their company's money and their personal influence with the heads of the university laboratories as means of advancing the search for new colors and color intermediates. . . .
>
> Cooperation with university chemists was so actively sought by the various German companies that a veritable competitive struggle

---

[16] *Ibid.*, pp. 184–97.
[17] Cf. Beer, *op. cit.*, chap. vi.

arose between them over the "control" of the most important academic laboratories; and in time each company managed to establish strong ties with certain schools to the exclusion of all other rivals. . . .

The means by which the competing dye firms tried to outdo each other for the favor of the professors is shrouded in mystery. It required a certain amount of circumspection to secure such cooperation without offending academic dignity and propriety . . . some of the ways generally used in rewarding professional cooperation are perfectly well known and were considered proper. First, there was the payment of royalties; second, there was the promise of expert technical and legal assistance to bring the discovery under the protection of an effective patent that would safeguard it from legal attack, infringement, or circumvention; third, there were consulting fees that were usually extremely handsome, considering the time and effort involved; and fourth, the dye firm could offer scientific cooperation which not only involved the already mentioned donation of rare and expensive chemicals, and the use of the company's laboratories and staff for tedious confirmatory and analytical tests, but went so far occasionally as to furnish the professor with one or more company chemists who would work in his laboratory on specific projects that were of special interest to the company.[18]

The indifference toward science exhibited by the British government until the middle of the last century stands in instructive contrast to the active concern and support provided by the governments of France and Germany. It is probably not much of an oversimplification to suggest that England's economic and military supremacy during the period explains the contrast. To us it seems ludicrous that the reward which the Crown saw fit to bestow on Newton for his monumental work was to take him from Cambridge and make him Warden of the Mint. It is no less strange that the state's only other major gesture toward science in the same century was even more economical: where the continental monarchies financed their academies, the British allowed its counterpart to *call* itself the Royal Society. Not until the middle of the nineteenth century, when the German-born Prince Albert threw his weight into the scales, did his Majesty's government, initially by establishing the Royal College of Chemistry in 1845 under August Hofmann (a student of Liebig), begin to press for the creation of institutions of higher scientific and technological education.

The scale of these early British efforts, however, was modest. Only when the Great Exhibition of 1851 and, even more

---

[18] *Ibid.*, pp. 64–65.

dramatically, the Paris Exhibition of 1867 revealed that French, German, and Swiss industry gravely threatened England's economic hegemony did state support of science and science education become appreciable in Britain. In the decade between 1871 and 1880, seven new colleges of higher education and the Cavendish Laboratory at Cambridge and Clarendon at Oxford were established.[19] That Britain's response in important respects proved in the long run inadequate to the challenge is interesting, but the instrumental character of that response is as apparent in her case as in the others.

II

The history of basic science in America repeats the story with differences only in the details. The promotion of science as an instrument of human betterment greatly appealed to the founding fathers, who numbered among their ranks the educated elites of Virginia and New England. The hope which many of them later shared of founding a national university vanished, however, with the rise of Jacksonian democracy, although the states' rights doctrine had never permitted it to burn brightly. The establishment of the land-grant colleges and universities after mid-century did little to promote fundamental research, partly because of Americans' concern with matters of immediate utility,[20] and partly because a local educational institution is a sub-optimal location for basic research since its utilitarian benefits are diffused and uncertain. The transplantation to American shores of the German university model in the form of Johns Hopkins University in 1877 marked the serious beginning of basic research in this country, but, according to I. Bernard Cohen, President Gilman's inaugural address and the university's early course offerings make its utilitarian orientation abundantly clear. Similarly, as noted earlier, the substantial research undertakings supported by the

[19] Cf. Ashby, *op. cit.*, chaps., ii, iii.
[20] Cf. Alexis de Tocqueville, *Democracy in America* (New York, 1959), II, 45–46.

Rockefeller, Carnegie, and Ford Foundations in this century have been motivated, not by a desire merely to advance our understanding of the world, but by a desire to change it, by advancing health and welfare.

In short, the recent spectacular involvement of the American government in basic science is not one of the new things under the sun. What is new in America is the combination of a sense of national peril and a recognition by the governing authorities that basic science can help to meet it and yield other benefits as well; but as we have seen, this combination has appeared elsewhere before. There is undoubtedly some merit in Tocqueville's contention that America neglected basic science because democracy promotes an interest in immediate material results, while Europe pursued it because aristocracies "facilitate the natural impulse of the mind to the highest reaches of thought, and they naturally prepare it to conceive a sublime, almost a divine love of truth." [21] One may grant, and not only for the sake of the argument, Tocqueville's premise, but at the same time question whether its weight is great enough to explain the great observed international differences in state support of science. A complacent English aristocracy ignored fundamental science when revolutionary French democracy energetically pursued it, while a later and more democratic English government initiated a much more active policy toward science. Undoubtedly the governing classes of Western nations were characterized by marked differences in their regard for science, both for its own sake and for its capacity to assist in the accomplishment of state purposes. Yet such differences apparently affected the level of state support less than did their different locations in the international constellation of power. Over the last two centuries or so, when states supported science, they did so primarily for utilitarian, not humanistic, reasons, as a way of accomplishing, by intellectual means, objectives beyond the reach of their material resources. A major reason that England ignored science in the eighteenth century and most of the nineteenth, while first France and then Germany vigorously

---

[21] *Ibid.*, p. 46. Cf. Also Richard H. Shryock, "American Indifference to Basic Science during the Nineteenth Century," *Archives internationales d'histoire des sciences,* No. 5 (1948).

fostered it, was that England was the pre-eminent power in the world and the others aspired to that position.

Marked increases in the level of state support of science seem generally to have been the by-product of large-scale changes in national posture arising from threatened or realized catastrophe, as we have seen in the case of post-Jena Germany, post-Paris Exposition England, and post-Sputnik America. It has apparently been not so much a difference in the value placed on science for its own sake, or in the abstract appreciation of the utility of science, as in the problems confronted, the urgency with which these problems were felt, and the effectiveness of the state in commandeering resources that accounts for the main international differences in the support of science.

III

Thus it would appear that the question with which this paper opened can be tentatively answered in the affirmative, at least with respect to the level of support for basic research. Just as inventive activity has been distributed among industries in accordance with the demand for inventions, so support of basic research has apparently tended to be distributed among nations in accordance with the demand for more general science. It may be conjectured that, as science became more useful, within each nation basic research tended to become distributed among fields roughly in accordance with demand, also; but I can only guess that this is so and hope that others better qualified will examine the possibility.

There are, of course, many differences between science and invention. From a utilitarian standpoint, scientific knowledge tends to be more of a general purpose tool than invention. Moreover, the former represents an expression in the indicative, the latter, in the imperative. For both these reasons, invention is usually more immediately useful and, therefore, in all likelihood, more immediately bound up with utilitarian considerations and more immediately responsive to urgent problems which are often dramatized by real or threatened catastrophes. Finally, unlike scientific discovery, invention is nothing if it is not useful. For these, and other reasons, it seems plausible to believe that scientific discovery, in the small as well as in the large, has been—and should continue to be—less affected by want-satisfying objectives than has invention. On the other hand, that, in a gross way, such objectives have played a substantial role seems undeniable.

HISTORIC CHANGES IN THE DIVISION
OF LABOR IN EUROPEAN RESEARCH

Hans Paul Bahrdt

BY "DIVISION OF LABOR IN SCIENCE," we shall refer to specialization according to branches of science. It seems that sicence is involved in an irreversible process of division into individual sectors of science. Smaller and smaller sections of the aggregate fund of knowledge acquired by scientific studies can be surveyed by individual researchers to the extent that they are capable of carrying out productive work. This specialization describes both the activities of teaching and the practical application of knowledge acquired in science.

I

Not long ago, there was much less division of labor in the sense of specialization by special fields; in antiquity and the Middle Ages, partly even in the early modern times, hardly any existed. It is true that the names of philosophers, mathematicians, historians, and geographers have come down to us in association with these special fields, but this does not mean that they were specialists in the modern sense, i.e., scholars and teachers, whose competences applied to one special field owing to a special education. To the extent that a division of labor evolved, it was along lines promoted by the professional training of students for practical life and not according to the natural requirements of modern scientific disciplines as we now understand them. Most of them were, first of all, disciples of a certain philosophical school: Pythagoreans, students of the Platonic academy, Peripatetics, or Stoics. Their works, as far as we know them, are predominantly concerned with scientific, mathematical, geographical, or historical subjects as a rule, but nevertheless they clearly indicate their standing within philosophical history and their intellectual association with one of the famous schools.

By and large, the sectoralization of the sciences already known in antiquity was probably more a classification of knowledge than a social division of the scientists.[1] I cannot say whether this assertion can be equally maintained for the later period of Hellenistic times. There is the question whether a man like Archimedes, for example, was not already a specialist in the modern sense who, however, combined mathematics with physics, astronomy, and the practical application of mechanical knowledge.[2] The process of extending fact-knowledge and the lessening interest in metaphysics is accompanied by a loosening cohesion of the great schools in the later period of antiquity. Windelband states: "With his entry into one of the big schools the individual man of science acquired a basic overall view and a determining principle for the treatment of the special questions and subjects of interest to him. It is true that the famous savants of (the late Antiquity) e.g., Archimedes, Eratosthenes, Aristarch, more or less maintained relations with this or that school but always showed themselves indifferent in the field of metaphysics."[3] Thus it happens that in this period very few theoretical principles of philosophy were found, whereas mathematical, scientific, grammatical, philological, literary-historical, and historical research produced a variety of rich and comprehensive results.

In the course of antiquity, progressive centrifugal research was gradually replaced by a classicism which repeated the knowledge and theories of the classics in an authoritarian-minded manner and predominantly demonstrated only literary ambition.[4] In this form, i.e., in the form of a literary traditionalism which wished to conserve traditions and endeavored to

---

[1] Pauly-Wissowa, *Realenzyklopädie des klassischen Altertums:* Articles on Geometry, Plato, and Aristotle.

[2] Pauly-Wissowa, *op. cit.:* Article on Archimedes

[3] W. Windelband, *Lehrbuch der Geschichte der Philosophie,* ed. Heimsoeth (14th ed.; Tübingen, 1948), p. 130.

[4] Lectures held by U. Karsteht at the University of Göttingen, Germany, unpublished.

keep them within the boundaries of old or new philosophies, the ancient science was passed on—very fragmentarily, as is well known—to the Middle Ages.

The Middle Ages knew even less than the epoch of Hellenism of a division of labor by specialities, to which the individual scientist is, so to speak, professionally committed. On the contrary, the interlacement of all knowledge by theology and the canonized Aristotelian philosophy prevented the specialties from being made independent by research. It prevented, too, a social differentiation of those engaged in scientific work. The scientists were to an even greater extent religious men in the Middle Ages than they had been philosophers in antiquity. The social forms of science were not determined by the requirements of research but by those of instruction and by factors only indirectly connected with science. To a certain degree this also applied to the universities of the late Middle Ages and of early modern times.

At the occidental universities a division into faculties and ultimately a division of the faculties into special subjects was in progress. The ground was being prepared for specialization in that the full professor was obliged to hold lectures in a special field of science so that this sector of science would be represented. But nobody prevented him from teaching other sciences as well. Nobody contested his competence; for, of course, he was well-versed in all the branches of science, above all the basic disciplines, theology and philosophy, and he had also pursued all-around research activities. This was in fact necessary because the individual disciplines, although they already had their own names, had no specialized formulations for their problems which would have rendered possible a delimitation from adjacent disciplines.

Today we may be able to abstract the natural-science content of the theory of Kant–La Place from Kant's philosophy, the principles of the infinitesimal calculus from the monadism of the metaphysician Leibniz, the astronomical discoveries of Kepler from his theological "Weltbild," i.e., his concept of the universe. But this approach of abstracting and sorting destroys the unity of the intellectual and social existence of the scholars of that time. It is precisely this unity that necessarily has to be comprehended as a whole when the history of intellectual development and the social history of the sciences is pursued. If one attempts to enumerate the enduring results of former scientific activity, frequently enough a specialized formulation is possible. But if one is to understand how they were achieved at that time, one should know, too, the moral-philosophical publications of Adam Smith and the moral philosophy upon which the philosophical works of the brothers Grimm are based. Indeed, relative to the early history of the natural sciences, one cannot but realize that what always mattered in alchemy was to discover the analogies between chemical processes, biological processes, and astronomy, and to think with the aid of conceptions originating in Christian theology, Platonic philosophy, and Greek mythology.

A division of labor already existed within the social systems of science and its institutions; however, it was not until very late and after a good deal of hesitation that the social system of science orientated itself to the already rather early discovered division of science into various disciplines. To express it in a simple way: "The science of" mathematics already existed at a very early date, but only later did "the" mathematician come into existence. The economy is older than "the" political economist.

II

A division of labor into specialties in line with modern specialization took place only after the acquisition of scientific knowledge was begun to be understood as work, i.e., a full-time, continuous, organized, and purposeful activity. It is only after this time that we can properly speak of research in its modern sense. It is true that meditation, contemplation, disputation, Socratic dialogue, etc., resulted in intellectual revelations, too, but they were not likely to have had the character of professional work, and they did not give rise to specialization of activity. This does not mean that the scholars of earlier epochs did not work. Doubtlessly, the writing of books, the study of the authorities, and teaching activity were often enough hard work. Research as work, however, occurred only every now and then. Therefore, there was hardly any reason for a separation of professional activities into specialties, as has long been customary with handicraft. Future pastors studied within the theological faculty, future civil servants, judges, and lawyers in the law faculty, doctors in the faculty of medicine. Prior to taking up their special occupational training, they all studied in the faculty of philosophy. Of course, future practitioners were bound to prefer certain branches of science and were free to neglect others, so that many subjects found a permanent home in a certain faculty. This development resulted in—from the scientific-theoretical point of view—highly doubtful limitations, borders which, as a matter of fact, continue to cause us concern even now.

The organizational difficulties of federal German universities dealt with in the "Suggestions of the Science Council with Regard to the Shape of New Universities" ("Anregungen des Wissenschaftsrats zur Gestalt neuer Hochschulen" [Bonn, 1962]) may not only be attributed to the imminent evolution of the sciences but also to the traditional faculty system, although it has been modified in the meantime, which was originally designed in conformity with the educational requirements for the ultimate practice of a profession which had long conflicted with the evolution of the sciences proper. We observe this dilemma in Germany especially since the comprehensive university reforms at the beginning of the nineteenth century. Then, and especially with the foundation of the University of Berlin, the deliberate attempt had been made to combine research and teaching.[5] In terms of organization, this meant that the Berlin Academy of Sciences was supposed to become the nucleus of the university. This idea was extremely unusual. In Germany, as well as in other countries, scientific academies and universities were by no means identical. The case of Göttingen, too, where the academy of sciences practically formed a privileged authoritative body within the university, was an exception, although it represented an example for the future. In the eighteenth century, a division

---

[5] *Idee und Wirklichkeit einer Universität,* ed. W. Weischedel (Berlin, 1960). A comprehensive documentation concerning the history of the University of Berlin, containing among other things the famous expert opinions of Fichte, Schleiermacher, and Humboldt.

of labor between research and teaching had first come into being. The academies formed privileged societies of individual researchers for the purpose of the advancement of scholarship whereas the universities became above all educational centers. There was a strong tendency to replace the universities, which were very much on the decline, by special technical high schools. These, of course, were designed exclusively to meet the educational requirements of the individual professions and promised to deliver outstanding work in this limited field.[6]

The prime concern of those who had planned the University of Berlin—which in fact set the standards for the entire reform movement within the German university system—was to improve the education for academic professions by allowing the students to participate in the world of research. Research, too, was expected to profit from a system in which professors and students were free to discuss together the most recent or eternal problems of science, in a Socratic dialogue, regardless of future utility.

Undoubtedly, this combination of research and teaching, of studying and researching, has tremendously accelerated the progress of science. That scientific working methods have become stricter and more practical and that the fund of knowledge has expanded immensely may be attributed in great part to this combination. The expansion of knowledge and multiplication of methods, combined with a stringent and critical yardstick for the legitimacy of scientific statements, eventually enforced that specialization of research activities common today and led also to a definite separation of the academic disciplines from one another.

Philosophy, the encompassing framework of all former scientific efforts, failed to keep pace with the individual sciences in the race for accuracy and became suspected of being scientifically unreliable. It maintained the status of a dispensable luxurious occupation wherever the circumstances permitted this. It was not only a general trend toward practical problems that dethroned philosophy as the queen of sciences and dissolved the venerable unspecialized learned profession; in addition it was precisely the philosophically orientated intensifica-

---

[6] A. Busch, *Die Geschichte des Privatdozenten* (Stuttgart, 1959), p. 12, and references cited.

tion of scientific thinking, the attempt to revive the Platonic academy within a reformed university, that encouraged an evolution whereby ultimately all sciences pursued ways of their own. Shortly after, the branches of science had re-organized themselves into guilds, each jealously watching over its competences within its respective special field. This was by no means only because of selfish motives, but rather for the sake of handicraft integrity and with a pronounced quality-consciousness: Any inroad on another field could not but result in bungling work.

III

The very division of labor in research and teaching gave strong impetus to scientific development so that science could not but differentiate also socially into special fields. By revealing social structural tendencies, research as such came into conflict with the formal organization of the universities, defined by educational requirements.[7] The result was a highly complex system of division of labor in science in accordance with special branches of knowledge, however coupled—in these branches themselves—with a peculiar interdependence of research, teaching, and studying activities. This entailed an evolution in which co-operation and communication among the different branches of science gradually faded away, and, on the other hand, a traditionalism alien to science and relatively ineffective was able to spread, a traditionalism which steadily called forth analogies with medieval handicraft.

In part, a medieval handicraft tradition was fostered by the very specialization of knowledge which accompanied its effective growth and led, in turn, to compartmentalization. The product of science is information which is obtained by means of complicated refining processes in which many other

---

[7] The new report of the Science Council of the Federal Republic of Germany attempts to take this problem into account by reforming the faculties, on the one hand, and by establishing central institutes overlapping faculty borders, on the other.

data are also made use of or applied for purposes of checking. In this way science long ago elaborated highly developed techniques of information storage and distribution. It has seemed natural ever since to live with a surplus of information and to invent expedients to keep this surplus available without being choked by it. (Information supply in the strict sense has always been understood in science as a "surplus economy," not just an economy in the sense of "allocation of scarce resources.") Moreover—and this, too, is inherent with science once it is understood as progressive research—science has a dynamic character. He who is on the move needs more information than he who stays in one place. Science not only continually produces new information but is always in need of additional information so that it can overcome the situation brought about by itself, i.e., in order to know the significance of the information freshly obtained and how to continue.

This additional information can result in part from one's own special research. In part it comes from other disciplines or from society. One would think that in science, if anywhere in the world, a very flexible, mobile system of labor division and a universal feed-back system ought to have been developed which supplies all scientists with the information from other disciplines, causing them to change their behavior. Now we doubtless have to concede that the technical mastery of such a task is much more difficult than it seems in other branches of society. Scientific data need a sort of a "cultivated soil," i.e., of previous learning processes, if they are to be dealt with successfully. Otherwise they remain enigmatic communications or provoke misunderstandings.

To be sure, there are many signs, even in Germany, of a tendency to transfer information from adjoining branches of science to one's own branch and to work one's way through adjoining fields. However, all such attempts encounter difficulties which are connected—I should say—with the working constitution of science. The defective efficiency of our university institutes in respect to teaching as well as research is that here, too, the work is wrongly distributed and insufficiently co-ordinated owing to an almost medieval status and corporation thinking. We discover above all an astonishing inflexibility. It is only by putting up with the greatest difficulties

that the work can be distributed in a different way than so
far has been the situation, despite that the development of
research—just as the technical progress in industry—calls for
a continuous adaptation of the working organization, too. Not
a few activities that are very heterogeneous remain concentrated in one hand although one would better leave them to
more than one specialist. The head of an institute and his
scientific assistants perform a lot of bureaucratic work on the
side. And being just as bad at being administrators as the
medieval craftsmaster was at being a businessman, they perform bad bureaucratic work. But whereas the craftmaster was
free to practice commercial sloppiness, the poor professor faces
an unrelenting governmental bureaucracy which does not
allow for any dilettantism in administrative affairs. It compels
him to deal over and over again with matters, which have
been inadequately handled until everything is according to
regulations, and it scares him with new deadlines. Ultimately,
he acquires the proficiency of a perfect administrative inspec-
tor and simultaneously that of a partisan in the jungle-war of
bureaucracy. However, he thereby loses the time needed for
research. He can hardly spare the time to meet his teaching
engagements.

It would be wrong, however, to make bureaucracy the
scapegoat. To be sure, its inflexibility does complicate a reasonable redistribution of the institute's work. But the tradition of
science, too, causes impediments which are anything but small.
The rigid status system within the institute (professor =
master, assistant = journeyman, student = apprentice) results
in an uneconomic organization or research group, provided
there is any group work done at all. Some group-subjects are
dealt with by just one person since it is the custom that a
thesis written by the individual be presented for a doctor's
degree or for habilitation. Theses for the doctor's degree or
theses for the habilitation make up a considerable part of
research in Germany, in some disciplines even the main part.
For example, today it can be observed in the field of sociology
that it is not so easy to find thesis topics which can be dealt
with properly by an individual. It is true, there are always
literary subjects suitable to be dealt with by one man working
alone. It is more difficult to find subjects which entail field
work and do not require a group of several collaborators. A

quantitative analysis of sociological subjects of doctoral theses would indicate an unjustified preponderance of literary subjects and quite a few empirical research works, the empirical bases of which are too weak just because they were carried out by a single person. In reality, though, this means that research is failing in quality because those pursuing it are not guided purely by motives of efficiency but by the requirements of a status system which had continuously to reproduce itself according to age-old codes.

It is not only in small university institutes that the negative effects of status-thinking can be observed but also in some large-scale research institutes which, on the whole, do no longer resemble so strongly an artisan undertaking. Thus, we frequently encounter a division of labor detrimental to research which is related to the fact that the collaborators are compelled either to advance rapidly within the status-hierarchy, where only the professor is of any importance, or to try to enter a career in industry, public administration, or the teaching field, careers whose courses have long since been fixed and which have to be taken up in early years. Thus it happens that the collaborators in large research institutes, too, are in reality not researchers by profession but senior students working for a fixed time as candidates for a doctor's degree, candidates for habilitation, aspirants for a chair or a good job in industry. As soon as it is possible for them to achieve a higher status, they quit research work or attempt to carry it on part-time, usually an unsatisfactory arrangement. In other words, they often work as research workers only for a period of transition or as a sideline. Their main profession is to climb the status pyramid of science, in which only the top grades grant social security, sufficient income, and adequate social prestige. For humanitarian reasons, perhaps even due to a sense of collegiality, the head of the institute will not try to hold back his collaborators. Sometimes he even commends them "away and upwards," thus giving a chance to the assistant who long since has wife and children, and runs the risk that research assignments come to an end or are carried on by new, perhaps less able, researchers.

There is yet another aspect which proves to be detrimental to research. There is a type of thinking which leads to a considerable "Autoritätsgefälle" ("difference in degree of author-

ity") which is not advantageous to the communication of those
who ought to co-operate. Differences in generation, differences
in prestige, different circles and ways of living, rigidly re-
spectful relations with superiors, etc., all erect walls of parti-
tion and make communication difficult. As a consequence,
even small institutes which require close personal contact are
prevented from acquiring the structure of a team. Surely it is
an illusion that, properly speaking, a research team ought to
be—formally and informally—democratic or its members even
equal in status. As a matter of fact, temporarily one collaborator and then another one is forced into a position of authority.
It would also be erroneous to believe that all hierarchical
structures in research teams can result only from objective
needs of the scientific work.

IV

Today there is a certain danger that, especially, younger
scientists who are discontented with the existing conditions
let themselves be intrigued by an image of a scientific team
that in reality can never be realized or, if it is, for very short
periods only. The general social structure also penetrates into
the world of science: Claims of the families, of the various
social classes from which the collaborators come, the prestige
order of the generations, the roles of the sexes, the different
burdens of the scientists by writing or teaching assignments,
and finally the civil professional ethos which understands the
way of life as a continual advance and creates frustrations
if a period of stagnation becomes obvious. All this penetrates
the spirit of the group task and impresses its mark on it. Only
in short periods of feverish activity are the general social constraints overshadowed by a common enthusiasm for one great
research goal linking all members of the institute together to
an unique community where the different economic situation,
different social background, and the different academic status
are no longer of importance. However, such phases of enthusiasm never last long. If it would be attempted to extend them

artificially, encystment, sectarianism, and sterility would take hold of the group. The spirit of science demands that periods of strong group cohesion—when the members are necessarily sealed off from the outside world to a certain extent, and might eventually even become entirely isolated—are followed by other phases with intense and world-wide communication, phases in which the scientists are integrating their results in the universe of science and themselves in human society. At this moment, the polyp's arms of society are newly getting hold of the scientist, and it would be fatal if he would have become intellectually unprotected and vulnerable by an exaggerated team-ideology. The reason why it is difficult for the scientist to find the social role which is his due does not lie only in the temptation of growing increasingly isolated from the outside world as an individual or member of a small separate group, it lies also in the problem of overcoming organizationally and psychologically the tension between international communication and the demand for concentration on individual or team-orientated research work. Part of this problem is also that he is aware of the "limits of the community"—to use a term by H. Plessner—and that he knows that a team of scientists is no partnership for life and may not be one, but rather a—perhaps very close—partnership for a limited time.[8]

A dispassionate assessment of the limits of team work also reveals the special chances of the research team. Above all, it reveals the lines to follow in order to make teams viable within the given limits. It would be utopian to plan research groups in accordance with an early Christian model, as a perfect community without any hierarchial structure. It rather has to be found how to keep the inevitable differences in rank informal and flexible enough so that those who are most efficient at a given moment may then gain the maximum influence, correspondingly. Moreover, formal rules and behavioral patterns have to be found to prevent the differences between the various ranks of the hierarchy from becoming too great.

---

[8] H. Plessner, *Grenzen der Gemeinschaft: Eine Kritik des sozialen Radikalismus* (Bonn, 1924). Compare H. Rittel's representations in: H. P. Bahrdt, H. Krauch, and H. Rittel, "Die wissenschaftliche Arbeit in Gruppen," *Kölner Zeitschrift für Soziologie und Sozialpsychologie*, XII, No. 1 (1960), 1–40.

They should not be so great that the leader of the investigation and the co-operators are living in two separate worlds
and have long stopped speaking a common language. A labor-
sociological and labor-psychological analysis of the different
social situations cropping up in the course of a research assignment, and of the different degrees of socialization and
capacity of integration of the different personality types in
such situations, could not only help to rationalize but also to
humanize co-operation in research.

Not only the status system renders team work difficult, but
there is another factor as well, one which also reflects an
analogy to pre-industrial craftsmanship. The guild-like isolation of the disciplines from each other, as well as the historical
differences between the faculties, which no longer correspond
to the present state of science, handicap the formation of interdisciplinary teams more than we are prepared to admit. In
Germany, too, of course, scientists are aware that there are
important topics which cannot be covered by one discipline
alone; chairs are established which belong officially to several
faculties. Nevertheless, I do believe it very difficult to build
a bridge from one speciality to another, not to mention from
one faculty to another one. It is touch-and-go for a junior
scientist who has not yet reached the top. All too quickly he
may find himself sitting between all the chairs: for example, a
Ph.D. candidate interested in the question of how patients
cured of tuberculosis can be reintegrated into their profession,
their family, and their circle of friends could get into the
following situation: The guild of sociologists hold the opinion
that properly speaking he is a statistician, the statisticians
consider the subject to belong to the science of medicine, and
the medical men do not display any interest on the grounds
that the whole subject belongs to psychology. The unfortunate
Ph.D. man finally loses all his self-confidence and may even
come to consider himself an unsound scholar belonging to no
respectable discipline. He is in the same boat as the wood-
carver of the Renaissance who fails when he wishes to make
a bronze figure. Unless he has a powerful patron who can
protect him in the no-man's land between the wood-carvers'
guild and that of the brass-founders and unless he feels himself a genius, he will fail.

In large industrial plants there are special groups of highly paid workers who, because of their experience rather than systematic training, are capable of working at quite different jobs wherever they may be needed. In Germany we call them "Springer," i.e., all-around men. Such a worker is not only capable of operating one certain crane but all the cranes in the plant. Such people are necessary although they make more money in a specific job than is usually paid for it, because labor shortages due to holidays and sick-leave, as well as variations in the production program, place a premium on flexibility. This type of worker is quite different from the specialized skilled worker of former days, who in Germany still resembles very much the craftsman. Nevertheless, no institutionalized occupational training is provided for him. This should not be a craft-training of the traditional type, but ought to be a polytechnical education of that kind that Marx proposed a hundred years ago.[9] In Western Europe so far there have only been theoretical discussions about the shape of such an education. Referring to Karl Marx explicitly, the East is carrying out practical experiments—I confess I do not know anything about the results.

At universities the claim has not yet been put that such all-around men ought to be trained. This would be too much of a contradiction to the guilds' esprit de corps. Nevertheless, it is symptomatic that quite a few scientists act as "Springers" on their own. The modern methods of problem analysis (for example, cybernetics) may be transferred from one science to another. Some scientists shifted to completely different disciplines by making use of these methods, for example, from economics to the military sciences or from physics to philosophy. More important is that the representatives of the various disciplines will have to learn to talk with one another in a language understood by all parties. And it is certain that in the future there will have to be specialists of non-specialization who by profession attend to the co-ordination of heterogeneous spheres of knowledge. A reappraisal of thinking and evaluating is necessary in order to consider such activities to

---

[9] Karl Marx, *Das Kapital*, Vol. I, chap. xiii. H. Klein, *Polytechnische Bildung und Erziehung in der DDR* ("Rowehts Deutsche Enzyklopadie," No. 144 [Hamburg, 1962]).

be acknowledged professions comparable to the old-established disciplines.

V

There remains the question why it was not until recent times that the guild-like working organization of German science began to cause such a lot of trouble, whereas fifty or a hundred years ago it made possible scientific successes of great importance, i.e., in an epoch which otherwise had long since lost its medieval characteristics. In my opinion, part of the answer is the following: The research work carried out in former times was such that in most cases it could be treated very well by one individual. He, too, of course, depended on world-wide communication. He needed intellectual contact with all directions and with the past if he was to develop a constructive method of proceeding, to eliminate many attempts at solution which had already failed elsewhere, to verify hypotheses, and to incorporate the results systematically into the knowledge of his generation. The complicated communication system of libraries, professional magazines, informal conversations with colleagues both of his own and of other disciplines proved to be sufficient to keep him "up to date." To express it sociologically: The medium of the unorganized public in science to which one entrusted one's own contributions and within which one collected on one's own the contributions of others necessary for the purpose of supplementation and checkup was surveyable and efficient enough. There was an anonymous market for scientific information which was easy to survey and did not require a special organization of the contacts between producer and consumer. The specialization and extension of the branches of knowledge had already progressed so far that it was no longer possible to be productive in every discipline like the scholars of the baroque period. Most important of all, the evaluation of the results of other sciences was still possible without outside help. Thus it was not

necessary to develop rationalized forms of constant scientific
co-operation. The institutionalized social framework could be
and was primarily determined by the requirements of teaching. The traditional artisan system was indeed rather well
suited for this purpose as long as the number of students remained manageable and the extra-official administrative functions were kept within limits.

The unity of research and teaching could be achieved; they
did not conflict with each other since research still had no
needs of its own as far as the social structure was concerned.
Today we know that the underorganized information market
is not able to provide satisfactory solutions for many a problem. Whenever a scientist needs the help of another science,
he can no longer search on his own in the libraries for the information needed. He needs direct contact and help from the
colleagues of the adjacent science. He would be best advised
to work in the same institute, next door. He is in a position
similar to that of the chief accountant in a company who
orders a computer after checking a catalogue and then sets
his subordinates to work, such as turners on commercial lathes.
From the time when the computer was installed, no matter
whether it was purchased or hired, the IBM salesman and
mechanic will frequently visit him. Permanent contacts between producer and consumer go along with a certain degree
of scientific development, as does, of course, also a—let us
hope, mutual—dependence which is inconsistent with the
market principle. This phenomenon, familiar to us from the
business sector, has a parallel in science. The communication
system within science, which is characterized by the frequent
but short contacts, no longer works once a certain degree of
complexity and scope of the sciences is achieved. Lasting
and well-organized direct contacts are needed, which undoubtedly restrict the independence of the scientist and, moreover, conflict with the existing guild regulations and status
hierarchies.

It would be reasonable to hypothesize that science will also
develop along the lines of the large-scale industrial enterprise. The big research centers with a staff of hundreds, sometimes thousands of people—as they are scarcely found in
Europe to date—already take care of a major part of the

research in the United States. They compete with the universities, at least as far as personnel is concerned. Their structure shows some similarity with the industrialized white-collar large-scale enterprises, despite all the academic airs they cultivate. There is little trace of the traditional academic hierarchy of the university, even though the architectural features of the research center remind one of a university campus. Here, the scientist is an employee working on a full-time job. The institute's directors, just like an employer, have the right to hire and to fire, and use this right within the framework of applicable labor legislation according to supply and demand on the scientific production market.

This icy draft from the world of industry need do no harm to science, as is illustrated by the results of these research centers. On the other hand, it must be stated that precisely the best achievements are brought about only when these big institutes have at their disposal sufficient scientists who learned their job where research and teaching form a unity, i.e., those who were lucky enough to study at a university where the established principle of the university had not yet petrified to a fiction. From this we might draw the conclusion that the university must be mindful not to confine herself to mere teaching tasks but must look ahead for new patterns for combining the research and teaching functions with each other. Achievement of this goal, however, presupposes that the crisis of the university be analyzed first.

Comment on Bahrdt and Schmookler

Everett Mendelsohn

A READING of the papers by Drs. Bahrdt and Schmookler makes one point quite clear: Regardless how infatuated we may become with the technical content of scientific discoveries and inventions, it is essential to remember that all science, as we know it, is a result of human activities and that in order to understand its functioning, we must be aware of the social context of science. As a social institution, science has a very distinct history, in many ways no less interesting than the knowledge it has discovered, harbored, and developed. The social patterns of scientific research and training have undergone no less change than the conceptual schemes and bits of data that make up the content of science.

Dr. Bahrdt's interesting paper provides an important part of the evidence of the last statement. If one were to ask "What was the last important innovation in scientific education?", we have to agree completely that the combining of research and teaching, on the one hand, and laboratory instruction by the senior scientist, on the other, are of great importance. History indicates that this is a relatively recent development. The celebrated chemical laboratory of Justus Liebig at Giessen, where the first sustained attempts at laboratory instruction were made, dates from the middle decades of the nineteenth century.[1] Many of the prominent chemists of the later part of the century received their training and developed their attitude toward chemistry in the center at Giessen. As von Meyer commented, Liebig "emphasized with all the force at his command that the true centre point of chemical study lay not in lectures but in practical work."[2] This is not to say

[1] Thomas Thomson had a teaching laboratory at Edinburgh, ca. 1807. The tradition, however, was not maintained.

[2] Ernest v. Meyer, *A History of Chemistry*, trans. by G. McGowan (London, 1898).

that earlier experimenters in chemistry had not learned the techniques of laboratory work as apprentices in the work rooms of a master—Humphry Davy is often said to have made his greatest discovery in the person of Michael Faraday, whom he had employed to help him with his chemical experiments. Empiricism had played an important role in chemical studies almost since the days of the alchemist; but the institutionalization of specific instruction being given to a group of men in a common laboratory was a new and important step. The practical aspects of chemistry were raised to the same level of importance as the theoretical. I wonder if it is mere coincidence that a successful synthetic chemical industry was first developed in Germany just slightly after Liebig pioneered in laboratory teaching?

The combination of research and teaching has become a hallmark of science in the modern period. Recall the classic picture of the medieval reader in anatomy with the Galenic text before him, sitting elevated in the lectum while the barber surgeon hacked away at the corpse.[3] The students, realizing that little connection existed between the words read and the motions of the barber's scalpel, chatted with each other and paid little attention to the dissection. In the sixteenth century the anatomist, Vesalius, has stepped down from the lectum and wields his own scalpel.[4] The students are pictured as paying direct attention. The anatomist is now as interested in things as in words and the possibility for research in nature is open. Other fields waited somewhat longer for the adoption of empiricism but there can be no doubt that the significant accomplishment of the scientific revolution of the seventeenth century was the introduction of new standards for the validation of theories—new definitions of truth. Observation and experiment in nature were proclaimed as the final arbiters of the truth about nature.

Science may have adopted empiricism in the seventeenth century, but with several notable exceptions the universities

---

[3] See the Frontispiece to an Italian translation of the *Anothomia* of Mondino reproduced in *Fasiculo di Medicina* (Venice, 1493).

[4] See the title page Andreas Vesalius, *De Humani Corporis Fabrica* (Basel, 1543).

failed to adopt science.[5] The experimental scientist did not
find a place in the university until well into the nineteenth
century. Experimentation was conducted either in private
workshops, in the halls of a scientific society, or in an ante-
room of a medical dispensary. Mathematics and some astronomy, however, were to be found in the university curriculum.
Attempts to broaden the scope to "natural philosophy" as a
whole met with little success—even Isaac Newton was unable
to attract more than a few students to his Cambridge lectures.
The humanistic spirit of the universities triumphed over the
experimental quest of science. Neither the teacher nor the
student was exposed to science in process, and there was no
direct way for a young man to be formally trained to become
a "scientist." Only in the medical faculties, where they existed
(Oxford and Cambridge were without one), might the student
stumble across his teacher in the course of research, and it
is consequently not surprising that a large proportion of all
the science done in the seventeenth and eighteenth centuries
was done by men trained to be physicians. Science itself was,
with some few exceptions, an avocation through most of its
formative period.[6]

All of this has been said to underscore the point that the
rise of science as a social institution has been accompanied
with a series of innovations which have evolved to the present
day. The division of research labor into specialized fields
dealing with specialized problems is part of both the growth
of knowledge and the re-evaluation of the most effective means

---

[5] Science did not enter the curriculum in a major way at Oxford and
Cambridge until the last quarter of the nineteenth century. Reform in
the German universities came somewhat earlier with the establishment of
scientific professorships in the middle decades of the century. France
developed a new institution, the Ecole Polytechnique as the most efficient means of providing scientific and technical training—thus establishing an example which others followed throughout the century.

[6] The Astronomer Royal, the members of the Académie Royale des
Sciences, the hired conductor of experiments of the Royal Society,
London provided the few "professionals" in the field. Private wealth,
whether one's own or someone else's, provided the leisure time of
several other full-time practitioners of the experimental arts. See my
detailed study, Everett Mendelsohn, "The Emergence of Science as a
Profession in Nineteenth-Century Europe," in *The Management of Scientists* (Boston, 1964).

of dealing with it. The "natural philosopher" of the seventeenth century might well have taken the whole of nature as his field. But the empirical study of nature came to demand an ever increasing proficiency in using specialized techniques and tools and the individual scientist came to learn more and more about less and less. It is probably this very phenomenon which caused a socialization of the process of research, brought scientific societies into being, encouraged wide scale and regular publication of research and speculative findings, and caused the creation of an international scientific community. As the physiological analogue indicated, division of labor can significantly increase the efficiency of the use of the parts and can operate highly satisfactorily if adequate communication and exchange is maintained. The values, universality, communality —so regularly associated with science—take on new meaning in this context. Specialization is not to be feared if it can be accompanied with innovations in communication.[7]

Although it is clear that a number of the points I have made obliquely refer to Professor Schmookler's exciting paper, let me come to terms with it directly. Dr. Schmookler's point is clearly stated: "Just as inventive activity has been distributed among industries in accordance with demand for inventions, so support of basic research has apparently tended to be distributed among nations in accordance with demand for more general science." Assumed in this statement is the ultimate utility of general science.[8] What must be demonstrated is that this utility was recognized and acted upon by the state or some organized part of society in those countries where history provides a record of a flourishing scientific community. What turns out to be even harder to prove is that the science practiced in the seventeenth, eighteenth, and early nineteenth century had any direct utility. There is no doubt that the image had been created. Bacon's dream of a science practiced in the service of man was just one of several similar statements. In the early years of the Royal Society, science was fostered

[7] The rapid change noticeable today should not be overlooked. The formation of research teams will probably have as far-reaching consequences as the establishment of the first research laboratory. It is still another attempt to accelerate the production of new knowledge.

[8] This point is made by Dr. Schmookler where he indicates that society has come to expect ultimate use even when the scientist may not claim this for his work.

for "glory of God and the benefit of all mankind." [9] But the appeals made for Royal support went unheeded in England, and with the exception of the establishment of the Royal Observatory at Greenwich and the salary paid to the Astronomer Royal, no monies went to support science.[10]

Although one of the major spurs to astronomical studies on the part of the Royal Society was supposedly the attempt to discover a method for determining the longitude at sea, success in solution came with the invention of a new and reliable chronometer by an unlettered technological inventor.[11] Even further, Robert K. Merton in his study "Science and Economy of Seventeenth-Century England" indicates that up to 70 per cent of the research carried out in the early years of the Royal Society had no explicit practical aim.[12] The major area where scientific research was directly related to practical needs grew out of the problems of marine transport. Similarly problems of the military and problems of mining left their mark upon the science of the day. But this may be more accurately interpreted as the scientist responding to his social context than society foisting support on science because, as Dr. Schmookler puts it, "society has become increasingly appreciative both of the cornucopia that is science and the unpredictable character of its results." Society at large provided just about no support for non–mission oriented research in the seventeenth and eighteenth centuries—and for good reason—the gap between what science was discovering and what society and its industries could utilize was great. The seminal discoveries of seventeenth-century science were far removed from the products and procedures of the manufacturing arts of the day. In England, at least, the scientist made a play for support based upon claims of utility. Their appeals were not unlike those heard now from the National Institutes

---

[9] See, for example, Thomas Sprat's *Apologia* for the Royal Society, *History of the Royal Society* (London, 1667).

[10] No maritime nation could afford to overlook the immediate aids to navigation to be gotten from an astronomical observatory.

[11] John Harrison (1693–1776) was a Yorkshire watchmaker who successfully constructed a series of chronometers achieving an accuracy of one-tenth of a second a day. He was awarded the Board of Longitude Prize in 1765.

[12] Robert K. Merton, "Science and Economy of Seventeenth Century England," in Bernard Barber and Walter Hirsch (eds.), *The Sociology of Science* (New York, 1962), pp. 67–88.

of Health and the National Science Foundation when they appear before the appropriations subcommittees. Utility, immediate or ultimate, provided the justification.

In France, where Colbert had convinced the crown to provide pensions or salaries for the members of the newly established Académie des Sciences, the scientists were expected to devote much of their time to the solution of practical and engineering problems. Not the least of their accomplishments was the design of the fountains in the gardens of the Palace at Versailles.

I can agree completely that where science was given major support, it was for supposed utilitarian rather than humanistic reasons. It is equally arguable, however, that general or basic science probably benefitted from "fallout" of support to mission-oriented science. The universities, where one might have expected science *qua* knowledge to flourish, were inhospitable to science until it was foisted upon them in the late eighteenth century in much of Europe and the mid-nineteenth century in England and the United States. Industry was in no way sensitive to the claims for its supports made by science in the mid-nineteenth century. Much of manufacturing saw little of advancing science, for it relied upon the most rudimentary science and rule of thumb technology. The first research laboratories were founded by those industries which had been directly created by new scientific discoveries— synthetic organic chemistry and electrical machines; these were late–nineteenth–century establishments directed at solving the complex scientific-technical problems of industries utilizing new knowledge.

Of course, as Dr. Schmookler has recognized, science has always been of two minds about its social function and consequently about the sources of its support. Today it is the politically liberal scientist who intuitively fears that a science too closely tied to the needs of the state—today, military needs—will have its traditional values warped and its freedom of choice seriously encroached upon.[13]

---

[13] There is considerable controversy, today, about the wisdom of the projected moon-shot program. This enterprise, it is feared by some scientists, will engage a disproportionate number of the already trained and newly trained scientists.

During the 1930's, when the socially liberal scientist wanted to see his efforts and those of his colleagues directed toward the solution of the problems of human want, it was the politically conservative practitioners who feared a science controlled by the government and allotted its place in a "state plan." The judgment, then, within science, is a social one. This raises the question of what the demand which brings support really is and what its social motivations really are. Is it the support of general science? Or is it the desire to apply science to the solution of some specific problem?

A brief look at the financial commitments that the United States Congress is willing to make may be instructive. The mission-oriented work of the National Institutes of Health—tinged as it is with the relief of human suffering—has each year received more money from Congress than originally requested by its administration. The National Science Foundation, however, the major supporter of pure science—even the National Science Foundation reads in a clause about long-range utility—has consistently been cut back below its original request.[14] Its utility is at best one step removed; and one step seems too many for a moribund legislature.

There are many more points in Dr. Schmookler's paper which deserve comment and several which demand historical clarification. Let me deal with one of the latter. The attempt to tie the amount of support given to science to a nation's position in the "international constellation of power" raises as many questions as it answers. Is the demand for science to be measured by the total of public funds allocated? If so, how does one explain the remarkable fecundity of the Netherlands as producers of pure science and basic scientists? Furthermore, England, in the late seventeenth century, stood as one of the major contributors to general science, yet the exchequer was not touched at all. During the nineteenth century, the "reform" of science and its increase in vitality in England was brought about primarily by the scientists themselves. No doubt that this was a response to new needs as seen by the new middle-class practitioners coming from

---

[14] See the provocative report by Robert Toth, "Congress Presses Funds on National Institutes of Health," *Science,* CXXXIV (1961), 822–24.

the Midlands of England. But this was in large measure due to the changing social background of the men of science and their need to earn a living at doing science. They achieved a "professionalization" no less successful than that induced in France during the few short years following the Revolution. What I am really asking is, How do you define "the demand for more general science"? I end where I began, recognizing with the two authors the important fact that science has a social context, but still believing that the relationship must be more sharply defined if we are to discover the dynamic for the production of new science.

Comment on Bahrdt and Schmookler

Melvin Kranzberg

THE COMBINATION of research and teaching which gave scientific pre-eminence to Germany during the latter part of the nineteenth century was imitated in the United States in our own development of science. Now we are told by Professor Bahrdt, whose paper is concerned with the relationship between the organization of science and science itself, that this organization no longer corresponds to the needs of science; instead, it hinders science because of the communications problems which it presents through the division of labor and because of certain defects in its administrative framework. Perhaps we have the opportunity now to repay our German colleagues for the many lessons which they have taught us in the past by informing them how we in the United States are coping with some of the same problems which beset them. Perhaps our German colleagues can learn both from our mistakes and achievements.

Although the specialization of sciences and division of labor among scientists has been proceeding apace in the United States, we find a countercurrent developing, namely, a joining together of two formerly separate disciplines into one area of mutual concern. Biophysics, biochemistry, and the other compound sciences have reversed the trend toward fragmentation.

In approach as well as in subject matter, the problem of division of labor among scientists is being overcome, or at least transformed from an obstacle to an advantage, through the development of such interdisciplinary approaches as systems engineering, materials sciences, operational research. The international development of science will probably force these same trends of interdisciplinary subject matter and approaches upon German science, thereby overcoming, at least partially, the difficulties arising from scientific specialization and division of labor.

The administrative difficulties which hamper European science also hinder our own; we, too, have made bad bureaucrats out of good scientists, and we have only begun to work out the training of a new breed of scientific administrator acquainted with the scientific process and with social and administrative problems. However, the stratification in structure which hampers German research institutes does not have its counterpart in American society, which is distinguished for both its social and geographical mobility. Changes in the German situation would probably involve a thoroughgoing transformation of social attitudes and other aspects of European society.

But it is Dr. Bahrdt's basic thesis that raises problems relevant to American science today, for in our universities we still use the formula of combined teaching and research which he finds outmoded. This provides the research scientist with adequate assistance and helps train the scientists of the future. Both American scientific research and education would suffer if this formula were dropped, and I know of no reasonable alternative to such a system.

Although I agree generally with Dr. Schmookler's thesis that the external support of science has had a primarily utilitarian basis, I do have reservations about some of his statements. One of my reservations smacks of semantic quibbling, for Dr. Schmookler talks of "humanistic or utilitarian reasons" for support of science, as if these were opposed to one another. In my private lexicon, utilitarianism includes human needs and desires of both a material and non-material nature.

Michael Polanyi, the physical chemist, has said: "We scientists are pledged to values more precious than material welfare and to a service more urgent than that of material welfare." This is the old "science for science's sake" argument; it is one of the myths that scientists live by. But there are elements of utilitarianism other than the satisfaction of material wants. If the scientists wish to delude themselves into thinking that they are pursuing science simply for the sake of "pure" knowledge, that does not mean that such a pursuit does not have utilitarian ends, and it certainly does not invalidate Dr. Schmookler's argument that the support of science has a utilitarian stimulus.

Nevertheless—and this is explicitly stated by Dr. Schmookler —there can be, and often are, differences in the motives of those who support science and those who actually do the scientific research. When Dr. Schmookler emphasizes the political objectives of France and Germany in fostering science, this helps prove that the politician's utilitarian ends differ from utility as conceived by the scientist.

Nevertheless, I am led to question some of Dr. Schmookler's statements such as "the quest for national power, more than any other influence, accounted for the growth of science and interest in scientific matters in France during the eighteenth century." I doubt if the contributions of the French scientists were owing to any concern for "national power" on their part. Modern nationalism did not even come into being until the French Revolution, and the dynastic struggles which occupied most of the eighteenth century would scarcely inspire scientists. I firmly believe that political and intellectual, including scientific, history are related, but, in this case, *not* in the way Dr. Schmookler suggests.

I also hold to the truism that Americans have been more indifferent to basic science than have Europeans. The support of science involves more than government encouragement. I offer only a couple of examples as proof of this. The theoretical contributions of one of America's greatest scientists, Willard Gibbs, were largely ignored by his countrymen because they did not seem immediately applicable, whereas they were immediately recognized by his European contemporaries. In this country the accolades went to the applied technologists—the Fords and the Edisons. At an earlier date Benjamin Franklin received international honors as the formulator of the "one-fluid" theory of electricity; in this country he was hailed as the inventor of the lightning-rod.

Even today I find less enthusiasm for "general non-mission oriented research" than Dr. Schmookler professes to find. All the studies of industrial research laboratories indicate that their support of fundamental and/or non-mission oriented science is founded upon the hopes of eventual utility—and profits. The same utilitarian factor has stimulated the tremendous expansion of government support of science since World War II. Thus Dr. Schmookler's case of the utilitarian basis for *support* of research is in some respects stronger than he makes it out to be.

This does not mean that scientists do not carry on "pure" scientific research in industrial laboratories or in universities under government grants and contracts. Indeed, the label "applied science" frequently serves as a disguise for fundamental research of a most recondite character. Even we social scientists are not immune to the lure of research grants—and what specious reasoning or tortuous arguments we employ to show how our pet projects are essential for national defense, public health, or the development of space or nuclear efforts!

Dr. Schmookler is noted for his statistical approach to problems of scientific and technological creativity, and I regret that he has not used a quantitative analysis in this paper. Such an approach might have made him think twice before stating that "basic research has tended to be distributed among nations in accord with the demand for more general science." How does he account for the fact that many of America's most prominent theoretical physicists came from the Austro-Hungarian Empire? I doubt if Dr. Schmookler can prove that "the demand for more general science" was greater in the Hapsburg Empire than elsewhere.

Despite my cavilling at these minor points, I agree with Dr. Schmookler's main thesis. Unfortunately so, for I find an element of danger in a support for science which arises largely from a utilitarian basis. If the social matrix of science is important in determining the amount and direction of scientific effort, we must continually ask if the utilitarian bias, and the government support based on it, is beneficial to science in the long run. Many scientists fear, for example, that our current concentration on the "space race" might lead to a one-sided growth in science which would be harmful for our future scientific development.

Fortunately, the organization of science in the United States is notable for its diversity and for the scientist's pursuing his research objectives without overmuch government control or direction. Let us keep it that way, and let us remember that the present structure for its support by no means represents the final organizational framework of American science; that will inevitably change in the future as it has in the past.

II

INDUSTRIAL RESEARCH AND DEVELOPMENT

ECONOMIC ANALYSIS AND THE RESEARCH AND DEVELOPMENT DECISION

Jesse W. Markham

ONE HAS ONLY to observe casually the present sources of research and development funds to conclude that the R&D decision is complex and multifaceted. Of the $12 billion expended for this purpose in 1959, $7.2 billion was financed by government, $4.5 billion by private business firms, and $0.3 billion by educational and other non-profit institutions. The factors that ultimately shape the R&D decision therefore include, among others, the persuasiveness of arguments presented before congressional appropriations committees, the demonstrated (or intuitively felt) "clear and present need" for defense, the support of scholarship for the sake of scholarship (and perhaps of scholars), and the profits incentive. The focus of this paper is on the R&D decision made inside the profits-motivated private firm, especially the $4.5 billion or so such firms have allocated out of their own funds in recent years for this purpose.

INDUSTRIAL STRUCTURE AND R&D

It is fairly obvious that the typical firm engaging in the R&D decision must make this decision within the structural and behavioral framework of some form of oligopoly (Table 1). The six industry groups ranking highest in R&D outlays in 1951, the year marking the beginning of the great outburst of industrial R&D, accounted for three-fifths of all the research performed by industrial firms. Fifty-eight of the 127 four-digit industries making up the six industry groups have concentration ratios exceeding 50 per cent. Four of the six groups

TABLE 1

STRUCTURE OF SIX INDUSTRIES ACCOUNTING FOR THREE-QUARTERS OF ALL INDUSTRIAL RESEARCH IN 1951

INDUSTRY	RESEARCH PERFORMED (IN MILLIONS OF DOLLARS)	NUMBER OF FOUR-DIGIT INDUSTRIES	RANGE IN CONCENTRATION RATIOS	FOUR-DIGIT INDUSTRIES HAVING CONCENTRATION RATIOS OF 50 PER CENT OR MORE	
				NUMBER	PER CENT OF TOTAL
Electrical equipment	$ 437	21	20–92	10	48
Aircraft	411	4	27–97	3	75
Motor vehicles and other transportation	214	10	18–95	5	50
Chemicals	221	41	13–84	24	59
Machinery (except electrical)	104	41	5–91	12	29
Instruments	100	10	28–65	4	40
Subtotal	$1,487	127		58	46
Petroleum	$ 98	3	25–53	1	33⅓
Primary metal	37				
Fabricated metal	35				
Food	34				
Rubber	24				
Stone, clay, and glass	21				
Paper	17				
Textile and apparel	16				
Total	$1,769				

Sources: R&D performed from Yale Brozen, "The Future of Industrial Research," *Journal of Business*, XXXIV (October, 1961), 436; concentration data compiled from U.S. Department of Commerce, Bureau of the Census, *Concentration Ratios in Manufacturing, 1958* (Washington, D.C., 1962).

have at least one four-digit industry with a concentration ratio exceeding 90 per cent, and three of these four have several such industries. It is also true, of course, that these six industry groups, as do others shown in Table 1, contain four-digit industries having relatively low concentration ratios, but in four of the six the lows equal or exceed 18 per cent. The essential point to which the data presented in Table 1 are addressed, however, is not that concentration ratios standing alone reveal a great deal about the competitive behavior of the industries to which they pertain, but rather that typically the R&D decision occurs in a structural framework in which most firms are large enough to affect the fate of their rivals. Hence, the a priori logic of the R&D decision is no more valid, and is probably less valid, than the present state of oligopoly theory itself.

OLIGOPOLY THEORY

Oligopoly, in spite of the heavy work-load imposed on the term in the past three decades,[1] has never been given an operational definition. Unlike the definitions of pure monopoly and pure competition, which establish bases for predicting certain behavioral patterns from given structural conditions, the definition of oligopoly reasons backward from an entrepreneurial "state of mind" to structural conditions; i.e., when firms are sufficiently few in number that each must take into account the indirect as well as the direct effects of its own actions, oligopoly is said to exist. But the meaningful portion of the definition is the behavioral aspect of taking into account the indirect effects, since the term "few" has no operational meaning when taken out of this context. In short, oligopoly simply denotes the behavior of oligopolists.

From Cournot, through Chamberlin, and down to present game-theory models, formal oligopoly theory has been cast

---

[1] The term "oligopoly" did not come into common usage in the English language until the early 1930's. See Edward H. Chamberlin, "On the Origin of Oligopoly," *Economic Journal*, LXVII (June, 1957), 211–18.

in terms of comparative statics, with each equilibrium point identified with given supply and demand conditions or, as in the case of game theory, a given pay-off matrix for a finite set of strategies. Even under these assumed static conditions, the equilibriums for such relatively simple variables as price and output fall over a relatively wide range according to the particular assumptions made concerning the oligopolist's "state of mind." In the Cournot model the price falls and the output increases monotonically as the number of firms increase; in the Chamberlin model a discontinuity occurs somewhere along the spectrum of firm numbers between one and many and the monopoly price and output solution suddenly evaporates and is replaced by a competitive solution; in the game-theory model a co-operative strategy with side payments produces a monopoly solution, whereas a strictly competitive game in which each competitor assumes the worst will lead to a maximin-minimax equilibrium, provided the strategies of all competitors are compatible.

It is clear that oligopoly theory in its present state is highly inadequate for purposes of generalizing on such traditional variables as price and output, and it is even clearer that the theory provides virtually no insight at all on the R&D decision within the private business firm. This decision, more than any other, involves a time dimension and is therefore dynamic in character. Moreover, R&D is undertaken for one or more of the following purposes: (1) to alter the demand for an existing product; (2) to alter the costs of a product; (3) to alter an existing product; or (4) to discover a new product. The traditional oligopoly theories generally dispose of all of these either by ignoring them or by assuming them away under *ceteris paribus* conditions.[2]

These deficiencies in the relevant theory of the firm in providing a logical framework for analyzing the R&D decision are most certainly attributable in large measure to the heterogeneity of both the decision and the market organization the theory encompasses. As stated earlier, the R&D decision

---

[2] However, see Edward H. Chamberlin, "The Product as an Independent Variable," *Quarterly Journal of Economics*, LXVII (February, 1953), 1–29.

typically occurs in a market setting which may be broadly described as oligopolistic. But oligopoly includes a wide variety of structural and behavioral patterns, and the correlation between the various structural and behavioral indexes is, at best, weak. For example, the synthetic fibers and cigarette industries both have concentration indexes of approximately .80; but over the period 1953–60, synthetic fibers had a price flexibility index[3] of 0.87, cigarettes an index of only 0.02; and primary aluminum with a concentration ratio of 1.00 had more flexible prices than paperboard boxes with a concentration ratio of only 0.16. Some oligopolists to which the kinked-demand-curve hypothesis might be expected to be applicable have more flexible prices than some oligopolies with price leaders[4]—a market feature which should eliminate the kink and its attendant price rigidities. The largest fifty corporations in the United States include twenty-six of the fifty largest corporations in terms of R&D expenditures but only nineteen of the largest in terms of advertising outlays, and the fifty largest in terms of R&D include only nineteen of the largest in terms of advertising. The statistical evidence on the variegations of oligopoly could be greatly expanded.

Similarly, R&D is a highly heterogenous business activity. A portion, but probably not a large percentage, of the R&D activity conducted in some of the best-known industrial laboratories would probably qualify as basic research. To borrow a variation of a definition of economists often attributed to Professor Viner, if we define basic research as "What basic researchers do," it is difficult to differentiate between the activities of certain Du Pont chemists, or Bell Laboratories mathematicians and physicists, for example, and their counterparts in university or government research laboratories. All are concerned essentially with scientific inquiry into "the fundamental laws of nature" rather than the discovery or improvement of a particular definable product or process. A characteristic of such research is that the outcome is un-

[3] Ratio of actual recorded monthly price changes to number of months covered.

[4] See George J. Stigler, "The Kinky Oligopoly Demand Curve and Rigid Prices," *Journal of Political Economy*, LV (October, 1947), 432–49.

certain.[5] A significant percentage of applied research also has this characteristic. At the opposite pole some industrial R&D (and probably some government and university R&D) is simply a matter of combining known technology to reach known, or at least reasonably predictable, results. The distinction among R&D outlays as to whether the results are (1) uncertain, (2) risky within a probability range, and (3) known or reasonably predictable, is clearly of considerable importance for economic analysis of the R&D decision. Outlays that fall into the third category conceivably may be approached through the traditional marginal revenue–marginal costs equation; those that fall into the first category clearly cannot; and those that fall in the second possibly may be, but subject to a large probable error on the revenue side of the equation.

THE RESEARCH DECISION AND UNCERTAINTY

The combination of the uncertainties inherent in heterogeneous oligopoly and the various categories of R&D make it extremely difficult to formulate testable hypotheses concerning the R&D decision. In the case of R&D outlays the results of which are known or predictable, the firm confronts only the uncertainties of rivals' actions and reactions inherent in oligopolistic market structure. This type of R&D is, therefore, not unlike any other factor payment the oligopolist incurs. But R&D outlays of the remaining two categories combine the uncertainties of oligopoly with either uncertainties or risks.

It is possible only to speculate on how those two combinations—uncertainties with uncertainties and uncertainties with risks—interact with each other. There are reasons to suppose that they may reinforce each other. If, as Professor Knight has argued, the uncertainty-bearing entails a price, the double uncertainty of research results and oligopoly market structure

---

[5] The term is used here in the sense defined by Frank H. Knight, *Risk, Uncertainty and Profit* (Boston and New York, 1921.)

combined would reinforce each other and act as a formidable barrier to research of this category. But it should be noted that this would probably hold only for the oligopolist first to venture into the uncertain areas of research. Once one firm in an industry has launched itself on the sea of this type of research, competing oligopolists may very well reason that imitation would reduce the total amount of uncertainty they confront. The strategic interdependence of oligopolists places a premium on reasonable assurance of parity. Hence, to any given oligopolist, a single venturesome rival may very well convert an obstacle into an incentive.

This, of course, does not explain why certain entrepreneurs venture into an R&D program with uncertain prospects in the first place, but it may very well explain why in certain industries research becomes an important competitive strategy; and hence, why they are characterized as research minded. The six or seven industry groups heading the list in Table 1 come first to mind, and some of the more narrowly defined industries these groups include, such as ethical drugs, are even more striking examples. Following World War II, no doubt in part because of the wartime success of penicillin and the sulfonamides, the drug industry suddenly graduated from the modest research class to the top of the manufacturing list. Between 1949 and 1959, R&D expenditures increased 5.5-fold; the spread of R&D activities throughout the industry accounted for a substantial part of the increase.

This interpretation of the interaction of oligopoly and R&D uncertainties is easily reconcilable with, and to some extent may explain, Professor Jacob Schmookler's findings that inventive activity as measured by patent grants tends to lag behind, or at least vary with, industrial growth as measured by production.[6] At some point in time, when the economic, social, and scientific conditions appear appropriate, some venturesome inventor-entrepreneur sets off a new industry with an invention that makes a significant break with known technology. If the product satisfies some significant demand, consciously recognized or latent, it inevitably adversely affects the

---

[6] Jacob Schmookler, "Economic Sources of Inventive Activity," *Journal of Economic History*, XXII, (March, 1962), 1–20.

fortunes of those firms competing with it. At this juncture, taking-on the uncertainties of R&D may very well be looked upon as a means of making the prospects for survival more certain. As more and more firms in a given oligopoly reach this conclusion, more and more patentable inventions in the industry are generated. But meanwhile the industry itself, under the stated conditions, is registering growth.

It does not necessarily follow that such imitative or defensive inventive activity must be limited to those who comprise the oligopoly. For analytical purposes it may be both useful and valid to regard the taking-on of R&D uncertainties as an "industry" itself. In this case we would then expect, even under oligopolistic market structures, to find that resources were allocated to the activity in accordance with its expected profitability. In the post–World War II period, as Professor Yale Brozen has recently pointed out,[7] the evidence indicates that the return on investment in R&D has exceeded that in alternative uses. According to Brozen's calculations, the coefficients of rank correlation between research performed as per cent of sales in 1949 and 1951 and return on net worth in 1952 were, respectively, .89 and .91. In short, the data for the past fifteen years have tended to reduce somewhat the uncertain revenue prospects for R&D activity; and this, combined with the countermoves certain R&D oriented oligopolists have forced on their rivals, may explain much of the postwar boom in the R&D industry.

While this essay is primarily concerned with joining economic analysis with the R&D decision, it is perhaps relevant to point out that Brozen's analysis suggests that the R&D industry is approaching an equilibrium; that is, the marginal returns to R&D are approaching the activity's marginal costs. The data he offers in support of this conclusion are the deteriorating rank correlation coefficients between R&D expenditures and profits for recent years.[8] An implicit assumption underlying Brozen's conclusion is that the numerous other factors affecting profits have remained constant over time, and therefore he ignores the much discussed wage-price squeeze

---

[7] Yale Brozen, "The Future of Industrial Research," *Journal of Business,* XXXIV (October, 1961), 435–36.

[8] *Ibid.,* p. 437.

and more intense competition from abroad as causal factors in the recent downward trend in profits in the heavy R&D industries.

There is other evidence, however, that would tend to bear out Brozen's basic conclusion. If we make the assumption that the annual average GNP growth rate of about 2.5 per cent for productivity increases represents the total return to R&D for the economy as a whole, then the total cost of R&D, both government and private, has just about caught up with this figure (Table 2), having reached 2.41 per cent of GNP in 1959. The difficulty with this line of reasoning is that much of the government R&D outlay is not designed to increase the output of goods and services. If we look only at privately financed R&D, total costs amounted in 1959 to only .93 per cent of GNP, which, while approaching the productivity growth rate of the economy, still has a long way to go. Unfortunately, nothing can be said about the over-all costs and revenues of R&D at the margins. However, that the productivity growth rate has not increased in the face of a fourfold increase in private industry R&D outlays over the past decade would suggest that R&D has encountered sharply rising costs and/or sharply diminishing returns. If so, we may be reaching an equilibrium as Brozen has suggested. In this case, the uncertainties and risks that attend the R&D activity may call for much more careful scrutiny of corporate allocations to this activity in the future than was necessary in the past.

RESEARCH AND DEVELOPMENT AND OLIGOPOLY

To summarize the points developed thus far, it has been argued, as an empirical fact, that the R&D decision typically is executed within the structural framework of oligopoly, that the significant and strictly creative research involves uncertainties and risks as to prospective revenues, and that these unknowns interact with the inherent uncertainties of oligopoly

TABLE 2

RESEARCH AND DEVELOPMENT IN RELATION TO GNP,
1930, AND 1945–59 (SELECTED YEARS)

YEAR	R&D EXPENDITURES (IN BILLIONS OF DOLLARS)				
	Industry	Per Cent of GNP	Government	Total	Per Cent of GNP
1930	$ .116	.13	$ .023	$ .139	.15
1945	.9	.42	.8	1.7	.80
1950	1.5	.53	1.8	3.3	1.16
1953	2.2	.65	2.5	4.7	1.29
1956	2.9	.69	5.2	8.1	1.93
1957	3.5	.79	6.2	9.7	2.20
1958	4.0	.90	6.7	10.7	2.40
1959	4.5	.93	7.2	11.7	2.41

Source: GNP data from *Economic Report of the President* (Washington, D.C., 1963); industry R&D data from Dexter M. Keezer, "The Outlook for Expenditures on Research and Development during the Next Decade," *American Economic Review*, L (May, 1960, supplement), 363.

in ways oligopoly theory, classical or contemporary, is incapable of handling. The principal contribution of oligopoly theory to an understanding of the R&D decision is the stress all theoretical models lay on the strategic interdependence of rivals. This essential feature of oligopoly may explain some of the historical relationships between inventive activity and other variables such as production, as described by Professor Schmookler. It may also explain why R&D, given considerable impetus during World War II, became a booming industry in the postwar period. Once certain firms adopted it as a competitive strategy, rivals reacted by following suit. In this period the rough approximations of the marginal profitability of the R&D activity were conducive to both its initiation and imitation.

None of this explains why R&D is essentially an activity largely centered in, if not confined to, oligopoly, although two historical arguments establish a strong presumption that the two should go hand in hand. The first is that uncertainty limits entry, and the limit varies in rough proportion to the degree of uncertainty. Hence oligopoly is to be the expected market form of industrial organization for industries based on a technology with unknown, and therefore uncertain, technological horizons. These are also the industries in which, by definition, the possible rewards to successful R&D are high, not only because significant technological discoveries are possible, but also because the number of firms exploring the possibilities is small. The second is the familiar thesis advanced by Schumpeter, namely, that the search for the new product and the new process requires both the past accumulation of uncommitted surpluses and the prospects of future profits higher than the competitive rate of return. Both conditions are more likely to be found in oligopolistic than in highly competitive industries.

The existence of uncommitted accumulated surpluses may be a necessary but certainly not a sufficient condition. Firms that have them may clearly use them to carry out a wide variety of prospectively profitable business ventures, and there are no logical grounds for assuming that R&D will rank high, or even be included, on the list. Expansion of existing plants, the invasion of other product lines, by merger or otherwise, or a new advertising campaign are equally possible ventures. On the other hand, R&D with uncertain returns generally cannot be financed by outside sources of funds. Accordingly, while we might expect R&D to be heavily concentrated in firms having a past history of greater-than-average profitability, there are no reasons for expecting all such firms to be heavily committed to R&D.

Data presented in a recent study by Jora R. Minasian are consistent with the foregoing line of reasoning.[9] By applying multiple regression analysis to the chemical and pharmaceutical industries, Minasian concluded that the causal relationship ran from R&D to profitability through increased productivity rather than from profits to R&D. The values of his partial regression coefficients are therefore consistent with the hypothesis that expected profitability rather than accumu-

---

9 "The Economics of Research and Development," *The Rate and Direction of Inventive Activity,* ed. Richard R. Nelson (Princeton, N.J., 1962), pp. 93–141.

lated past profits induce allocations to R&D. Moreover, as corroborative evidence, he found that R&D and expenditures on plant and equipment were negatively correlated, thereby suggesting that the two are considered within the firm as competing rather than complementary means to profits. Minasian's results on this point are borne out by those of Brozen obtained by using completely different data.[10]

A COMMENT ON PUBLIC POLICY

The essential conclusion of this essay is that the R&D decision involving the most significant type of research is necessarily made in an environment of uncertainties—those that inhere in the nature of the activity and in the nature of oligopoly. Where they reinforce each other, as they may in the case of the first oligopolist to employ it as a competitive strategy, they deter R&D. For those who follow, they may tend to offset each other. However, even the initial uncertainty may make it an attractive competitive strategy in that, if successful, it is less quickly neutralized by rivals, at least under the existing patent system, than such easily imitated strategies as price reductions, new advertising campaigns, new packaging techniques, and modest product change. These speculative conclusions scarcely dictate policy proposals, although they may help clarify some of the current policy controversies.

One such controversy surrounds the size of firm and R&D outlays. Unfortunately, the controversy has failed to differentiate clearly between absolute size of firm and the market environment in which the firm finds itself. On the one hand, proponents of big business have argued that large firms are the source of industrial progress, and for this reason bigness is a social asset.[11] On the other hand, ardent defenders of the

---

[10] Brozen, *op. cit.*, p. 437.

[11] Cf. David Lilienthal, *Big Business, A New Era* (New York, 1952); A. D. H. Kaplan, *Big Enterprise in a Competitive System* (Washington, D.C., 1954); and J. D. Glover, *The Attack on Big Business* (Boston, 1954).

antitrust laws, opponents of big business, and students who simply question the "Big Business" thesis have presented persuasive statistical rebuttal designed to show that correlations between firm size and R&D outlays are at best weak, or at worst non-existent.[12] This controversy has, it seems to me, bypassed the essential policy issue. Bigness as such is not to be equated with oligopoly, otherwise the notion of the conglomerate firm would have to be discarded. In a society where monopoly in its most extreme form is illegal, the prevailing forms of market organization are various shades of oligopoly and various shades of competition, and the borderline between the two is both factually and theoretically difficult to locate. What is important is that R&D is centered heavily in oligopolistic industries as a factual matter and that, given the high order of uncertainty the R&D activity involves, the facts are consistent with the received theory of market structure. But the highly unsatisfactory present state of economic theory establishes no expectation that within any given oligopoly a strong correlation should be found between firm size and R&D expenditures. What we would expect is a strong relationship between R&D outlays and the willingness to shoulder uncertainties, but there is no logical reason for supposing that the latter is correlated with mere size.

Finally, one is likely to be charged with negligence if he explores the theoretical underpinnings of the R&D decision without relating it to the patent controversy. The substantive content and the practical administration of the patent system have been vigorously attacked, and equally as vigorously defended, since their beginnings in 1790. This inquiry into the analytical framework of the R&D decision sheds no new light on this ancient debate. However, if, as has been argued above, the obstacle to R&D is the uncertainty of its revenue possibilities and its attractiveness as a competitive strategy is the inability of rivals quickly to imitate or offset its successes, the existence of the patent system leads to the allocation of more resources to R&D than would be the case in the absence

---

[12] Cf. Jacob Schmookler, "Bigness, Fewness, and Research," *Journal of Political Economy*, LXVII (December, 1959), 628–32; and James S. Worley, "Industrial Research and the New Competition," *ibid.*, LXIX (April, 1961), 183–86.

of the system. Whether this is socially desirable depends on other factors about which very little is known, namely, the optimum quantity and quality of R&D resources, the relative social value of prospectively patentable, as compared with non-patentable, research results, and the relative efficiency of the existing patent system as compared with other institutional means of attaining the same ends.

Comment on Markham

W. Eric Gustafson

I FIND Professor Markham's stressing that research-oriented
industries generally are oligopolistic most useful. The observation itself is, of course, a commonplace; what Markham
contributes is an emphasis on oligopolistic interdependence
as a determinant of the volume of research expenditures.
Most of the literature on R&D does not even pay homage
to our lack of knowledge in this area. Markham's suggestion
that oligopolistic interdependence may be useful in explaining Schmookler's results points to further interesting work
which can be done. But let me underline that while the
notion of oligopolistic interdependence helps to explain what
one might call "reactive research," it does not seem so helpful in explaining the initial impulse toward research—or
its absence.

On another point, however, I should like to differ with
Markham. He says, that "the productivity growth rate has
not increased in the face of a fivefold increase in private
industry R&D outlays over the past decade would suggest
that R&D has encountered sharply rising costs and/or sharply
diminishing returns." To begin with, I cannot find a set of
figures which shows a fivefold increase in private industry
R&D outlays, assuming that the phrase means research
financed by private industry. A rather lower figure is called
for. But the problem still remains. Let me suggest two
alternative explanations which seem to me equally as plausible
as Markham's, if not more so.

In view of the association over the long period between
productivity growth and growth in output which Nelson
cites in his paper for this volume, might one not lay the
lack of increase in the rate of productivity change at the
door of sluggish growth in output rather than ascribe it to

diminishing returns or rising costs in R&D? (A closely related factor is, of course, the declining ratio of business fixed investment to total output since 1948.[1])

One might also suggest that a long lag between the performance of research and its economic results would go some distance toward explaining the phenomenon. It is not uncommon to hear businessmen talk about an average lag of seven years between research and its effects. If that is the case, we have yet to feel most of the effects of the rise in R&D spending over the last decade.

In any case, the factors which Markham suggests are scarcely the only possible set—nor even, in my view, the most likely ones—and it behooves us to look more carefully at the whole issue.

---

[1] See *Economic Report of the President* (Washington, D.C., 1963), p. 62.

R&D DIFFERENCES AMONG INDUSTRIES

Yale Brozen

SCHUMPETER'S hypothesis that monopolistic or oligolistic industries innovate more rapidly or often than competitive industries,[1] and Villard's corollary that such industries do more research and development,[2] is the most prominent statement in modern economic literature bearing on the reason for differences among industries in research and development expenditures. Its prominence is, perhaps, largely due to its heretical nature. Schumpeter's own earlier view was that innovation was the result of new men entering industries rather than a consequence of the existence of oligopolies.[3] He continued to stress in his later work that the constant threat of entry kept the oligopolists striving for improvement and caused them to behave as competitors would. His monopolists and oligopolists researched and innovated, then, not so much because they were monopolists in the structural sense as because they were competitors in the behavioral sense. "Effective" competition was at work, not classical "atomistic" competition.

The inference to be drawn from Schumpeter's argument is that those industries which have firms with large investments to protect and which suffer a greater likelihood of new entrants appearing in the field will do more research than those where the opposite conditions prevail. Oligopolists or monopolists secure in their position or with investments which would suffer little loss when re-allocated to other uses would not be Schumpeter's R&D heroes.

---

[1] J. A. Schumpeter, *Capitalism, Socialism, and Democracy* (2nd ed.; New York, 1947).

[2] H. Villard, "Competition, Oligopoly, and Research," *Journal of Political Economy*, LXVI, No. 6 (December, 1958).

[3] J. A. Schumpeter, *Business Cycles* (New York, 1939), p. 87–109.

I

In earlier economic writing, increased division of labor was the most discussed condition for invention and innovation.[4] Since the degree to which labor is divided and specialized depends upon, among other things, the extent of the market, those industries with a wider market were expected to enjoy a greater supply of inventions. This helped account for the greater development of new technology in the eighteenth-century textile industry, whose product value was higher relative to its bulk and weight than in, for example, the brick industry. Schmookler and Brownlee's recent work relating the rate of invention to the level of activity in an industry is a corollary hypothesis.[5]

In my own work I have indicated that there are other reasons—such as the varying quality of the science base among industries—for the differences in the amount of R&D.[6] Granted that more R&D is done in large industries than in small ones, other things equal, why is it that when we remove the scale effect by measuring R&D per dollar of sales, per dollar of value added, or per dollar of investment, we find large differences between categories of industry (see Table 3)? I have argued that when research must be done by the Edisonian try-every-bottle-on-the-shelf empirical approach, the production of a result of given value may be very expensive. Unless the demand for results is inelastic, as it may be in the drug industry, research is not profitable, and little is invested in R&D. On the other hand, with a good base in theory and a large heritage of information, experiments may

---

[4] A. Smith, *The Wealth of Nations* (New York, 1937); A. Young, "Increasing Returns and Economic Progress," *Economic Journal,* XXXVIII (December, 1928), 527–42.

[5] "Determinants of Inventive Activity," *American Economic Review,* LII, No. 2 (May, 1962). See also Schmookler, "Economic Sources of Inventive Activity," *Journal of Economic History,* XXII (March, 1962).

[6] "The Economic Future of Research and Development," *Industrial Laboratories,* Vol. IV (December, 1953).

TABLE 3

RESEARCH PERFORMED AND FINANCED, 1951–60

(Dollar Amounts, Percentages of Sales and of Investments)

INDUSTRY	RESEARCH PERFORMED						COMPANY FINANCED RESEARCH					
	Millions of Dollars		Per Cent of Sales		Per Cent of Investment		Millions of Dollars		Per Cent of Sales		Per Cent of Investment	
	1951	1960	1951	1960	1951	1960	1951	1960	1951	1960	1951	1960
Food	$ 34	$ 104	0.08	0.19	5	12	$ 33	$100	0.08	0.17	5	11
Tobacco	2	11	0.06	0.23	11	25	2	11	0.06	0.23	11	25
Textiles and apparel	16	32	0.06	0.12	3	......	14	25	0.05	0.09	3	6
Lumber and furniture	5	13	0.04	0.13	2	4	......	11	0.04	0.11	2	39
Paper	17	54	0.20	0.42	4	9	17	56	0.20	0.44	4	8
Chemical	218	1,000	1.20	3.70	20	64	206	848	1.10	3.00	19	52
Industrial	140	664	......	......	......	......	130	545	......	......	......	......
Drug	48	171	......	......	......	......	48	181	......	......	......	......
Other	30	165	......	......	......	......	28	122	......	......	......	......
Petroleum	98	298	0.50	0.99	5	11	95	281	0.48	0.91	5	10
Rubber	23	119	0.44	1.90	20	50	20	81	0.38	1.30	17	35
Leather	1	11*	0.03	0.25	5	66	......	22	0.03	0.52	......	......

TABLE 3—Continued
RESEARCH PERFORMED AND FINANCED, 1951-60
(Dollar Amounts, Percentages of Sales and of Investments)

INDUSTRY	RESEARCH PERFORMED						COMPANY FINANCED RESEARCH					
	Millions of Dollars		Per Cent of Sales		Per Cent of Investment		Millions of Dollars		Per Cent of Sales		Per Cent of Investment	
	1951	1960	1951	1960	1951	1960	1951	1960	1951	1960	1951	1960
Stone	22	82	0.35	0.94	6	13	22	78	0.35	0.89	6	13
Primary metal	37	162	0.15	0.64	3	9	34	152	0.14	0.50	3	8
Fabricated metal	41	112	0.29	0.58	11	15	30	80	0.21	0.40	8	11
Machinery	104	949	0.50	3.60	16	85	80	584	0.37	2.20	12	52
Electrical	467	2,434	3.60	7.00	35	63	207	816	1.60	2.70	16	21
Motor vehicle and other transportation	226	852	1.00	2.70	51	89	214	660	1.00	2.00	48	69
Aircraft	411	3,621	11.90	27.00	270	850†	61	434	1.80	3.30	40	110†
Instruments	93	339	3.00	7.50	109	250†	40	199	1.30	3.70	47	130†
Other manufacturing	17	139	......	......	......	......	......	......	......	......	......	......
Total	$1,832	$11,392										

* 1956.
† Approximately.

Source: Bureau of Labor Statistics and Department of Defense, *Scientific Research and Development in American Industry* (Washington, D.C., 1953), p. 24. Additional data inferred from *Research and Development Personnel in Industrial Laboratories, 1950* (Washington, D.C., 1951); and D. C. Dearborne, R. W. Kheznek, and R. N. Anthony, *Spending for Industrial Research, 1951-1952* (Cambridge, Mass., 1953). National Science Foundation, *Research and Development in Industry, 1960* (Washington D.C., 1963). Manufacturers' sales from *The Economic Almanac, 1962* (New York, 1962), p. 261. Corporate manufacturers' sales from *Quarterly Financial Report for Manufacturing Corporations* (Washington, D.C., 1962). Expenditures on new plant and equipment from statistical series releases of the Securities and Exchange Commission; *Survey of Current Business;* and *Census of Manufacturers.*

be run cheaply with paper and pencil. Theoretical principles and prior knowledge can guide applied research and development workers to high pay-off, low-cost projects. With this help, much will be invested in R&D, provided the demand for results is elastic.

I have also argued that the structural characteristics of an industry will influence the amount of R&D, although a different concept of structure was emphasized than that discussed by Schumpeter. When analyzing the Schumpeterian aspect of structure, I reached conclusions which were opposite of those reached by Schumpeter.[7] The non-Schumpeterian concept of structure concerned the supplier-customer relationship. The electric-generating and farming industries, for example, buy most of their research and development from the industries supplying them with equipment and materials. The extent to which R&D is conducted by these industries does not depend on their concentration ratios.

It is frequently argued that the atomistic competition among farmers and the lack of R&D by farmers are causally related. I would argue that there is no such relationship. Farmers are in the business of producing certain standard commodities. Those who become interested in producing a better variety of corn or potatoes end up, not as suppliers of feed or food, but as suppliers of seed to other farmers. Those who are interested in developing more productive processes end up as supplers of machinery, fertilizers, and insecticides. Successful R&D by a farmer graduates him, so to speak, into a supplier industry. As a consequence, agricultural R&D is classified in the machinery and chemical industries. Only the small part that is done on the development of new strains might be classified in the agricultural industry, and even this frequently appears in the R&D accounts of tobacco, food preserving, and packing industries.

The R&D of the electric-generating industry is small for the same reasons and for an additional one. Most power

---

[7] "Research, Technology, and Productivity," *Industrial Productivity* ("Industrial Relations Research Yearbook" [Chicago, 1951]); and "Determinants of Entrepreneurial Ability," *Social Research*, Vol. XXI, No. 3 (Autumn, 1954). See also J. Jewkes, D. Sawers, and R. Stillerman, *The Sources of Invention* (New York, 1958).

companies are limited to a rate of return on capital set by state regulatory authorities, and their expenditures must be accepted as "prudent" by these regulators. This severely limits the inducement to engage in research activities.

This leaves us with the problem of explaining the motivation for R&D outlays by the telephone company. The answer appears to me to lie in the concluding phrase of the preceding sentence. We speak of the telephone company, not the telephone industry. The Bell companies were the major market for telephone inventions. The fact of one major buyer exposed investors in telephone R&D and production of telephone equipment to such hazards that few found this a favorable climate for economic activity, to put the matter in a highly over-simplified fashion. In part for this reason, "the" telephone company found it necessary to become its own supplier of equipment and R&D. I would assert that less R&D has been performed than would have been if there had been a more competitive telephone-equipment manufacturing industry,[8] and there would have been a more competitive equipment industry if there had been more independent major telephone companies.

II

Before examining possible evidence of relationships between Schumpeterian structural concentration and R&D, it is well to raise the question of whether one would expect to find in general a separation of R&D organizations from manufacturing organizations. Why is it that most R&D departments are closely connected with the potential users of their output instead of operating as independent companies selling their

[8] "Organizing the Economy into a series of oligopolistic industries would certainly reduce the number of centers of research initiative. . . . This, by itself, would reduce the probability that any given research opportunity would be explored."—J. Schmookler, "Bigness, Fewness, and Research," *Journal Of Political Economy*, LXVII (December, 1959), 628.

new knowledge to many different users for a royalty or a lump sum? If R&D could be produced in this manner, it would then make little difference in Schumpeterian terms whether the producing organizations in each industry were organized as a few large units or many small ones.[9]

A few R&D organizations do exist as independent suppliers of new knowledge producing knowledge on their own risk for their own account. Universal Oil and Hazeltine, for example, have both operated in this fashion. Yet, even they are moving into the production of items embodying the new knowledge they produce.

The reasons appear to lie in the areas of tax structure, the impingement of the anti-trust laws on the use of patent rights, the non-patentability of large areas of new knowledge, and the need for intimacy of development and production to complete the development in application of new knowledge. First, there are tax advantages to launching research and development in an organization which has current taxable income against which R&D expenditures can be expensed. In these circumstances, what amounts to an interest-free loan from the government is obtained which is not available to a new independent R&D organization which has no taxable income when it is first launched.

Secondly, the yield from patent rights has been severely limited by the finding under the anti-trust laws that certain methods of discriminating pricing to maximize the return from R&D investment are illegal. As a consequence, greater yields are available from patented information by using it for some purposes than by restricting the return only to that obtainable from royalties.

Thirdly, those involved in developing new knowledge must often work intimately with the men applying it in production to "debug" the processes and products in which the knowledge is embodied. Valuable information, mostly non-patentable, is produced which an independent R&D organization might retail to competitive firms. Producing organizations first applying new knowledge frequently find it necessary to

---

[9] W. Nutter, "Monopoly, Bigness, and Progress," *Journal Of Political Economy,* Vol. LXIV (December, 1956).

control the suppliers with whom they work in order to realize a return on the information they help develop.

Schumpeter's idea that monopoly is necessary to realize a return from the work of developing and introducing an innovation is correct, but the monopoly does not have to occur in the form of the structure of an industry. The producers of new knowledge can monopolize it without previously monopolizing an industry. They can do this, in part, through the use of patent law, as Schumpeter indicated, in part by the fact of prior knowledge with a lag in application by competitors, in part by secrecy, and in part by being in a position to maintain a lead over others by always evolving further from an advanced position in the field.

III

If Schumpeter, in his late writing, and Villard are correct, we should expect to find more R&D and a higher rate of innovation in concentrated industries. Also, we should expect more R&D in the large firms in an industry than in the small firms after allowing for the scale effect. That is, there should be more R&D per sales dollar or value-added dollar or more per dollar of investment.

A correlation of manufacturing industries ranked by the ratio of R&D expenditures in 1949 to sales and by degree of concentration (using Warren Nutter's data for 1939 given in *The Extent of Enterprise Monopoly in the United States, 1899-1939* [Chicago, 1951], p. 82) yields a coefficient of 0.29. If we accept this as significant and not simply the result of chance, then the degree of concentration may be said to account for 9 per cent of the variation in research rank among industries. This still leaves us with 91 per cent of the variation to be explained on other grounds.

A large part of the variation among industries may be explained on three grounds. The first is that being second best in some fields has little value. A second-best automobile in terms, let us say, of gasoline consumption may still be a

valuable automobile. Consumers will be willing to purchase
such a car equal in other aspects to the best if the lower
price compensates for the difference in gasoline operating
costs. To put this another way, it is not worthwhile spending
very large sums on research and development of gasoline
saving methods if the amount of gasoline saved in the future
life of the car does not have a very large present value. On
the other hand, a second-best military aircraft may lose the
war or it may take several such craft to combat the best.
Since the difference in value of second best and best may
be very large, it is worthwhile making great efforts to develop
the best aircraft. For this reason, large research and development appropriations are provided by the federal government for expenditure in those industries producing crucial
military items.

Military product industries spend large amounts of their
own funds in addition to those provided by the government
for the same reason. That is, a design competition for a
military contract yields a contract only to the company
entering what is presumably the best design. The second-best
design is worth zero to the company submitting it.

A second factor, affecting the cost of research and development, is the cost of capital. In the petroleum and motor-vehicle
industries, a slowing in the growth of demand has reduced
the return from investment in expansion of capacity for the
standard lines. The reduced return from alternative uses of
capital reduces the cost of capital for research and development and leads to an expansion of R&D. The tripling of
company funds used for this purpose in the nine years from
1951 to 1960 is in part a result of this situation.

On the other hand, a reduced rate of investment in an
industry has dampening effects on R&D. To some extent,
R&D investment is a substitute for plant and equipment and
other types of investment spending, but those industries
spending little for investment find little use for research and
development as a substitute.[10]

---

[10] Brozen, "Trends in Industrial Research and Development," *Journal
of Business,* XXXIII, No. 3 (July, 1960), 211–15; and "The Future of
Industrial Research," *Journal of Business,* XXXIV, No. 4 (October,
1961), 437–38.

The third ground accounting for much of the variation between industries is the different quality of the science base available to different industries. Electrical, chemical, and mechanical industries find a well-developed body of science with an excellent theoretical structure available to guide their research and development. Mechanics is among the oldest of sciences, and chemistry and electricity are old enough to have led to the founding of industrial-research laboratories in this country over half a century ago. These, of course, were predated by chemical-research organizations founded earlier in Germany.

The importance of the science base in determining relative research performance becomes very obvious when the content of research programs in the industries other than the chemical, electrical, and machinery (including motor vehicle) is examined. Much of the R&D in the food industry is chemical and machinery research and development. The petroleum and rubber industries devote much of their research and development effort to chemical projects. Even the machinery industry devotes great effort to electronic research.[11]

The science base of the chemical, electrical, and mechanical industries has been expanded by fundamental discoveries in recent years with the result that R&D growth has continued in these industries in the past decade, despite its early founding which might have been expected to have provided enough time to reach maturity, since new areas for applied research and development have been opened by the discoveries. Newness in product as well as in fundamental science is also of great importance in determining which industries will do more or less research. This becomes very apparent when industry trends and relative positions are examined during the period of great expansion of R&D since the 1920's.

During this period of enormous expansion of industrial research, the instrument industry—which is now, excepting aircraft, ranked at the top in terms of research spending (Table 4)—came into existence, as far as business census-

---

[11] National Science Foundation, *Funds for Research and Development in Industry, 1959* (Washington, D.C., 1962), pp. 70–71.

TABLE 4

RESEARCH EXPENDITUTES AS A PERCENTAGE OF SALES,
BY INDUSTRY, 1927–60

Industry	1927*	1937†	1949‡	1960§
Aircraft and parts	. . .	. . .	5.0	27.0
Instruments	. . .	. . .	3.0	7.5
Electrical equipment	0.54	1.5	3.1	7.0
Chemical	0.42	1.1	1.7	3.7
Machinery	0.19	0.43	0.52	3.6
Rubber	0.36	0.96	0.75	1.9
Petroleum	0.09	0.45	0.57	0.99
Stone, clay, and glass	0.13	0.43	0.56	0.94
Motor vehicle	0.07	0.4 ⎫	0.9	2.7
Other transportation equipment	0.07	0.07 ⎬		
Primary metal and products..	0.07	0.17	. . .	. . .
Fabricated metal	. . .	. . .	0.19	0.63
Primary metal	. . .	. . .	0.14	0.64
Paper	0.06	0.17	0.32	0.42
Tobacco	. . .	. . .	0.03	0.23
Food	0.02	0.04	0.10	0.19
Forest products	0.013	0.036	0.03	0.13‖
Leather	0.01	0.025	0.03	0.25#
Textile and apparel	0.007	0.022	0.07	0.12

* F. S. Cooper, "Location and Extent of Industrial Research Activity in the United States," in National Resources Planning Board, *Research: A National Resource* (Washington, D.C., 1941), p. 181.

† J. V. Sherman, "Research as a Growth Factor in Industry," in *ibid.*, p. 122, provided data on research expenditures by industry. Industry research expenditures have been modified to take account of differences in cost per research worker for different industries, instead of using $4,000 per worker to compute expenditures. Data on sales from *The Economic Almanac, 1953-54* (New York, 1955), p. 320.

‡ Research expenditures in each industry estimated from data on professional R&D employees and total R&D employees reported in *Research and Development Personnel in Industrial Laboratories, 1950* (Washington, D.C., 1952), p. 11; data on spending per professional employee and total employees reported in Bureau of Labor Statistics and Department of Defense, *Scientific Research and Development in American Industry* (Washington, D.C., 1953) adjusted to 1949 price levels. Manufacturing corporate sales are from *U.S. Income and Output* (Washington, D.C., 1958), p. 215. Aircraft sales estimated from data for twenty-nine companies.

§ Computed from data on the number of research workers provided by *Research and Development Personnel in Industrial Laboratories, 1950.*

‖ Based on 1959 data.

Based on 1956 data.

takers were concerned.[12] (However, three companies in this category were among the one hundred largest spenders on research and development, measured in absolute number of personnel, in 1927, and two were among the one hundred largest in 1938. The companies were in three separate sub-categories—photographic, instrument, and optical—and declined in rank at successive survey dates through 1955.) The next ranking industry, electrical equipment, held top position in the 1920's and has remained there relative to all other manufacturing industries ranked at that time. It outranked instruments until 1957. It employed two thousand researchers (approximately 10 per cent of all reported research personnel) in 1927, more than any industry other than electrical communication, and spent a higher percentage of sales on research than any other industry except electrical communication, which spent 1.3 per cent.

The electrical industry was relatively new in the 1920's, as is a significant portion of the instrument industry today. Its continuing high level of spending today is in part a consequence of the work in a new segment of the industry, in electronics, and in applications of recent discoveries in solid-state physics. From this we might infer that new product categories will spend large amounts on research relative to sales. The relationship is expected partly because sales are low until a product is established and partly because much needs to be learned to perfect new products, develop applications, and improve production processes. As these problems are solved and sales grow, the percentage of sales spent on research may be expected to drop, although absolute amounts continue to grow. The instrument and electrical-equipment industries have not yet reached this stage despite a very rapid growth of sales. Electrical equipment is, however, closer to this point than instruments. The instrument category is adding products and possibilities of new applications at such a rapid rate that (excluding aircraft from the ranking) it has spurted from second place, with 3.2 per cent of sales revenues spent on research in 1951, to first place since 1957, with more

---

[12] The instrument category includes a number of subgroups which were in existence much earlier (medical instruments, photographic equipment, watches and clocks, etc.) but which were lumped into other categories.

than 5.5 percent of sales spent on research in that year, and 7.5 per cent in 1960. Electrical equipment has dropped from first place in 1951, with 3.6 per cent of sales spent on research, to second place since 1957, with 5.5 per cent spent on research and development in that year, and 7.0 per cent in 1960.

Perhaps 1927's third-ranking industry, rubber, illustrates the decline in percentage and rank to be expected after an industry is well established and the early problems of product development and application are overcome. Rubber rose from 0.36 per cent of sales spent on research in 1927 to 0.96 per cent in 1937, with a doubling of research personnel employed. It then dropped back to 0.54 per cent in 1951, with a continued increase in research personnel amounting to approximately 50 per cent of its 1937 research employment. When facilities for producing synthetic rubber were acquired, the relatively new material raised problems which played a role in pushing research above 1.5 per cent of sales in 1956 (the acquisitions occurred in 1955). Despite the surge in spending, the rubber industry fell two ranks because of an even greater surge by the motor-vehicle and machinery industries.

Part of the failure to maintain research performance relative to sales in the 1940's and early 1950's in the rubber industry, despite the appearance and use of synthetic rubber in the 1940's, can be attributed to the role of the United States government in the synthetic industry. It owned the plants, required patent pooling and exchange of information until 1948, and subsidized research by private companies, with the government retaining rights to all discoveries. The latter arrangement continued into the 1950's. The companies doing research on government subsidy had no profit motive, and those doing research without subsidy found profit potentials severely limited by what amounted to government pre-emption of the field both in research and in ownership of production facilities. With the end of government dominance in 1955, increases in private research spending more than made up the reduction in government subsidy.[13]

If high rates of research activity are to be expected in relatively new industries, should we expect low rates in old

---

[13] R. Solo, "Research and Development in the Synthetic Rubber Industry," *Quarterly Journal Of Economics*, LXVIII (February, 1954), 61.

industries? Textile, leather, food, paper, lumber, and pottery products have an ancient history. As expected, we find these industries in the bottom ranks in 1927, except the stone, clay, and glass group. Despite the long lineage of these industries, however, the percentage of their sales spent on research has risen. The percentage is increasing as fast as, and sometimes faster than, the newer industries. The occupant of the bottom rank in 1927, textiles and apparel, more than tripled its research relative to sales by 1937. Between 1937 and 1953, textiles increased research relative to sales by another five times, a greater rate of increase than that in any other category except two other bottom-ranking, old industries—leather and forest products.

What happened in textiles? The development of new materials for use in the textile industry is largely responsible; the usual problems had to be solved. Also important, development of a scientific base for improvements in textile technology occurred. The invention of synthetic fibers not only provided new materials and new aspirations for what might be done with old materials but also stimulated the development of a body of knowledge approaching a science of textile fibers. With at least a semi-scientific base, the cost of discovering and developing new technology could be reduced, and research became an economically worthwhile outlet for investment. The trial-and-error methods of research, which were too costly for the results they could produce, were partially replaced by cheaper, deductive, paper-and-pencil techniques.

This experience, and others, provides a clue to the future direction of inventive activity in the form of research-and-development programs. Where a scientific base which can replace empirical methods has been developed fairly recently, or where basic advances are made which add to an old scientific base, research spending may be expected to begin growing rapidly or continue growing. The more basic research in any given field, the greater the prospect for the development of a scientific base. An inventory of basic research can, then, provide some clues concerning the prospects for surges of research-and-development activity in various fields.

We should also add that the more research-and-development activity there is in a field, the more rapid, usually, will be the improvement in the scientific base for the field, and the more probable will be a maintained or, even, increased rate of spending. This is a major factor accounting for the maintenance of high rank and the failure of the percentage spent on research to decline in the electrical equipment and chemical industries since 1927, despite an enormous growth in sales. In the case of electrical equipment, an added factor increasing the percentage of sales spent on research is the provision of funds by the federal government, which accounted for 68 per cent of the industry's total performance in 1960, although the experience of the rubber industry should be kept in mind when interpreting the effects of government subsidies of research.[14]

Although high applied research-and-development activities in a field will result in some improvement in its scientific base, even greater improvement will flow from application of funds directly to basic research. In those fields in which a larger proportion of research-and-development funds is allotted to basic work, there are better prospects for the growth of research and development than in converse instances. The instrument industry may have forged ahead of electrical equipment, in spite of—or because of—governmental provision of only 50 per cent of the total funds available for research and development, as against 68 per cent in electrical equipment, because, in 1953, it used 7 per cent of its funds for basic work as against the less than 3 per cent used by electrical equipment (Table 5). The latter industry has since doubled its basic outlays, while the instrument industry has not raised its basic performance. This may bring about a reversal of ranks if this pattern of spending, along with such factors as the maturation of the instrument industry, continues.

The over-riding principle governing the differences in research and development among different industries is the difference in opportunities for profitable investment in this activity. A science base, on the one hand, makes for low cost relative to given values for results. Supplier-customer

---

14 G. J. Stigler and D. M. Blank present evidence which may indicate that government spending replaces private spending on research and, perhaps, reduces total private performance (*The Demand and Supply of Scientific Personnel* [New York, 1957], p. 59).

TABLE 5

Basic Research Performance, By Industry, 1953, 1956, 1960*

Industry	1953†		1956†		1960§	
	Millions of Dollars	Per Cent of R&D	Millions of Dollars	Per Cent of R&D	Millions of Dollars	Per Cent of R&D
Chemical	$ 37.8	10.5	$ 55.0	10.7	$117.0	12.0
Electrical equipment	19.1	2.6	49.9	4.8	78.0	3.0
Aircraft	18.1	2.4	41.1	2.0	44.0	1.0
Non-manufacturing	13.7	7.0	16.4	5.9	23.0	16.0
Manufacturing (n.e.c.)	12.3	1.6	16.4	1.7	6.0	4.0
Instruments	11.7	6.8	13.2	6.0	9.0	2.0
Machinery	11.5	3.6	15.3	2.5	22.0	2.0
Petroleum	11.1	7.6	19.7	9.8	55.0	18.0
Primary metals	4.2	7.1	7.4	8.4	10.0	6.0
Stone, clay and glass	3.6	9.6	3.2	4.8	6.0	7.0
Food	3.5	6.4	3.8	5.0	8.0	7.0
Rubber	3.1	5.7	2.8	3.4	4.0	3.0
Motor vehicles and other transportation	....	....	....	....	8.0	1.0
Fabricated metal	....	....	....	....	1.0	1.0
Paper	....	....	....	....	1.0	2.0
Textiles and apparel	....	....	....	....	1.0	1.0
Total	$149.7		$244.2		$393.0	

* Total annual expenditures on basic research in the United States amounted to $432 million in 1953-54 ($151 million performed in industry, $47 million by federal agencies, $208 million by universities, and $26 million by other institutions). Basic research in the United States grew to $1,302 million in 1960-61 ($382 million in industry, $245 million in federal agencies, $575 million in universities, and $100 million in other institutions).

† National Science Foundation, *Science and Engineering in American Industry* (Washington, D.C., 1956), p. 67.

‡ National Science Foundation, *Funds for Research and Development in Industry, 1959* (Washington, D.C., 1962), p. 28.

§ *Reviews of Data on Research and Development* (September, 1961), p. 7; and National Science Foundation, *Research and Development in Industry, 1960* (Washington, D.C., 1963). Basic research in electrical equipment in 1960 includes telecommunication research, classified in non-manufacturing in 1953 and 1956.

relationship, newness of product, and the valuelessness of second best, on the other hand, govern the schedule of result values. Two other factors should be mentioned, one affecting the value of results and the other the cost of obtaining new knowledge.

Rapid growth in demand in some markets, resulting from the growth in per capita income, has been frustrated by an equally rapid growth in cost. The demand for maid service, for example, has a very high income elasticity, but the price of maids has risen as rapidly as demand has grown. This frustrated demand has presented opportunities for the profitable development of new products by the food and appliance industries. The food industry has developed new products incorporating maid service (prepared and partially cooked foods) and the appliance industry has developed mechanical maids (automatic home laundries, instrument regulated stoves, mechanical garbage disposers and dishwashers, etc.). Applied research and development in these industries, as a consequence, has grown, relative to such industries as textiles and apparel, where research and development has stagnated since the spurt associated with new fibers and new science ended in the early 1950's.

IV

The differences in research and development spending among different industries are very largely the result of the differences in opportunity for profitable investment in R&D. Industry structure may have a slight influence insofar as patent protection is not available for some kinds of knowledge, but the aspect of structure which is most directly relevant is ease of entry or ease of imitation of appliers of non-patented knowledge. The evidence that less concentrated industries provide a better market for new knowledge is fairly strong.[15]

---

[15] In addition to the previous sources cited, see G. J. Stigler, "Industrial Organization and Economic Progress," in *The State of the Social Sciences* (Chicago, 1956).

Opportunities for profitable investment in R&D differ among industries according to the quality of the science base and cost of capital, on the one hand, and potential value of results, on the other. The potential value of results increases with the competitiveness of the buyers; the newness of the product, and, therefore, the potential opportunity for developing new uses or for improving the product; the appeal of the best as contrasted with the second best to buyers; and the size of the market.[16]

---

[16] This point has been discussed in Y. Brozen, "Trends in Industrial Research," p. 214.

ENGINEERING AND PRODUCTIVITY CHANGE: SUSPENSION-BRIDGE STIFFENING TRUSSES*

Robert S. Merrill

THE AIM of the study reported here is to identify some of the kinds of engineering knowledge that have significant productivity effects by means of an exploratory case analysis of one aspect of suspension-bridge design.

Recently, there has been increased recognition of the role of technological advance in productivity change and economic growth. The influences of inventions, of advances in fundamental science related to invention, and of "research and development" in general have been increasingly stressed and their relations to economic change deeply studied. At the same time, there are other kinds of knowledge which have significant effects on economic productivity. In particular, it seems to me, as a result of previous work (Merrill, 1959, 1962), that surprisingly little attention has been paid to the role of engineering knowledge. Also, there seem to be few studies which enable us to really identify the various technological sources of particular economic changes.

Yet such knowledge seems essential if we are to establish with some precision the role of technological change in productivity advance, the economic relevance of different bodies of technological knowledge, or the institutions and activities which are significant sources of economically relevant technology. One way of furthering our knowledge of these subjects appears to be studies of engineering advances focussed on assessing their economic effects and tracing the kinds of knowledge which make these effects possible.

*The research on which this paper is based was partly supported by a National Science Foundation grant; by a Ford Foundation senior research fellowship at the Graduate School of Industrial Administration, Carnegie Institute of Technology; and by the Department of Economics, University of Minnesota. It is an outgrowth of earlier work at the Research Center for Economic Development and Cultural Change, University of Chicago. This support and assistance, financial and otherwise, is gratefully acknowledged.

With these considerations in mind, suitable subjects for exploratory case studies were sought. The one partially reported here is a study of improvements in the design of the stiffening trusses of American suspension bridges in the period from about 1909 to 1940. Stiffening trusses are the vertical steel frames or girders attached to each side of the suspension-bridge deck for the primary purpose of reducing the undesirable slopes along the bridge floor which are caused by uneven distributions of traffic on the bridge. This appears to be a case where an important advance in engineering knowledge has led to a series of economically significant changes. A noted bridge engineer has said (Steinman and Watson, 1957, pp. 366–67):

> The introduction of the "Deflection Theory" for suspension bridge design revealed that prior spans had been proportioned with needlessly excessive depth and section, and placed a premium of economy on more flexible design. Increased emphasis on artistic appearance placed a further premium on grace and slenderness. Stiffening trusses were made of shallower and shallower depth. . . . Thus improvement in analysis, the demands of economy, and considerations of aesthetics —all combined to accelerate the trend toward increased slenderness of proportions.

An attempt to identify the magnitude of the improvements connected with the introduction of the deflection theory, and, at the same time, to uncover any other advances in knowledge that had played a role in the making of more economical stiffening trusses should reveal some of the specific ways in which advances in engineering knowledge can produce identifiable economic effects.

So far, my explorations have been limited to printed sources (engineering journals, textbooks, treatises, handbooks, etc.) supplemented by discussions with a few academic engineers. I plan later interviews with bridge designers and a search for other relevant data. The results presented here are, therefore, tentative.

The introduction and bringing into use of the deflection theory posed a series of problems for engineers. I will outline some of these problems, give the evidence I have for the ways they were solved, and present the few estimates I have found of the magnitude of the economic effects associated with the resulting advances in knowledge.

Two uses of the deflection theory will be examined. The first is use of the theory to design trusses of a *given* stiffness which were less heavy, and therefore less expensive, than those designed before. Here the role of the deflection theory in "final design" calculations is of primary importance. The second use is in making shallower, less stiff trusses, which were more economical for *that* reason. This change is connected with the influence of the deflection theory on "preliminary design" decisions. These uses combined to produce the improvements in stiffening trusses with which we are concerned.

DESIGNING LIGHTER TRUSSES OF A GIVEN STIFFNESS

The deflection theory is an example of a very important kind of knowledge in structural engineering. It is a method of "stress analysis" or "structural analysis" used to calculate the stresses (forces) which are generated in a suspension bridge by the action of traffic loads, temperature changes, and other influences. The engineer needs to know the largest stresses that will occur in each part of a bridge in order to make the part strong enough but, at the same time, not so strong as to be uneconomical. In addition, the magnitude of the stresses affects how much the parts deflect, that is, bend or stretch or contract. Thus, knowledge of stresses is important in designing structures for rigidity as well as strength.

Theories of stresses are approximate. No theory includes all the factors in any actual physical situation, nor does any one show with full accuracy how each factor that is included behaves. At the time the deflection theory was formulated (largely by J. Melan, 1888), two other theories of suspension-bridge stresses were available. The oldest and simplest was the rigid theory. The second, the elastic theory, was quite new and considerably more complicated. The deflection theory itself was by far the most complicated of the three. Each successive theory made fewer simplifying assumptions than the preceding one, which explains the increasing complexity.

Around the turn of the century, suspension-bridge designers were making increased use of the elastic theory, but had not actually used the deflection theory. Here is our first problem: What led to the first actual use of the deflection theory? Why the apparent delay in using a less approximate and presumable more accurate theory?

Introduction of the Deflection Theory into Use

The reason for the delay appears to be quite simple: Nobody thought it was worth the trouble, including the theory's primary originator and developer, Melan. Of Melan's 1888 presentation, Moisseiff (1935, p. 1206) remarks: "Strangely, Melan did not put much emphasis on the practical results of the theory." Later, in 1905, Melan (1905, pp. 208–13) used approximations derived from the elastic theory in discussing proposed East River bridges where deflection theory considerations would have been most relevant. Even in 1908, Moisseiff reports (1925, p. 458) that in an interview in Prague, Melan still did not realize the importance of his "more exact" theory, i.e., the deflection theory.

What, then, happened to change the situation? Luckily we have an account by the first user of the deflection theory, Moisseiff, of the circumstances which led him to adopt it (1935, pp. 1205–6). He states that, in the summer of 1901, some of the suspender rods of the Brooklyn Bridge broke. This aroused much interest, and Moisseiff made an analysis of stresses and deformations of the bridge (*ibid.*, p. 1205): "He found that while there were no official measurements of the deflection of the bridge under load, such deflections as could be observed were of much less magnitude than would result from computations based on the Elastic Theory." This was the first discovery: There was a significant discrepancy between the stress theory in use and the roughly observed behavior of an actual structure.

Moisseiff then discovered he could get calculated results which agreed more closely with observation if he neglected the effect of the light stiffening trusses of the bridge and

merely calculated what the deflections of the unstiffened cable
would be. (Methods for doing this had been established long
before and were relatively simple.) The deflections of an
unstiffened cable depend primarily on the dead-load weight
of the cable itself and of the structure suspended from it.
This finding, therefore, led Moisseiff to the conclusion that the
reason the elastic theory gave "large errors" for the long-span
Brooklyn Bridge was because that theory neglected the influence of the dead load. This, in turn, implied that the
deflection theory, which took into account both dead load
and truss stiffness, would be significantly more accurate than
the elastic theory for large bridges. Moisseiff then developed
the deflection theory so it could be used for bridges with
suspended side spans and in 1904 used it in making the
design for the Manhattan Bridge that was actually constructed
(main span 1,475 ft., completed 1909). This was the first
actual use of the deflection theory in suspension-bridge design.

To the first discovery had been added a second: the
discovery that one particular theory, the deflection theory,
would give significantly better results than the elastic theory.

This episode suggests a more general conclusion about the
introduction into use of a new theory of stresses or similar
types of engineering knowledge. A bare mathematical theory,
though it may involve fewer simplifying assumptions than
another, does not, in and of itself, tell you whether it is
significantly more accurate in use. It is perfectly possible for
added complications to make very little difference if simpler
assumptions are sufficiently close to the facts. Therefore, use
of a theory requires additional knowledge, knowledge of the
relative accuracy of a new method as compared with old
ones. This is another kind of engineering knowledge, in
addition to theory, that can be expected to have important
economic effects.

A second episode connected with the Manhattan Bridge
reveals still another significant kind of engineering knowledge:
knowledge of the safety of a new method of stress calculation.
When the Manhattan Bridge was nearing completion, enough
doubts were expressed about its safety that an outside consultant was called in to check the design. The report was
favorable ("The Design . . . ," 1909), thus allaying doubts

about possible computational errors. However, I think it a fair inference that doubts about the bridge and its method of design were far more convincingly allayed by the successful behavior of the actual structure than by the report. This example and Moisseiff's work on the Brooklyn Bridge illustrate the role that actual structures can play as sources of knowledge as well as objects of use.

Establishing the Range of Usefulness of the Deflection Theory as a Method of Stress Calculation

There is a gap in Moisseiff's account which we should now pursue: What does he mean by "large errors" (Moisseiff, 1935, p. 1026) when the elastic theory is used? How big or significant does an improvement in accuracy need to be before it becomes worthwhile to use a much more complex method rather than a simpler one? This is no mere academic question, for the much simpler elastic theory continued to be used for a variety of purposes along with the deflection theory after the latter had come into general use. Considerations of convenience can, therefore, compete with those of accuracy, so we need to know how the outcome is determined.

The basic consideration leading to the actual use of the deflection theory becomes clear in a paper in which Moisseiff (1925) seeks to persuade engineers of the practical usefulness of the deflection theory. The core of the argument is a quantitative calculation of the amount of savings that were obtained by using the deflection rather than the elastic method in the final stress calculations for the Philadelphia-Camden Bridge (main span 1,750 ft., completed 1926).

The method Moisseiff uses to compare the economic effects of this use of the two methods is an approximate one common in structural engineering. The cross-sectional sizes of each part of a structure are generally made proportional to the maximum stresses which are expected to act on them. Therefore, the weight of a structure of given linear dimensions will be approximately proportional to the average of the calculated maximum stresses. And if costs are assumed to vary about proportionately to the weight of metal, then one can estimate the difference in costs of the same structure designed by two different methods of stress calculation.

After correcting this theoretical saving slightly (since all
cross-sections can not be reduced proportionately), Moisseiff
(1925, pp. 461–62) arrived at a saving of truss metal in all
three spans of 42 per cent, 3,211 tons of steel, or $548,000.
This was made possible by using the lower stresses calculated
by the deflection theory rather than the higher ones calculated
by the elastic theory. Moisseiff then adds the indirect savings
resulting from the fact that suspenders, cables, towers, and
anchorages would have to carry less weight, and obtains a
total saving of $850,000 or, as I calculate it, about 10 per cent
of the cost of the Philadelphia-Camden Bridge. Elsewhere,
Moisseiff (1927, p. 923) also gives the theoretical direct saving
in truss weight for the Manhattan Bridge as 26 per cent.

These figures tell us what was meant by "large errors."
These are errors whose size and direction meant that large
relative and absolute savings could be made by eliminating
them with the deflection theory. More difficult and complex
computations were justified when they had effects of this
magnitude on stiffening truss designs. Extrapolating from
scattered and incomplete data, I estimate that the savings
obtained through this specific use of the deflection theory in
designing American suspension bridges during the period
1909–40 were probably at least 50 per cent of the metal "in
place" that would have been required had the elastic method
been used. Translated into physical productivity terms, this
is an increase in productivity of 100 per cent. (I hope to much
improve this estimate.) The deflection theory clearly did have
significant economic effects.

However, our discussion shows that these economic effects
depended not only on the deflection theory per se, but also on
the discovery of its accuracy and safety. Furthermore, the
Moisseiff argument clearly suggests that widespread use of
the deflection theory also depended on specific demonstrations
of the magnitude of its economic advantages by means of
comparative calculations of the savings to be obtained in
particular cases.

The role of accumulating data on the magnitude of the
savings obtainable by use of the deflection theory in final
stress calculations is reflected in changes in statements about
cases in which the method should be used. For example, Stein-

man, who certainly knew the deflection theory, since he had translated Melan (Melan, 1913), introduced his presentation of the *elastic* theory in 1922 by saying (Steinman, 1922, pp. 18–19):

> The resulting theory is the one ordinarily employed, and is sufficiently accurate for all practical purposes; any errors are generally small and on the side of safety.
>
> If the stiffening truss is not very stiff, or if the span is long, the deflections of truss and cable may be too large to neglect. To provide for such cases, there has been developed an exact method of calculation [i.e., the deflection theory] which takes into account the deformations of the system.

In the 1929 edition of the treatise, the statement concerning the elastic theory is modified as follows (Steinman, 1929, p. 18):

> The resulting theory is sufficiently accurate for shorter spans and those having comparatively deep stiffening trusses; any errors are on the side of safety.

Furthermore, an appendix was added presenting the deflection theory in which it is stated (*ibid.*, p. 246):

> The values of the bending moments and shears yielded by the Elastic Theory are too high, satisfying safety but not economy. The method is expeditious and therefore convenient for preliminary designs and estimates. It is generally sufficiently accurate for short spans and for designs having deep rigid stiffening systems that limit the deflections to small amounts.
>
> In designs with long spans, shallow trusses, or high dead load, the results of the approximate method become too wasteful, and the Deflection Theory should therefore be applied.

The dependence of efficient use of the deflection method on knowledge of the magnitude of the savings involved is also suggested by evidence concerning the actual use of the method. As the statements from Steinman indicate, once the size of elastic-theory errors for large bridges was shown, engineers would expect errors at least as great for larger bridges and decreasing errors as shorter and stiffer spans are approached. It is, therefore, not surprising that, with two probable exceptions, all the American suspension bridges with main spans of eight hundred feet or longer, built after 1909, appear to have been designed by use of the deflection theory for final stress calculations. The first large bridge completed after 1909, the Bear Mountain Bridge (main span 1,632 ft., completed 1924), was apparently not designed by the deflection method. In the case of another early bridge, the American-designed Florianopolis Bridge (main span 1,114 ft., completed 1926), deflection-theory calculations were made. However, the results were not used to modify the elastic-theory design, but rather to show that the "actual" strength and rigidity of the bridge were greater than appeared from the design calculations (Steinman and Grove, 1928). Apart from these early exceptions, use of the deflection theory in the design of larger suspension bridges apparently became universal.

But for short spans, the situation appears to have been quite different. I have not found information on how such bridges were actually designed, but there is evidence that data on the magnitude of elastic-theory errors for suspension bridges with a span of seven hundred feet or less accumulated remarkably slowly. In 1939, Fischer (1939, p. 609) asserted that the elastic theory could be used for spans of 750 feet or less. Others sharply disputed this (Hardesty and Wessman 1939*b*, p. 630), but no one cited specific figures. The first real comparison of the two methods for short-span bridges was apparently a study based on sixteen different theoretical designs for a main-span suspension bridge of 450 feet. This was made, interestingly enough, by engineers of a public body, the Oregon State Highway Commission, and published in 1940 (McCullough *et al.*, 1940). They found even for this very short span, average values of the errors increasing from 14 to 35 per cent of the elastic-theory values as the flexibility of the designs increased (*ibid.*, p. 122).

It seem likely that expectations of small relative errors, coupled with smaller absolute savings for a given relative error, reduced incentives to find out how big the short-span discrepancies actually were. Even with such data available, it is not clear that designers think deflection-theory calculations would be worth the trouble. For example, we find the author of the article on steel bridges in a standard handbook published in 1957, *American Civil Engineering Practice,* saying this about the use of the elastic method (Granger, 1957, p. 189): "It is impossible to fix a dividing span length, but probably at about 800 ft. enough comparisons should be made to see whether more exact analysis is justified." All this evidence shows that actual application of the deflection theory depended on knowledge of the savings to be expected by its use, and on an assessment of whether they justified the more laborious and difficult computations involved.

Extensions of the Deflection Theory

There is still another kind of advance in knowledge connected with the use of the deflection theory in final design which can have economic effects. This is extension of the mathematical theory to cover bridge types not included in the original formulation. One such extension has already been mentioned without comment: Moisseiff's extension of the theory to cover bridges with all three spans suspended from the cables. Another case is the extension of the deflection theory to cover a special kind of stiffening trusses, "continuous" trusses.

Continuous stiffening trusses provided possibilities of increased economy for shorter-span suspension bridges. Relevant information is available on two bridges where they were used. One was the Roundout Bridge (main span 705 ft., completed 1922) which was designed by the elastic method with no reduction made in the calculated stresses (Steinman, 1933, p. 491). In the second instance, the General U.S. Grant Bridge, the designers (*idem*) "calculated the stresses and sections by the common elastic theory and then assumed a reduction of 10 per cent for the deflection correction." At the time these bridges were designed, there was no way to make final design calculations for continuous truss bridges with the deflection method.

Then, by 1933, Steinman had developed a "generalized deflection theory" which could be used to design such suspension bridges (Steinman, 1933; full description, Steinman, 1935). With his new method Steinman (1935, p. 1135) was able to show that, had this theory been available, "the stresses calculated could have been reduced approximately 30 per cent for the Roundout Bridge, and 18 per cent for the Portsmouth Bridge [i.e., General U.S. Grant Bridge, main span 700 ft., completed 1927]."

Thus, a direct saving of some 30 per cent in the first case, and one of about 8 per cent in the second, could have been obtained had the "generalized" theory been available when these bridges were designed. I do not know the extent the theory has actually been used in practice, but these data suggest the order of magnitude of the economic effects that could be involved. We therefore have at least an indication that extensions of stress-analysis methods to new cases can have economic effects.

Conclusions

To summarize the results of the preceding analysis:

1. Advances in engineering knowledge, such as the deflection theory, do have significant productivity effects.

2. The magnitude and timing of these economic effects depends, in addition to the bare theory, on the accumulation of other important kinds of engineering knowledge. These include new knowledge concerning the actual accuracy of the theory compared to others available; its safety in use; the magnitude of the savings to be obtained by using a new method, rather than another, in various designing situations; and extensions of the theory to cover additional designing problems. In some cases, at least, it would be possible to estimate the magnitude of the economic effects that could be imputed to advances in these areas of knowledge.

3. Some of the sources of these additional kinds of knowledge are rather surprising. I am especially impressed by the role of actual structures and of numerical results of computations as sources of generally significant knowledge as well as items of direct practical use. Actual bridge designing emerges as a remarkably important producer of broadly useful design knowledge.

Let us now turn from the use of the deflection theory for designing trusses of a given stiffness to its role in deciding how much stiffness trusses need to have to obtain satisfactory suspension-bridge performance.

STIFFENING TRUSS PROPORTIONS AND THE DEFLECTION THEORY

As stated in the introduction, the primary purpose of suspension-bridge stiffening trusses is to make the bridge sufficiently rigid to eliminate excessive slopes or gradients caused by traffic. For any given bridge, the stiffer the trusses, the more rigid the bridge; but the quantitative relation between the two varies from bridge to bridge.

The stiffness of a truss of given length is measured by a number, the moment of inertia, which is equal to the square of the height (depth) of the truss multiplied by one-half the cross-sectional area of one chord of the truss. (The chords are the horizontal top and bottom members of the truss, assumed here to be of equal cross-sectional area.) The chords are primarily subjected to stress from the bending forces, or bending moments, produced by loads acting on the bridge. It is usual, as a first approximation, to assume that the weight of a truss of given length, and its cost, varies in proportion to the cross-section area of the chords.

To design economical trusses, it is therefore important to know how the cross-section areas of the chords required to provide adequate strength change with changes in the stiffness—the moment of inertia—of the truss. Early in the use of the deflection theory, it was apparently recognized that this theory, unlike some others (especially the rigid theory), led to the conclusion that, for a given bridge, the more flexible the truss—the lower its moment of inertia—the smaller the required chord areas and, therefore, the cheaper the truss. (This contradicted beliefs held by at least some engineers. See, e.g., Steinman, 1913; Waddell, 1916, pp. 655–56; Steinman, 1922, p. 83.)

If the foregoing theory were correct, then the problem of the designer attempting to provide adequate bridge rigidity at lowest cost was to find, for each particular bridge, the truss with just enough moment of inertia to give the bridge the required rigidity. This was a much more complicated job than following the simple rule, derived largely from the rigid theory, that the most economical truss for a suspension bridge was one whose truss height-to-span length ratio was about one-fortieth of the span. (See above references. It should be noted that, for a given bridge, truss height and truss moment of inertia vary together so that the former is an index of the latter.) Hence the problem: Was it worth the trouble to find the most flexible truss that gave adequate bridge rigidity?

Establishing the Significance of More Flexible Trusses

The earliest published statement I have found which stresses the magnitude of the economic effect of changing truss moments of inertia was based on the designing of the Philadelphia-Camden Bridge. In this connection, Dana (1927, p. 915) provided the following semiquantitative analysis:

> The Delaware River Bridge [Philadelphia-Camden] is a good example of an intermediate case because the trusses as designed reduce the cable deflections [a measure of *bridge* rigidity] to about one-half the natural or unstiffened amounts. . . . To have designed them . . . [so they caused no reduction] would have necessitated a depth of truss about one-half that actually used, in order to keep the unit stresses [in the chords] down to the permissible amounts. Such shallow nominal trusses were not considered adequate, however, as it was felt desirable to resist to a considerable extent the motion of the cables and towers. . . . If somewhat shallower trusses had been used their weight would have been much less, or if somewhat deeper trusses had been used their weight would have been much greater. . . .

Dana thus asserts that truss weights vary more than proportionately with changes in truss height, which suggests the quantitative importance of truss-height decisions. However, no actual numerical data are given.

So far as I can tell, the really convincing demonstration that significant economies could be achieved by using shallower, less-stiff trusses was provided by the design of the George Washington Bridge (main span 3,500 ft.). Though the bridge was not completed until 1931, Ammann had published a preliminary design with shallow trusses in 1924 (Ammann, 1924; I have not yet seen this article). And, by 1927, he had published a quantitative estimate of the amount of savings involved (1927, pp. 935–36). This comparison was elaborated, using additional data, and the revision published in 1933 as follows (Ammann, 1933, pp. 42–43):

> Some formulas would increase the weight of stiffening roughly in proportion to span and live load. On that basis, when compared with the stiffening of any of the bridges in Table 2 [Manhattan, Bear Mountain, Philadelphia-Camden], the system of the George Washington Bridge, with silicon steel chords, would weigh roughly from 13,000 to 14,000 lb. per ft. Actually, it is about one-sixth this comparative weight in the final condition and about one-twelfth in the initial condition [as a single deck highway bridge as it remained till 1960]. Considering also the fact that every dollar spent for steel in the floor and stiffening trusses in a span of this length requires at least an equivalent expenditure for materials in the cables, towers, and anchorages to carry the floor steel, the total saving by the adoption of the flexible trusses is estimated to be almost $10,000,000.

This impressive estimate does exaggerate, however, the effect of reducing the truss-height ratio from the average ratio of around 1/60 for the three earlier bridges to the 1/121 final condition ratio and to a ratio of less than 1/1000 for the "initial condition" bridge. The formulas referred to, and the comparative data used, provide an estimate of what the George Washington Bridge trusses would have weighed if they had a truss-height ratio of 1/60 of the span and had been designed by a mixture of elastic and deflection methods. The estimate does not show what the George Washington Bridge trusses would have weighed if their height had been 1/60 of the span and they had been designed by the deflection theory alone. The estimate thus measures the effects of the truss-height decision together with some of the savings from using the deflection method for final design calculations. Nonetheless, the implied productivity increases in the efficiency of use of truss steel—500 per cent—are sufficiently great to make it obvious that efficient truss proportioning *can* make an important economic difference, especially in very large bridges. We do get an idea of the order of magnitude of the upper range of productivity increases made possible by the deflection theory.

Let us now see how this design advance was made (Ammann, 1933, pp. 41–42):

Stiffening trusses of the Manhattan and Delaware River [Phila-delphia-Camden] Bridges may be called semiflexible, while those of the George Washington Bridge are practically "flexible," that is, they exert almost no restraint upon the distortions of the unstiffened cables. . . .

The permissibility of an almost flexible system in the case of the completed bridge—that is, with rapid transit trains running over the bridge on the lower deck, or of an entirely flexible system in case the bridge carries only vehicular traffic on the upper deck—was not obvious to the writer at the inception of his studies.

The general tendency, both in the United States and abroad, had been toward a rigid stiffening system, and the textbooks and many modern treatises on suspension bridges had confined themselves entirely to that system and to the elastic theory, without respect to span length, dead weight of bridge, or character of traffic.

Extensive studies convinced the writer that for a long-span suspension bridge a rigid system was not necessary. He was also familiar with the fact that by the application of the correct or so-called deflection theory, as distinguished from the "elastic theory," to a more or less flexible system, material economies can be effected. . . .

Aware of the ample rigidity of the Manhattan Bridge under actual traffic conditions, and of the sufficiency even of the much more flexible Brooklyn Bridge under all ordinary conditions, the writer became convinced that in the George Washington Bridge—with its much longer and heavier center span (the latter weighing four times that of the Manhattan Bridge and ten times that of the Brooklyn Bridge), its comparatively shorter side spans with almost straight cables acting as rigid back-stays, and the more effective distribution of concentrated loads by reason of its wide rigid floor—stiffening trusses of relatively greater flexibility than those used in the aforementioned smaller bridges, were permissible and economically required.

As a result of lengthy theoretical investigations, supplemented by observations on mechanical models, made in an endeavor to find the appropriate degree of rigidity of the stiffening trusses for the George Washington Bridge, the writer came to the conclusion that the arrangement of nearly flexible trusses in the finished bridge, and the omission of trusses [except for the top chords] in the initial stage of a single highway deck, were perfectly permissible and would secure a degree of rigidity at least equivalent to that of any of the aforementioned large modern bridges.

Ammann's work provided a concrete demonstration that some suspension bridges could be made adequately rigid by the use of very flexible trusses, or even no trusses at all. This fact was established by means of extensive numerical computations, checked by model tests, and was based on taking seriously the underlying implications of the deflection theory.

With evidence such as this available, it clearly became important for designers interested in economical truss design to consider the possibility of more flexible trusses. To do so posed two different problems. First, if reductions in truss moments of intertia could yield appreciable economies, then having good *criteria* for deciding how rigid a bridge really had to be became much more important than it had been. This is because the factor limiting how flexible trusses could be designed was how rigid the bridge had to be. Second, there was the problem of *finding*, for each particular bridge, just what was the smallest allowable moment of inertia for the truss. As can be seen from the quotation from Ammann, the deflection theory indicated that the truss stiffness required to give a given degree of bridge rigidity depended on a large number of factors. Thus, no simple rules for finding an optimum truss stiffness were available. This, coupled with the difficulty of deflection-theory calculations, made finding efficient trusses a definite problem.

Let us consider each of these problems in turn.

Determining Criteria for Bridge Rigidity

Establishing criteria for suspension-bridge rigidity is an intricate problem and would require at least another paper for adequate discussion. Here I will merely state briefly a few key points to show the implications of the subject for efficient stiffening-truss design.

Discussions in the engineering literature make it clear that it was very difficult for designers to arrive at reasonable and specific criteria of bridge rigidity. The criteria mentioned, and presumably those used, appear to have been relatively vague and somewhat variable from designer to designer. If one assumes that advances in knowledge of such a subject are possible, the apparently slow advance of knowledge concerning bridge-rigidity criteria probably limited, at least to some extent, the economies that could have been obtained by use of the deflection method. This field of knowledge and technique, therefore, probably had significant economic effects.

There is also evidence that, when bridge engineers *did* decide that less stringent criteria of bridge rigidity were reasonable, they proceeded cautiously, paying close attention to the results of actual experience with previously constructed bridges. For example, by at least 1933, Ammann held the following beliefs (1933, p. 42):

> For vehicular and electric passenger traffic the limiting grade [i.e. maximum longitudinal slope of the bridge floor], under severe loading conditions, can safely be assumed at 5%, in view of the improbability that it would ever be produced, and even then it would prevail only over very short stretches.

Yet, as we have seen, he designed the George Washington Bridge to be at least as rigid as previous comparable bridges. This meant, for the above type of traffic, a maximum grade from both live load and temperature change of less than 2.25 per cent (*idem*). When Ammann did design a more flexible bridge, the Bronx-Whitestone Bridge (span 2,300 ft., truss ratio 1/209, completed 1939), he thought of himself as taking "a further radical step" (1939, p. 626). He justified this (1946, p. 102) by the trend toward shallower trusses and the proven adequacy of such bridges as the George Washington and Ambassador bridges (main span 1,850 ft., truss ratio 1/84, completed 1929). And, before the Bronx-Whitestone Bridge was completed, he said (Ammann, 1939, p. 626):

> The Bronx-Whitestone Bridge still requires the test of actual operation. If it proves to be amply rigid, as the writer does not doubt, it should set a precedent for spans of that magnitude and similar proportions. It should also indicate that some of the bridges of shorter span might well have been designed with shallower, more economical, stiffening trusses or girders. . . .

Here we see again knowledge of the behavior of actual structures playing an economically significant role in suspension-bridge design.

Finally, the sensitivity of suspension-bridge design to bridge–rigidity requirements made the total economic effect of the deflection method and related knowledge depend on the changing character of the demand for types of suspension bridges. Freight-railway bridges, for example, have to be very rigid. Therefore, if the demand for suspension bridges had been confined to them, the deflection theory would have had a much smaller economic impact, because the savings obtained by its use are much smaller for rigid than for more flexible bridges. An appreciable part of the total savings attributable to the deflection theory and related bodies of knowledge was dependent on the fact that highway bridges, with their much less strict rigidity requirements, came to be the most common form of suspension bridge built.

Finding the Most Flexible Adequate Truss

Assuming the problem of criteria of bridge rigidity solved, we now turn to the problem of finding the cheapest truss that will meet whatever standards have been set. If it is difficult, as we shall see it was, to find the optimal truss stiffness, this would have the economic effects associated with making stiffer, more expensive trusses than were really thought necessary. For very understandable reasons, it is impossible to tell whether this actually happened from the engineering literature I have examined. The nearest approach to direct evidence is provided by Ammann's judgment (1939, p. 624) that there were "widely varying degrees of rigidity of stiffening trusses, even in recently built suspension bridges." However, he made this statement in discussing criteria of bridge rigidity, and differing criteria would also cause such variations.

It is, therefore, impossible to determine, from the direct evidence at hand, whether, or to what extent, difficulties in actually finding optimum truss designs actually led to the design of uneconomical trusses. What we do have is circumstantial evidence that the designing process was difficult, and that efforts were made to make it easier and thus, possibly, better. However, the processes of gaining new knowledge to overcome these designing difficulties do have, at a very minimum, one effect of economic significance. Such knowledge would make for a more efficient use of resources in the engineering work of designing. It may be possible to find evidence bearing on both these possibilities in sources not yet tapped.

To find, for a particular bridge, the least expensive truss providing adequate bridge rigidity could be solved if the engineer could make deflection-theory stress calculations for a range of assumed truss moments of inertia and thus determine the quantitative relations between moment of inertia, truss weight, and bridge rigidity as measured by maximum deflection, grades, or other criteria. However, there is considerable evidence that this was not done.

Setting aside the marginal case of the Florianopolis Bridge, mentioned earlier, I have found two accounts which give the changes in truss design made *during deflection-theory calculations.* (In these and other cases, elastic-theory calculations were always made in the course of preliminary design. These were made, at a minimum, to provide approximate values for variables that were needed to start the final calculations and make them less laborious.) In one case, the Isle d'Orleans Bridge (Banks, 1936*a*, 1936*b*), only slight changes were made: the truss height was reduced from an initial 13.5 feet to a final 13 feet and the truss moment of inertia was reduced from 4,600 to 4,200 in.^{2} ft.^{2}, which implies that the chord areas probably were not changed at all. In the other case, the Ambassador Bridge (Portas, 1936), the changes in moment of inertia were larger, from about 44,000 to about 18,000 in.^{2} ft.^{2}, with proportional changes in chord areas, but the truss height was kept constant at 22 feet. And in this case, it *is* stated that the major change in truss height (and moment of inertia), from 36 feet (1/51 of the span) to 22 feet (1/84 of the span), was made in the course of *elastic-theory* calculations.

From this evidence, it appears that deflection-theory calculations are used to make the usually moderate changes in truss proportions necessitated by the smaller stresses found, but not to explore the consequences of alternative decisions concerning truss stiffness. This inference is supported by the negative evidence that I have found no comparative deflection-theory data for any one bridge, giving truss stresses, chord areas, or bridge deflections for different assumed values of the truss moment of inertia. These various facts suggest that the difficulty of deflection-theory calculations exerted a remarkably restraining influence on the extent to which it was actually used in computations.

If designers did not make major decisions concerning truss stiffness on the basis of comparative calculations with the deflection theory, what did they do? The decisions must have been made in the course of "preliminary design" studies. Published information on how preliminary design decisions were made in particular cases is most conspicuous by its absence. We must, therefore, rely on less specific information.

For one extreme type of bridge, bridges with "flexible" or "almost flexible" trusses in Ammann's sense, designers were in a favorable position. As a result of work on the George Washington Bridge, and possibly other work as well, a relatively simple method of stress calculation and designing, based on the old theory of the unstiffened cable, had been developed. Concerning the former, Ammann writes (1933, p. 42):

> In his studies the writer became aware of the fact that even the so-called exact or deflection theories (a number of which had been advanced by that time), became unreliable and inapplicable in the case of trusses of relatively great flexibility, and that the simplest and most reliable method was to calculate the deflections of the unstiffened cables and the corresponding bending moments produced in the trusses, and, subsequently, correct the results slightly to allow for the comparatively very small stiffening effect of the trusses.

The quite simple procedure for determining truss heights which applies in this extreme case has been described by Dana (1927, p. 915):

> For this case the design of the trusses would consist merely in finding the unit stresses in the chords corresponding to the curvature into which the trusses would be forced by the deflection of the cables. The unit stress for any given amount of curvature is directly proportional to the truss depth, and obviously a depth of truss would have to be selected which would give permissible unit stresses.

This development provided designers with an easily usable designing procedure for those bridges in which "flexible" trusses were permissible.

For the more complex cases in which the deflection theory was relevant, one strategy was to use accumulated data on the differences between elastic- and deflection-theory stress calculations. Steinman (1929, p. 247) reports:

> In the course of the professional practice of Robinson and Stein-man, as successive bridge designs were calculated by the Deflection Theory, data were gradually accumulated on the percentages of reduction from the corresponding stresses by the approximate theory for different lengths and proportions of spans. These data soon indicated that there was some law of relationship between the amount of reduction and the flexibility of the span. The plotted records were used to indicate the reduction percentages for use in approximate estimates and preliminary designs on new bridge projects.

How widely this procedure was used, I do not know, but in this case at least, the dependence of the designer's work on accumulated data from design calculations is clear.

Another procedure was to develop more general semi-rational relationships between percent reductions and bridge characteristics. Here again, Steinman was involved (1929, pp. 247–48):

> In 1927 the author suggested to A. H. Baker, as a thesis problem, the development, from the office data and from further computations, of graphs what would give the corresponding percentages closely as functions of the span constants. After a year of computations and comparisons, Mr. Baker developed the graphs reproduced in Fig. D5 and described in the accompanying text. These graphs afford a short-cut method for figuring the "more exact" stresses, with little error, directly from the results of the more expeditious Elastic Theory.

Baker's work was published (Baker, 1928), but again I do not know who used it besides Steinman himself (e.g., Steinman, 1932).

Such efforts, and perhaps other activity I have no evidence of, did affect the prevailing view concerning optimum truss proportions. Steinman, who had translated Melan (1913), and who in 1922 adhered to the old 1/40–1/60 "economic proportions," changed his views radically by 1929 (Steinman, 1929, pp. 82–83):

> For highway bridges, the depth may be made as low as 1/50th to 1/70th of the span, for spans up to 1000 feet; 1/70th to 1/90th of the span, for spans up to 2000 feet; 1/90th to 1/150th of the span, for spans up to 3000 feet; and the stiffening trusses may be dis-

pensed with for longer spans. The increasing ratio of dead-load to live-load reduces the need for extraneous stiffening.

Still, engineers were not satisfied with the situation. In 1935, Frankland complained that the opaqueness of the deflection-theory equations limited their use "almost entirely" to making computations on designs obtained in other ways. He thought this "has hindered economic development of suspension bridge design," and hoped for simpler formulae showing directly the main relationships (Frankland 1935, p. 1204). In the same discussion, Johnston (1935, p. 1211) added: "The practice of utilizing the dead load as a stiffening factor is of comparatively recent origin, and its economic importance is probably not yet fully appreciated."

Just at the end of our period, a new advance in knowledge demonstrated by its own usefulness the difficulties designers had been contending with. This advance was a very carefully worked-out approximate deflection theory designed specifically for use in preliminary design by Hardesty and Wessman (1939a). The method met with immediate acclaim. And with it came the first published examples I have seen of basic aids to rational truss design: curves showing, for individual bridges, the numerical relationships between changes in truss moments of inertia and bending forces on the trusses, deflections, truss heights, and chord areas (Wessman, 1936; Hardesty and Wessman, 1939a; Karol, 1939). Simultaneously, and also based on computations with the new preliminary method, came the first published cost comparison of different ways of obtaining increased stiffness in a particular bridge (Woodruff and Raab, 1939). Designers now apparently had a tool with which to study the many complex interactions between bridge characteristics and truss design, which I have not even mentioned in this simplified presentation. Suspension bridges could now be effectively designed as systems.

Unfortunately, it will be difficult to test the effects of this new method and of more recent preliminary-design methods (see, for example, Pugsley, 1957, chap. x). Their use falls largely into the period after 1940. And, in 1940, the collapse of the Tacoma Narrows Bridge ushered in a new era in suspension-bridge truss design, dominated by the study of the previously ignored aerodynamic forces whose importance became so dramatically evident in that disaster.

Conclusions

I will now sum up what we have learned concerning the improvement of truss-height design with the advent of the deflection theory.

1. The large economic effects obtainable by improvements in truss proportioning were indicated by one estimate for an extreme case near the upper range of possibilities. However, from the evidence examined, we could not trace the average magnitude and timing of the design improvements. Nor could we establish really specific links between advances in designing knowledge and changes in truss-height decisions, or between changed truss heights and productivity increases. There appear to be methods and data which would make it possible to fill, at least partially, these gaps. I hope to explore them in the future.

2. The kinds and sources of knowledge which appear to have influenced truss-stiffness design include those we encountered earlier, but we saw additional ways in which they may have economic effects. We also found still other kinds of knowledge. These included simpler design procedures for special cases (e.g., for flexible trusses), empirical correlations, and semi-rational curves permitting more effective use of computations by a convenient but erroneous theory, and rational, approximate, preliminary-design theories. These methods are closely related to the importance of numerical results in structural engineering, since they serve as ways of obtaining more such results more easily.

3. We also encountered a rather different kind of knowledge from any of these: the procedures and knowledge used to establish criteria of adequate bridge rigidity. Such knowledge is similar to that used elsewhere, as for example, in specifying traffic "live loads" for design purposes. There is evidence, not presented here, that changes in loading specifications and in "allowable unit stresses" under various loads also have economic effects on suspension-bridge design. When a more complete picture of the role of knowledge related to structural

analysis has been developed, it should be possible to trace the consequences of changes in these fields. Studies of their economic role should then prove fruitful.

REFERENCES

(ASCE = American Society of Civil Engineers)

O. H. AMMANN

1924 [Preliminary design for the Hudson River Bridge], *Connecticut Society of Civil Engineers, Proceedings.*

1927 Discussion of Waddell (1927), *ASCE Transactions,* XCI, 932–37.

1933 "George Washington Bridge: General Conception and Development of Design," *ASCE Transactions,* XCVII, 1–65.

1939 Discussion of Hardesty and Wessman (1939), *ASCE Transactions,* CIV, 624–26.

1946 "Additional Stiffening of Bronx-Whitestone Bridge," *Civil Engineering,* XVI, 101–3.

ANONYMOUS

1909 "The Design and Construction of the Manhattan Bridge," *Engineering Record,* LX, 372–75.

ARVID H. BAKER

1928 "Suspension Bridge Analysis by the Exact Method Simplified by Knowledge of Its Relations to the Approximate Method," *Rensselaer Polytechnic Institute, Engineering and Science Series,* No. 24, I and II.

SHEWELL REGINALD BANKS

1936a "The Superstructure of the Island of Orleans Suspension Bridge, Quebec, Canada," *Institution of Civil Engineers, Journal* III, 357–421.

1936b Authors Reply, *Institution of Civil Engineers, Journal,* III, 457–70.

HARDY CROSS

   1936   "The Relation of Analysis to Structural Design," *ASCE Transactions*, CI, 1363–1408 (including discussion).

ALLSTON DANA

   1927   Discussion of Waddell (1927), *ASCE Transactions*, CI, 914–17.

A. W. FISCHER

   1939   Discussion of Hardesty and Wessman (1939), *ASCE Transactions*, CIV, 609–10.

J. M. FRANKLAND

   1935   Discussion of Steinman (1935), *ASCE Transactions*, C, 1204.

ARMOUR T. GRANGER

   1957   "Steel Bridge," Sec. 28, Vol. III, of Robert W. Abbett (ed.), *American Civil Engineering Practice* (New York).

SHORTRIDGE HARDESTY and HAROLD E. WESSMAN

   1939*a* "Preliminary Design of Suspension Bridges," *ASCE Transactions*, CIV, 579–608.

   1939*b* Discussion of above, *ASCE Transactions*, CIV, 629–34.

STERLING JOHNSTON

   1935   Discussion of Steinman (1935), *ASCE Transactions*, C, 1210–11.

JACOB KAROL

   1939   Discussion of Hardesty and Wessman (1939), *ASCE Transactions*, CIV, 610–14.

C. B. McCULLOUGH, G. S. PAXSON, and DEXTER R. SMITH

   1940   "Rational Design Methods for Short-Span Suspension Bridges for Modern Highway Loadings," Oregon State Highway Department, *Technical Bulletin*, No. 13.

J. Melan

1888   *Theorie der eisernen Bogenbrücken and der Hangebrücken*,
        2nd. ed. (Berlin)

1905   Discussion of Lindenthal, *ASCE Proceedings*, XXXI, 208–13.

1913   *Theory of Arches and Suspension Bridges*, trans. D. B.
        Steinman (New York).

Robert S. Merrill

1959   "Routine Innovation," Unpublished Ph.D. Dissertation, Uni-
        versity of Chicago.

1962   "Some Society-wide Research and Development Institutions,"
        in National Bureau of Economic Research, *The Rate and
        Direction of Inventive Activity* (Princeton), pp. 409–34.

Leon S. Moisseiff

1925   "The Towers, Cables and Stiffening Trusses of the Bridge
        over the Delaware River between Philadelphia and Camden,"
        Franklin Institute, Journal, CC, 436–66.

1927   Discussion of Waddell (1927), *ASCE Transactions*, XCI,
        918–23.

1935   Discussion of Steinman (1935), *ASCE Transactions*, C,
        1205–6.

John Portas

1936   Discussion of Banks (1936a), *Institution of Civil Engineers,
        Journal*, III, 446.

Alfred G. Pugsley

1957   *The Theory of Suspension Bridges* (London).

D. B. Steinman

1913   *Suspension Bridges and Cantilevers*, 2nd rev. ed.; "Van
        Nostrand Science Series," No. 127 (New York).

1922   *A Practical Treatise on Suspension Bridges* (New York).

1929   *A Practical Treatise on Suspension Bridges*, 2nd ed. (re-
        vised), (New York).

1932   "The Design and Construction of the St. Johns Bridge,"
        Civil Engineering, III, 490–91.

1933 "A Generalized Deflection Theory," *Civil Engineering,* III, 490–91.

1935 "A Generalized Deflection Theory for Suspension Bridges," *ASCE Transactions,* C, 1133–70.

D. B. STEINMAN and WILLIAM G. GROVE

1928 "The Eye-bar Cable Suspension Bridge at Florianopolis, Brazil," *ASCE Transactions,* XCII, 266–342.

DAVID B. STEINMAN and SARA RUTH WATSON

1957 *Bridges and Their Builders,* (revised ed.), (New York).

J. A. L. WADDELL

1916 *Bridge Engineering* (New York).

1927 "Quantities of Materials and Costs per Square Foot of Floor for Highway and Electric-Railway Long-Span Suspension Bridge," *ASCE Transactions,* XCI, 884–945 (including discussion).

HAROLD E. WESSMAN

1936 Discussion of Cross (1936), *ASCE Transactions,* CI, 1393–94.

GLENN B. WOODRUFF and NORMAN C. RAAB

1939 Discussion of Hardesty and Wessman (1939), *ASCE Transactions,* CIV, 614–17.

Comment on Brozen and Merrill

Frederic M. Scherer

PROFESSOR BROZEN'S correlation between sales-deflated R&D expenditures and concentration in manufacturing industries aroused my curiosity. Concerned about the possible invalidity of a concentration index for two-digit industries, I checked the original tabulation by Nutter which Brozen employs. It turned out that Nutter's concentration index—the proportion of a two-digit industry's value added, accounted for by product lines in which four firms held a total market share of 75 per cent or more—is about as good as one can do under adverse conditions. But a look at the data suggested something unexpected. If we eliminate only the tobacco industry, which is well known to be a peculiar kind of beast, the rank correlation coefficient jumps from 0.25 (by my calculations, which apparently involve slightly different assumptions from Brozen's) to 0.53. With thirteen observations, this is significant in a one-tail test at the .05 level.

This result warns us that the possible influence of market structure on R&D investment decisions should not be dismissed as lightly as Brozen does. And there are other grounds for believing that market structure might be a relevant variable. Mansfield's impressive work has suggested that innovation may be related to firm size, although the relationship is by no means a simple one. A recent study by James Worley revealed that, in six industries out of eight, the number of R&D personnel employed by firms increased more than proportionately with total company employment, although the results did not attain the statistical significance levels demanded by his null hypothesis.[1] Markham has argued on largely qualitative grounds that R&D spending tends to be

---

[1] "Industrial Research and the New Competition," *Journal of Political Economy*, LXIX (April, 1961), 183–86.

concentrated in oligopolistic industries. Some work of my own
is also relevant. In an exploratory cross-section study of thirty-
five non-conglomerate firms employing largely mechanical
and/or empirical technologies, I found that company patenting increases as a function of both market share and sales
volume. The three variable R^2 was 0.45, with partial r^2 of
0.33 for market share and 0.13 for sales volume. On the other
hand, the Hamberg study cited by Brozen seems to show
contrary results. In sum, the Schumpeterian pot has come to
a vigorous empirical boil during the past few years. But
unfortunately, the broth is still too hot and turbid for us to
reach in and discover exactly what has been cooked.

My cross-section study also indicated that inter-industry
differences in technological opportunity are more important
determinants of patenting variations than either market share
or firm size. Here my findings coincide broadly with Brozen's,
since he attributes a predominant role to the "varying quality
of the science base among industries."

It is necessary, however, to question points of detail in
Brozen's science-base analysis. Two brief comments must
suffice. First, the available evidence does not support the
hypothesis that relatively high spending on basic research
leads to relatively high rates of growth in total R&D expenditures. When 1953 basic research expenditures as a percentage
of sales are correlated with the percentage growth from 1953
to 1956 in the total R&D expenditures/sales ratios for nine
two-digit industries surveyed by the National Science Foundation, an r^2 of ($-$) 0.0005 is obtained. When the same 1953
basic research expenditure percentages are correlated with
the growth from 1953 to 1959 in total R&D expenditures/sales
ratios, r^2 is 0.0036. Clearly, no simple relationship between
basic research outlays and R&D growth is revealed, although
a multiple correlation which took demand variables into
account might show some relationship. Second, it is difficult
to accept Brozen's statement that "little is invested in R&D"
when a good theoretical base is lacking. The industry with
the highest company-financed R&D spending per dollar of
sales in 1959 was, according to National Science Foundation
data, *drugs and medicines*. Organic chemical theory is generally in a primitive state; and, especially in the drug field,

much research necessarily embodies the "try-every-bottle-on-the-shelf" approach. The industry with the second highest company-financed R&D spending per sales dollar was *optical, surgical, photographic, and other instruments.* An optical scientist described his industry's theoretical base as follows:

> Optics is one of the most conservative of sciences. Attempts to improve the performance of optical systems are subject to severe but still not well understood limitations which apparently are of a basic nature. . . . It seems that despite all the theoretical and experimental work in lens design there are some obscure factors which usually do not permit bringing the performance of an optical system to its natural limit—determined by diffraction phenomena.[2]

Thus, we find the highest rates of private R&D investment in two industries which, while science oriented, do not enjoy well-developed theories facilitating accurate prediction of experimental results. Rather, the kind of situation most conducive to high R&D spending appears to be one in which theory is well enough developed to suggest the existence of economically important new results, but not well enough developed to predict solutions in any detail.

Merrill's paper reflects the kind of solid empirical work much needed to advance our understanding of technological innovation. It lends support to Herbert Simon's hypothesis that the calculation effort associated with finding an optimal solution may deter efforts to achieve the optimum. I should like, however, to know more about the role which risk played in retarding the application of deflection theory. Did the potentially catastrophic consequences of a mistake exert a special restraining influence? (In many other fields of engineering, it is possible to reduce uncertainty considerably through the testing of relatively inexpensive models.) What were the risks of error to the bridge designer? Reputation damage? Outright financial loss? It would also be interesting to learn what specific factors motivated those designers who *did* accept the risks of innovation and the burden of calculating new optimal solutions. Could competitive forces have had some bearing? How do bridge designers secure new

---

[2] Pestrecov, "Myopia in Optics," *Industrial Research,* IV (September, 1962), p. 18.

design contracts? Competition on the basis of reputation? On the basis of design effort cost? Expected bridge cost? In weapon-systems designing, which may in many ways be analogous to bridge designing, variables such as the criteria for contractor selection, the size of potential contractors' order backlogs, and the degree to which financial risks are assumed by the buyer rather than the designer have an important influence on the propensity to innovate. I hope Merrill's further interview research will yield answers to some of these questions.

Comment on Merrill and Brozen

Edward Ames

PROFESSOR MERRILL's paper is particularly interesting to students of the sequences in which technological change occurs. The deflection theory is an engineering theory formulated in 1888, the third in a sequence of such theories. It was formulated at about the time the second in the sequence was coming into general use, and it was not applied at all for thirteen years. When applied, it was first used as a cross-check on other calculations, and as a means of explaining a fault in a bridge designed according to the earlier theory. Another eight years elapsed before a new bridge designed with this theory was completed; it then was adopted for large bridges, and gradually came into use for smaller ones.

The number of suspension bridges built annually is small, I suppose, as compared to the number of new machine tools designed annually. If new engineering theories are adopted in a pattern which reflects the flow of information within the profession, then Professor Merrill's paper may be taken as a slow-motion movie of a process which would take much less time in an industry with large production batches.

But is such a hypothesis entirely suitable in explaining why a theory which, as experience ultimately showed, was worth adopting was nevertheless adopted with such a long delay? Here is a theory which, by the 1920's, would reduce the total cost of a large bridge by 10 per cent, and the metal costs in the order of one-third. But by 1920, as compared with 1890, there had certainly been changes in both the costs and the quality of metals used in bridge construction. Would comparable savings have been possible in 1890? If not, the adoption of the deflection theory would depend upon the development of the steel industry, which certainly underwent rapid change over this period.

It may be asked why the new theory was first used on large bridges, and only later for small ones. For it might seem wise to experiment with a new technique on a project where the cost of failure was less. Two hypotheses at once are suggested. The first is that the large bridges are known to be challenges, and their design is entrusted to leaders in the profession. Only gradually is their experience transmitted to those who design the smaller, and less difficult, projects. Such a hypothesis is a theory about the flow of information through the profession. A second hypothesis is that the ratio of metals cost to total cost increases with the length of the bridge; that the price of metals changed differently over time from other prices. If so, then in the 1910's, the deflection theory would not in fact have provided money savings on the smaller bridges; but at a later date it would have. Therefore, the pattern of adoption was superficially contrary to the principle of minimizing risk.

These interesting questions require an analysis of the extent to which engineering practices reflect the flow of information within the profession, and the extent to which they reflect changes in the cost of the various components of a bridge. In the first case, Professor Merrill's paper may well be a slow-motion view of engineering change in general. In the latter case, it is not clearly so.

Let us now turn to Professor Brozen's comments on the "science base" existing in different industries. He suggests that a basic determinant of how much research and development is carried on by an industry depends on how much basic scientific knowledge there is about inputs, processes, and products of the industry. He says that basic science reduces the cost of research by making possible "paper experiments" (that is, by having an appropriate theory). Since scientific advance has been concentrated in electricity, chemistry, and mechanics, he expects to find the readiest market for the output of scientists in those industries which depend on the application of these branches of knowledge.

But here I find a difficulty. One way of expressing the foregoing hypothesis is to say that the supply of new scientific output in electricity, chemistry, and mechanics is relatively large and price-elastic, while the supply of scientific output in other areas is relatively small and relatively price-inelastic. As we know, however, the existence of supply functions alone does not tell us what equilibrium output will be, unless we also know what demands are for the various products.

Let us consider several plausible statistical hypotheses. First, assume that business researchers have knowledge distributed among sciences in the same way as the knowledge of scientists and that the more science they know, the more applications to business they see. Then we should expect the demand for science by business to be correlated with the supply of basic science; prices of different sciences will tend to equality and actual use of the different sciences by industry to be proportional to basic scientific discoveries. This is Professor Brozen's hypothesis.

Next, however, we assume that the demand for science of various types by business is statistically independent of the supply of scientific output. This situation could occur because scientific advance follows a path of least resistance: scientists push hardest into areas where they expect to obtain the best results. Business, in contrast, has problems which arise from economic conditions, and these are independent of laboratory results. Then there will be no tendency toward price equalization, and no particular correlations between the value of expenditures on research by different industries with the quantity of research used by these industries.

The third possibility is based on a principle of declining marginal utility. Suppose that the usefulness of additional science to a business varies inversely with the amount which has been bought in the past (an existing stock of capital). In this case, the demand for science by business would be inversely correlated with the long-run supply of scientific output. Therefore, the prices of different kinds of science would be negatively correlated to the amounts actually used.

Suppose, now, that we attempt to correlate research and development by particular industries with other attributes of these industries. We are then correlating values, products, that is, of prices and quantities. If Brozen's hypothesis is correct, his method will indeed yield statements about the quantities of research; but otherwise his results in part must be taken to apply to an association between unit costs of research and development in industries and other attributes of the industries. This difficulty was evaded by Professor Mansfield, who was cautious about inter-industry comparisons. Unfortunately, Professor Mansfield was unable, as a result, to consider the interesting type of question considered by Professor Brozen.

What does Professor Merrill's paper suggest about Professor Brozen's thesis? To the extent that a new *engineering* theory tends to be adopted as knowledge of it spreads through a profession, or to the extent that it is adopted as prices in the economy change so as to make it profitable to use, we would use Professor Merrill's results to cast doubt on correlations such as those of Professor Brozen's. To the extent that new *engineering* theory is empirical rather than theoretical in the scientific sense, it can develop independently of the scientific base, and casts further doubt upon Brozen's procedure.

Both papers are pioneering efforts to explore a subject that is little understood. It is not surprising that they are not really consistent. Properly compared, however, they illuminate several fundamental problems which must be resolved before we can say that (as the econometricians would say) we have an identified model, or that (as we say in English) we can interpret what we see around us.

THE PROCESS OF TECHNICAL CHANGE*

Edwin Mansfield

INTRODUCTION

IN RECENT YEARS, there has been an enormous increase in the amount of attention devoted by social scientists, government officials, businessmen, and labor leaders to the subject of technical change. At least four factors account for this. First, there has been a growing conviction in government and elsewhere that the American economy is not growing as rapidly as it should, and a growing awareness that our rate of economic growth depends very heavily on our rate of technical change. Second, the advent and continuation of the cold war has made it painfully obvious that our national security depends on the output of our military research and development effort. Third, economists and others are coming to realize the full importance in various markets of competition through new products and processes rather than direct price competition. Fourth, unemployment created or aggravated by technical change has become increasingly acute, the problem reaching such dimensions that the President recently labeled it one of the foremost problems of the sixties.

Despite the considerable amount of space devoted in newspapers and professional journals to the various problems associated with technical change, we know surprisingly little about the process by which new processes and products are invented, developed, commercialized, and accepted. The pur-

* The work on which this paper is based was supported by a contract with the Office of Economic and Statistical Studies of the National Science Foundation, by a Ford Foundation Faculty Research Fellowship, and by the Cowles Foundation for Research in Economics at Yale University. It is part of a larger project under my direction concerned with technical change and economic growth, financed currently by a grant from the National Science Foundation.

pose of this paper is to summarize some of the findings of a continuing study of this process that I have been conducting. These findings pertain to a number of aspects of the process of technical change. Rather than try to integrate the results into a single, all-inclusive theoretical structure, we shall consider a number of important questions regarding this process and summarize very briefly the results to date which bear on them. Because of limitations of space, it is impossible for the paper to include all of the qualifications and limitations of the results. Those interested in more detailed discussion are referred to my papers listed in the Bibliography which accompanies this paper.

THE EXPENDITURES OF THE FIRM ON RESEARCH AND DEVELOPMENT

Most of the nation's R&D is financed by the federal government, principally for defense and space activities. The amount spent for such purposes is, of course, dictated very largely by military and political considerations. Besides these expenditures, there is also an enormous amount of R&D being financed by private industry; and an important question is: What determines the amount spent on R&D by a firm in an industry where government financing plays a small role—like chemicals, petroleum, drugs, glass, and steel?

I propose the following set of relationships to help answer this question: (1) A firm sets its expenditures so as to move part way from the previous year's level toward a desired level that depends on (a) the firm's expectation regarding the average profitability of the R&D projects at hand, (b) the profitability of alternative uses of its funds, and (c) its size, as reflected in annual sales adjusted for certain inter-industry differences.[1] (2) The firm's speed of adjustment toward the desired level depends on the extent to which the

---

[1] A complete description of the interrelationships is given in [5] in my Bibliography.

desired level differs from the previous year's level and on the per cent of its profits spent during the previous year on R&D.

These relationships taken together constitute a model which was formulated in part on the basis of interviews with research directors and other executives of a number of firms in the chemical and petroleum industries. For eight firms from which the necessary data could be obtained, this model, in more specific and operational form, could fit historical data regarding these firms' expenditures quite well. Moreover, when supplemented with additional assumptions, it could fit the 1945–58 data for thirty-five firms in five industries (petroleum, chemicals, drugs, glass, and steel) quite well, and it could do a reasonably good job of "forecasting" their 1959 expenditures. Of course, the model is a more apt description of decision-making regarding applied research and development than basic research, but the latter is quite small in this content.

Because of the small number of observations and the roughness of the basic data, the results are obviously tentative. But if reasonably trustworthy, they have at least three significant implications. First, they allow us to make rough estimates of the effect of certain kinds of government policies on the amount a firm spends, in money terms,[2] on research and development. For example, what would be the effect on a firm's expenditures of a change in tax policy that increased the prospective profitability of each of its R&D projects by 1 per cent? Assuming that the model holds and that the firm's actual and desired expenditures would be approximately equal, the effect in 1958 would have been to increase the expenditures of the petroleum firms for which we have data by about 2 per cent. Among the chemical firms, the effect would have been to increase expenditures by about 3.5 per cent. Given current data, estimates of this sort could be made on a current basis.

Second, the fact that the model fits the data so well seems to imply that the process by which a firm's R&D expenditures

---

[2] It would be preferable, of course, to estimate the effects in real, not money, terms. If estimates of the supply functions for various R&D inputs can be obtained, it is possible that estimates of this sort can also be obtained. See [5] and [7] in my Bibliography.

are determined is not so divorced from profit considerations as some observers have claimed. If firms "establish research laboratories without any clearly defined idea of what the laboratories could perform" [11], and blindly devote some arbitrarily determined percentage of sales to R&D, it is difficult to see why the model fits so well.

Third, the results provide new evidence regarding the effects of a firm's size on the amount spent on R&D. They indicate that, among large and medium-sized firms in the petroleum, glass, steel, and drug industries, there was no tendency in 1959 for the percentage of a firm's sales devoted to R&D to increase with the size of the firm. If anything, the opposite was the case. However, in the chemical industry, the larger firms spent more on R&D, relative to sales, than did somewhat smaller firms.

RESEARCH AND DEVELOPMENT AND INVENTIVE OUTPUT

The second subject I wish to consider here is the productivity of industrial research and development, an area in which measurement problems are extremely acute. On the basis of the crude measurements that could be made, does it seem that a firm's output of significant inventions is closely related to the amount it spends on R&D? Is there any evidence that the productivity of a firm's R&D activities increases with the amount spent on R&D? Is there any evidence that productivity is greater in large firms than in small ones?

To help answer these questions, detailed studies were made of the chemical, petroleum, and steel industries. To measure the inventive output of firms in the chemical industry, we used Langenhagen's data [1] on the number of significant inventions (weighted roughly by a measure of their importance) carried out by various large chemical firms. In the petroleum and steel industries, we used Schmookler's list [12] of important inventions in petroleum refining and my list [4] of important petrochemical and steel innovations. Results were obtained for about ten large firms in each industry.

Calculations based on these crude data suggest the following three conclusions. First, holding the size of the firms constant, the number of significant inventions carried out by a firm seems to be highly correlated with the size of its R&D expenditures. Thus, although the productivity of an individual R&D project is obviously very uncertain, it seems that there is a close relationship over the long run [3] between the amount a firm spends on R&D and the total number of important inventions it produces.

Second, the evidence from the cross-section analysis seems to suggest that increases in R&D expenditures, in the relevant range and holding the size of the firms constant,[4] result in more than proportional increases in inventive output in chemicals. But in petroleum and steel, there is no real indication of either economies or diseconomies of scale within the relevant range. Thus, except for chemicals, the results do not indicate any marked advantage of large-scale research activities over medium-size and large ones.

Third, when a firm's expenditures on R&D are held constant, increases in size of firm seem to be associated in most industries with decreases in inventive output. Thus, the evidence suggests that the productivity of an R&D effort of given scale is lower in the largest firms than in the medium-sized and large ones.

THE SIZE OF INNOVATORS

The significance of the innovator has been stressed repeatedly by Schumpeter and others. One of the most important questions regarding the innovator is concerned with its size. Is it true that the largest firms have been the first to introduce a disproportionately large proportion of the

---

[3] The data on inventive output pertain to periods of about fifteen years after 1940. The data on R&D expenditures pertain to somewhat earlier periods. See [5] in the Bibliography.

[4] It should be stressed that all the firms included here are large. See [5].

important new processes and products that have been developed in recent years? Is it true that they dominate the picture to a larger extent now than in the past?

To help answer these questions, studies were made of the iron and steel, petroleum, and bituminous-coal industries. Using lists, obtained from trade journals and engineering associations, of the important processes and products first introduced in these industries since 1918, I determined whether, in each case, the largest four firms seemed to introduce a disproportionately large share of these innovations. Then a simple model was constructed to explain why the giant firms accounted for a disproportionately large share of the innovations in some cases, but not in others; and an attempt was made to estimate whether innovations would have been introduced more slowly if these large firms had been broken up.

The principal results are as follows: First, although it is often alleged that the largest firms do more than their share of the pioneering, this is not always the case. For example, in petroleum refining and bituminous coal, the largest firms accounted for a larger share of the innovations than they did of the market. But in iron and steel, they accounted for less.

Second, the evidence seems quite consistent with a simple model which predicts that the largest four firms will do a disproportionately large share of the innovating in cases in which (1) the investment required to innovate is large relative to the size of the firms that could use the innovation, (2) the minimum size of firm required to use the innovation is large relative to the average size of firm in the industry, and (3) the average size of the largest four firms is much greater than the average size of all potential users of the innovation. The reasoning underlying this model is spelled out in my article "Size of Firm, Market Structure, and Innovation" [4].

Third, some very rough estimates suggest that, in the petroleum and bituminous-coal industries, the six largest firms were of about optimal size from the point of view of maximizing the rate of innovation. In the steel industry, much smaller firms seem to have been optimal in this respect. However, before relaying the news to the attorney-general, two things must be considered. (1) The underlying theory and data are extremely rough. (2) The results are based on the past behavior of these companies, which may be different in important respects from their more recent and future behavior.

Fourth, there is evidence that the smallest steel, bituminous-coal, and oil firms did less innovating during 1939–58— relative to large and medium-sized firms—than in 1919–38. With the rising costs of development and the greater complexity of technology, this is not surprising.[5]

INNOVATION AND THE GROWTH OF FIRMS

Having considered the size of the innovators, another important question is: How large has been the payoff for a successful innovation? Perhaps the best single measure of a firm's rewards is the rate of return on its investment; but because of data limitations, I investigated the effect of a successful innovation on a firm's growth rate, another interesting, if incomplete, measure of its success. First, I determined which firms were first to introduce about one hundred new processes and products regarded by trade journals and engineering associations as being the most important that occurred in the iron and steel and petroleum industries since World War I. A comparison of the growth rates of these innovators— during the period in which the innovation occurred—with those of other firms of comparable initial size helps to indicate how great the payoff was, in terms of growth, for a successful innovation.

The results show that, in every time interval and in both industries, the successful innovators grew much more rapidly (during a five- to ten-year period after the innovation occurred) than the other firms, their average growth rate often being more than twice that of the others. According to my best estimates, the average effect of a successful innovation was to raise a firm's annual growth rate by four to

---

[5] For a complete discussion of the topics considered in this section, see [4].

thirteen percentage points, depending on the time interval and the industry. Taking each innovator separately, the difference between its growth rate and the average growth rate of other comparable firms seems to have been inversely related to its size. As one would expect, a successful innovation had a much greater impact on a small firm's growth rate than on a large firm's.[6]

THE TIMING OF INNOVATION

Another study in this series [9] is concerned with the timing of innovation and its effects on the timing of expenditures on plant and equipment. The dates of first commercial introduction were determined for the 150 processes and products regarded by trade associations and trade journals as being the most important introduced during 1919–58 in the iron and steel, petroleum, refining, and bituminous coal industries. Using these data, we see whether the rate of innovation in these industries seems to have increased in accord with the spectacular rise in R&D expenditures and whether the rate of occurrence of innovations has varied appreciably over the business cycle. In addition, we formulate and test an investment function that includes the effects of the timing of innovation on the timing of an industry's expenditures on plant and equipment.

The principal conclusions of this study are as follows: First, there was some apparent, but statistically non-significant, tendency for the rate of occurrence of innovations to increase over time in these industries. However, the rate of increase was significantly less than the rate of increase in R&D expenditures, indicating perhaps that the expenditures on R&D required to produce a significant innovation have increased considerably. If this is true in most other industries, too, the

---

[6] For a complete discussion of the topics considered in this section, see [3].

much publicized increase in total R&D expenditures greatly exaggerates the increase in the rate of innovation.

Second, it appears that process innovations were most likely to be introduced during periods when the industries were operating at about 75 per cent of capacity. Contrary to the opinion of many economists, there was no tendency for process innovations to cluster during the periods when operating rates were extremely high or extremely low. Apparently, innovation at the trough was discouraged by the meagerness of profits and uncertainty regarding the future. At the peak, some executives in the industries claim that it was discouraged by the lack of unutilized capacity where alterations could be made cheaply and without interfering with production schedules.

Third, a simple investment function combining the flexible capacity accelerator with a simple model of innovation-induced investment can explain the behavior of the level of investment in steel and petroleum more adequately than the accelerator alone. The timing of innovation is shown to have had a statistically significant and quantitatively important effect on the level and timing of expenditures on plant and equipment.[7]

THE DIFFUSION OF INNOVATIONS

Finally, having considered the origin and initial introduction of an innovation, it is necessary to look at the subsequent diffusion process as well. Once an innovation has been introduced by one firm, what factors determine the rate at which other firms follow the innovator? What factors seem to determine whether one firm will be quicker than another to begin using a particular technique? Do the same members of an industry tend to lag behind in introducing innovations, or are the leaders in one case likely to be the followers in another?

An intensive study of the diffusion of more than a dozen major process innovations in the railroad, brewing, steel, and

_____

[7] For a complete discussion of the topics considered in this section, see [9].

bituminous-coal industries seems to indicate the following answers to these questions. First, there seems to be a definite "bandwagon" or "contagion" effect. As the number of firms in an industry using an innovation increases, the probability of its adoption by a non-user increases. This is because, as experience and information regarding an innovation accumulates, the risks associated with its introduction grow less and competitive pressures mount. Moreover, in cases where the profitability of an innovation is difficult to assess, the mere fact that a large proportion of a firm's competitors have adopted the innovation may prompt the firm to consider it more seriously. Second, the rate of diffusion tends to be higher for more profitable innovations and for those requiring relatively small investments. The rate of diffusion also differs among industries, there being some slight indication that it is higher in less concentrated industrial categories. The relationship between these variables and the rate of diffusion is in accord with a simple model of the imitation process. This model gives a surprisingly close approximation and may be useful for forecasting purposes, although one should note that in none of the cases considered were patents a relevant factor, since they were held by the equipment producers.

Third, there may be some tendency for the rate of diffusion to be higher when the innovation does not replace very durable equipment, when an industry's output is growing rapidly, and when the innovation's introduction into an industry is relatively recent.

Fourth, the speed with which a particular firm begins using a new technique is directly related to the firm's size and the profitability of its investment in the technique. But a firm's rate of growth, its profit level, its liquidity, its profit trend, or the age of its management seem to have no consistent or close relationship with how soon a firm adopts an innovation.

Fifth, in most industries, only a relatively weak tendency exists for the same firms to be consistently the earliest to introduce different innovations. The leaders for one innovation are quite often followers for another, especially if the innovations become available at widely different periods of time.[8]

---

[8] For a complete discussion of the topics considered in this section, see [2], [6], [8], and [10].

CONCLUSION

In conclusion, these findings should be useful in formulating more adequate theories of firm behavior and economic growth and in guiding public policy regarding science and technology. However, in the space that remains, it would obviously be impossible for me to deal adequately with the implications of the findings for these matters. This must be postponed to another occasion.

BIBLIOGRAPHY*

1. LANGENHAGEN, D. "An Evaluation of Research and Development in the Chemical Industry" (Master's thesis, M.I.T., 1958).

2. MANSFIELD, E. "Technical Change and the Rate of Imitation," *Econometrics,* Vol. XXIX (1961).

3. ———. "Entry, Gibrat's Law, Innovation, and the Growth of Firms," *American Economic Review,* LII (1962).

4. ———. "Size of Firm, Market Structure, and Innovation," *Journal of Political Economy,* LXXI (1963).

5. ———. "Industrial R and D Expenditures: Determinants, Prospects and Relation to Size of Firm and Inventive Output," *Journal of Political Economy,* LXXII (1964).

6. ———. "The Speed of Response of Firms to New Techniques," *Quarterly Journal of Economics,* LXXVII (1963).

7. ———. "Comment," in *The Rate and Direction of Inventive Activity.* Princeton, N. J., 1962.

8. ———. "Intrafirm Rates of Diffusion of an Innovation," *Review of Economics and Statistics,* XLV (1963).

9. ———. "Timing of Innovation and the Investment Function" (mimeo, revised version, 1963).

10. ———, and HENSLEY, C. "The Logistic Process: Tables of the Stochastic Epidemic Curve and Applications," *Journal of the Royal Statistical Society,* Ser. B, Vol. XXII, No. 2 (1960).

---

*EDITOR'S NOTE: The Mansfield references have been updated since the paper was originally presented.

11. ORGANIZATION FOR EUROPEAN ECONOMIC CO-OPERATION. *The Or-
    ganization of Applied Research in Europe, the United States, and
    Canada* ("Report of Technical Assistance Missions," Nos. 81, 82,
    83). Paris, 1954.

12. SCHMOOKLER, J. "Changes in Industry and in the State of Knowl-
    edge as Determinants of Inventive Activity," in *The Rate and
    Direction of Inventive Activity*. Princeton, N. J., 1962.

Comment on Mansfield*

Zvi Griliches

IT IS HARD to discuss a summary of a set of studies, particularly if not all of the original studies are available to the audience. Mansfield is reporting on a very large body of work, and he should be congratulated for working, almost alone, in this very important area and for producing so many interesting and significant results. All I can do in this context is to reiterate Mansfield's caveat that some of his conclusions rest on quite shaky data and mention a few other scattered pieces of work having some relation to the range of topics covered by him.

To illustrate some of the difficulties of empirical research in this area, consider Mansfield's first model, dealing with the determinants of R&D expenditures by the firm. The important variables in this model, as explained in his paper "Industrial R and D Expenditures: Determinants, Prospects, and Relation to Size of Firm and Inventive Output," *Journal of Political Economy* (August, 1964), were derived from answers to a questionnaire or interview. They are not "data" in the usual sense. Thus, Mansfield finds that firms that would like to do a lot of research *say* that their expected returns are high relative to their cost of capital. This does not prove that profitability affects investment, it tells us only that when asked to explain why they invest in research, these firms can provide a "sensible" answer. The same objection applies with

---

* EDITOR'S NOTE: The references which Griliches makes here to Mansfield's articles "Industrial R and D Expenditures: Determinants, Prospects and Relation to Size of Firm and Inventive Output," and "Timing of Innovation and the Investment Function" were from preliminary drafts differing substantially in relevant places from the final versions cited in Mansfield's Bibliography. For those interested in the preliminary versions, see "The Expenditures of the Firm on Research and Development," Cowles Foundation Paper No. 136, and "Timing of Innovation and the Investment Function" (mimeo., 1st version, 1962).

somewhat less force to Mansfield's calculation of the rate at which a firm adjusts its expenditures on R&D toward the desired level. In another part of Mansfield's paper "Industrial R and D Expenditures," forecasts are made of R&D expenditures; the crucial coefficient used in these computations is not significantly different from zero or has the wrong sign in twenty out of thirty-five cases.

Similar problems arise in Mansfield's paper on the influence of inventions on investment ("Timing of Innovation and the Investment Function" [Cambridge, Mass., 1963]). There are several difficulties here: (1) so much depends on the definition of what is an important invention. Since it is essentially a scaling device, it may not be surprising that at any point of time people may not be able to think of more than three to five "important" inventions in the field. Thus the observed lack of growth in the number of "important" inventions may reflect nothing more than a certain constancy in the scaling procedure. We have not been giving many more A's than previously. This does not prove that our students have not become better or worse. (2) The crucial finding of the influence of past inventions on investment is based on a coefficient which is just twice its standard error for steel and only one-and-a-half times its standard error for petroleum refining. When the period of summation of past inventions is reduced from eighteen to fifteen years, both numbers being somewhat arbitrary, this coefficient becomes insignificantly different from zero in both equations.

As to the substance of his findings of an influence of inventions on investment, I would like to note that, in some of the work that Schmookler and I have been doing, whatever little evidence we have on this matter points more in the direction of investment influencing innovations rather than vice-versa. There is no reason, though, why both effects could not be present simultaneously.

A few "other literature" notes: for additional evidence on the returns to research expenditures, see Griliches [3] and Minasian [5] in the Bibliography to this paper. For the results of a diffusion-of-an-innovation study that are very similar to Mansfield's, see Griliches [2]. Most of the diffusion studies have been done by sociologists rather than economists. This fact notwithstanding, some of them are very good and should be better known to economists. Among others, see the work of Coleman, Katz, and Menzel [1] on the diffusion of a new drug among physicians and a similar study by Ryan and Gross on the diffusion of hybrid corn. See also Katz [4] for a comparison of these studies.

BIBLIOGRAPHY

1. COLEMAN, J.; KATZ, E.; and MENZEL, H. "The Diffusion of an Innovation among Physicians," *Sociometry,* Vol. XXI, No. 4 (December, 1957).
2. GRILICHES, Z. "Hybrid Corn: An Exploration in the Economics of Technological Change," *Econometrica,* Vol. XXV, No. 4 (October, 1957).
3. ———. "Research Costs and Social Returns: Hybrid Corn and Related Innovation," *Journal of Political Economy,* Vol. LXVI (October, 1958).
4. KATZ, E. "The Social Itinerary of Technical Change: Two Studies on the Diffusion of Innovation," *Human Organization,* Vol. XXI (Summer, 1961).
5. MINASIAN, J. R. "The Economics of Research and Development," in NATIONAL BUREAU OF ECONOMIC RESEARCH, *The Rate and Direction of Inventive Activity.* Princeton, N.J., 1962.
6. RYAN, B., and GROSS, N. *Acceptance and Diffusion of Hybrid Seed Corn in Two Iowa Communities.* ("Iowa State College Bulletin," No. 372.) Ames, Ia., 1950.

III

INTERNAL ORGANIZATION

THE PERSONALITY FACTOR
IN RESEARCH PLANNING

Paul Matussek

MAN IS of central importance in research planning. He is its beginning and its end. He determines the efficiency of planning and the application of results.

Modern research planning is, therefore, dealing ever increasingly with the human factor, a task which has been taken over mainly by psychologists, psychiatrists, and sociologists. As far as psychology is concerned, there are primarily two areas which have been treated by different methods and been approached from different angles: (1) The psychological problems of team work; and (2) The characteristics of the creative scientist.

With respect to the first problem, we are dealing with investigations which endeavor, by means of a better understanding of the psychodynamic peculiarities of a group of scientists, to increase the efficiency of their work. One of the many results of such studies is the cognition that a team's efficiency increases with the amelioration of the interpersonal relationship and declines with its deterioration.[1]

These studies are especially important in areas where scientists of different disciplines are co-operating on a joint project. If the personal relations of the group members are deficient, then they will fall back upon their professional authority and close their minds to free discussion and possible criticism. Eaton stated in a rather general form: "In absence of good personal relations conflicts tend to arise between the

---

[1] See, for example, G. P. Bush and L. H. Hattery, *Teamwork in Research* (Washington, D.C., 1953); and, by the same authors, *Scientific Research: Its Administration and Organization* (Washington, D.C., 1950); also R. N. Anthony, *Management Controls in Industrial Research Organizations* (Cambridge, Mass., 1952); and J. W. Eaton, "Social Processes of Professional Teamwork," *American Sociological Review*, XVI (1951), 707–12.

formal status of each collaborator, as he conceives of it, and the realistic assessment by others in the research group of their performance in this situation."[2] These and similar cognitions, which could be easily documented by additional references, stress the importance of the individual personality.

Interpersonal relations first and foremost are not a function of sociological or group-dynamic characteristics but primarily one of the individual personality. Not even the best working conditions can coerce a crank into contributing to productive group work. Similarly, the most ideal institutional conditions will fail to transform an unproductive scientist into a productive one. Thus, studies of group and institutional conditions are likely to be most successful when we have exact knowledge of the various personalities with their unique personality structure and abilities.

It is, therefore, not surprising that the majority of the studies are concerned with the second complex of problems, i.e., the personality attributes of the productive scientist. The studies center on the question of which prominent intellectual and emotional features a scientist should have in order to be creative. To answer this problem many diverse methods are used, such as factor-analysis methods (e.g., the questionnaire technique) and personal observations over prolonged periods in organizations and institutions.

The results generally agree irrespective of differences in method. The work of Brown,[3] which is based upon fifteen years' experience as director of scientific institutes, may be quoted as an example. Brown proceeded from the question: How does the creative scientist differ from other professionals, say a politician. He considers the following characteristics to be significant criteria for the scientist:

> an inquiring mind
> powers of analysis and accumulation
> the attribute of intuition
> a tendency to self-discipline
> a tendency toward perfectionism

---

[2] *Op. cit.*

[3] D. J. Brown, *A Climate for Discovery* (Princeton, N.J., 1960).

a tendency toward introspection

a tendency to resist external authority.

Other authors, e.g., Eaton,[4] have arrived at a similar result and anyone having observed scientists over a long period will agree more or less with Brown's views.

Valuable as these and similar studies are in singling out significant characteristics of the creative scientist, they are, nevertheless, too general, since they refer to creative scientists in general. This fact renders them usable only to a limited degree for the purpose of research planning. The search for such characteristics leads one to a high level of abstraction, at which one is no longer able to interpret correctly the concrete scientific activity. We are not concerned with the description of an ideal image, but rather our objective is to deal with the problem of research planning, that is the evaluation and smooth working together of large numbers of scientists.

In the first place, scientists differ according to their field of specialization. For example, a physicist clearly requires other personality qualifications for his scientific creativity than a biologist, psychologist, surgeon, or historian. Moreover, every scientist has his very special individuality, in spite of certain common features, which he shares with other scientists. These emerge if one asks the following questions:

Which motives underlie his work?

Does he value his accomplishments adequately?

Where and how can he best employ his abilities?

Is he capable of co-operating with others?

When does he cease to be truly creative, and
will he realize it or not?

How does he react to a decrease in his creative
abilities?

The answers to such questions, however, are not synonymous with mere descriptions of the scientist's personal working style. Rather they point to the creativity which constitutes an integral part of the scientist's personality.

---

[4] *Op. cit.*

This assertion is easily illustrated by reference to recent American publications on the problem of creativity, e.g., by Ott.[5] Concerning the process of creativity Ott distinguishes between the following phases:

1. Problem-finding
2. Preparation
3. Frustration
4. Incubation
5. Illumination
6. Verification
7. Communication

Various scientists pass through these phases in a rather individual manner which is decisive for their creativity. Differences become more apparent if we regard the single steps of the process from the viewpoint of the structure of the individual personality. Thus we might ask the questions:

Which problems does he perceive and how does he perceive them?

How does he prepare himself for the solution of the problem?

When and for how long does he feel frustrated and by what situations?

How does he cope with these difficulties?

What is the relationship between the experience of frustration and incubation?

What part of the problem is being liberated from the incubation phase and enters the illumination phase?

Is there any relationship between the subjective feeling of the illumination and the objective value of the illumination?

What appears to the scientist in question the proper approach to verification?

How and to whom does he communicate his results?

Ott and other authorities have correctly emphasized that the questions relate not only to the scientist's "style" but that they are central to the problem of creativity itself.

---

[5] E. Ott, "Stimulating Creativity in Research," *Chemical and Engineering News*, XXXIII (1955), 2318–21.

Thus, for example, the frustration experiences decisive for the creative process do not depend exclusively on the difficulties of the problem to be solved nor on the intelligence of the scientist in question. Rather, a whole series of personality factors are involved. For instance, some scientists seem to need a high degree of extra-scientific frustration in order to be creative at all—you will remember some geniuses who only worked if they were short of money. There are others who become unproductive if the slightest frustration occurs in their personal lives. They have to be "spoiled" by their environment if they are to produce creative solutions.

These suggestions may suffice to characterize the problem dealt with in this paper. In order to solve the problem—that is, to highlight the importance of the scientist's personality for research planning—I am relying on psychoanalytical experiences with scientists and on psychodynamically oriented observations made by me in English and German institutes. Thus, the experiences are clinical experiences. However, in order to remove them from their individual context, I have tried to schematize somewhat those aspects which are relevant to the problem of research planning. In this way, a model of psychodynamics of the various personality structures suggests itself as a classification scheme. Let me distinguish between the following personality structures: the compulsive, the depressive, the hysterical, the schizoid. Two remarks may be made prior to a detailed description of these personality types with regard to their effects on science:

1. If terms are used here which to the layman signify only abnormalities, this is admittedly an imperfection, but little else. Clearly, the structural concepts which I shall use do not imply that the personalities in question are abnormal. Whether they are depends on a number of factors which are not under discussion here. In any case, they are not relevant to the fact that we are dealing with a scientist. It is true that there were times when scientists were considered to be more or less abnormal; even today we occasionally encounter the same opinion. This attitude is not based on empirical facts but on the generalization of single cases.

2. Any typology runs the risk of distorting reality in favor of an abstract scheme. This holds true especially

when the types mentioned are conceived of in either-or terms and not as transitional. Therefore, if we distinguish between the different personality structures, we are not proposing mutually exclusive entities but types which in their pure definition would represent an ideal case. Properly speaking, every man has a few of these peculiarities if we stick to the developmental laws known today. All that matters is which personality structures are dominating. Or to define it in a different way: The ideal case would be a personality combining harmonically all the structures which, in their turn, represent certain possibilities of their relation to the world. This ideal, however, is the exception. In practice, certain characteristics always seem to be predominant.

The following sketches of the personality structures are, due to the lack of space, not supposed to reflect an exhaustive representation of the various types regarding their scientific work. We have to confine ourselves to a few features and, what is more, to such which, on one hand, are characteristic for the personality structure concerned and, on the other hand, are especially important for questions of research planning.

THE COMPULSIVE PERSONALITY

Throughout the world there is hardly an institute in which scientists of this personality type are not to be found. Here we deal with people who, due to their particular correctness and their lack of spontaneity, are likely to be conspicuous in the daily life. Their scientific career, too, is sometimes characteristic. It is planned and thought over in advance and with respect to every detail. They complete their courses strictly as prescribed, and it is not seldom that they graduate with brilliant marks. Instead of thinking through a subject, they prefer to dutifully memorize it. Wherever independent and creative work is concerned, they show traits of pedantry which, doubtlessly, can often contribute, too, to scientific success. In that case they are mostly extreme specialists rendering valuable services on a limited special subject. Truly creative accomplishments are likely to be rare. Their scientific *curriculum vitae* is frequently restricted to the pursuit of second-rate assignments conceived by others. It is true they can be very valuable, provided they can rely on effective leadership by others. Their instructions, however, have to be meticulously elaborated. This applies especially to younger scientists. The proficiency of compulsive personalities is mediocre if they do not have this guidance and if the problems at hand provide their own initiative with a certain latitude because the matter is not suitable for advance planning. As things go, they are apt to irritate a whole team by criticizing forever the project's insufficiency. Due to their personality structure, they fail to understand that the nature of some problems does not tolerate detailed advance planning and hence they are unable to comprehend that every question which arises cannot be tested empirically.

In principle, the compulsive personalities can be said to lack the imagination leading to the formation of fruitful hypotheses. They often substitute astonishing knowledge of technical literature for something which is of importance within the team, acting as if they were the recorders of the group. They are likely to become troublesome once it is not a question of conveying objective data, which are already known, but of discussing new problems. Here, due to the rigidity of their mental schemes, they often become downright unbearable. They are not capable of accommodating themselves to another, unknown, model of thinking. Many a team effort has failed owing to the stubbornness and rigidity of a compulsive personality, at least much time has been wasted in fruitless discussions. One can discuss problems with such people for hours hoping they will become impressed by stringent data and results and change their way of thinking but one has finally to accept that such attempts are doomed to failure. The compulsive personality is completely unfit to readjust to another model of thinking; or, at least, he finds it extremely hard to do so and then only after a protracted process.

As soon as a project becomes stalled, such experimental scientists will, as already been remarked, blame others or, in case they are working independently, try to clear up the diffi-culties by means of undue pedantry: the repeated study of the minutes, and reiterated controlling of the experiments, the repeated reading of the technical literature are then supposed to bring about the new working plan. Should this design, too, fail after repeated attempts and the sphere of activities be changed as a result, the scientist will typically say: "there was not much in the problem" or "it was not sufficiently pre-pared." Repeatedly I could observe how a scheme having been abandoned as settled by a compulsive personality was taken up again by another person and subsequently finished in an extremely efficient manner.

In the past the above phenomena have usually been ex-plained in terms of rational abilities and/or intelligence with-out examining in this context the much more decisive motiva-tional variables.

It was with an university professor that I experienced the fear of unplanned, unexpected situations in its crassest form. He could give his lectures, which were attended by a mere four or five students, only if he had prepared them verbatim, and was thus able to read off his manuscript. The lectures, it is true, were very good. Surely, this is a very drastic example which can show us, however, how the effectiveness of a per-formance can be impaired by the individual's personality structure. In the laboratory this scientist manifested the same circumstantiality, pedantry, and fearful working method.

The question of the economy of a scientific effort, which is so frequently discussed in the literature, i.e., the question concerning the relationship between expenditure of effort and result, can further be elucidated by studying the personality structure of the scientist. Therefore, a few remarks may be interpolated here in this context.

All authors dealing with the psychological problem of planning in science stress the necessity of granting the scientist sufficient time for his work—and they are fully justified in doing so. In general, creative ideas are neither generated at will nor under time-pressures. However, the correctness of this general principle cannot be allowed to conceal the ques-tion—as has been done very often by various authors—whether the scientist, in fact, uses the time granted him for creative purposes. Of course, the working method of each scientist has a rather personal style, he has a personal rhythm of activity and recreation, of productivity and leisure.

In this connection, the importance the personal style of the scientist far exceeds that of the number of working hours or that of the number of publications. The last is a rather doubtful criterion of productivity anyway. And then it is a question of how, for instance, the director of a large research organization or the member of a scholarship commission is to decide which personal working and life style can be justified as economic and which one not?

The example of the professor cited above permits us to realize at a glance that three days' preparation for one lecture was uneconomic, all the more since, as in this case, the fear manifesting itself was not limited to the lecture but showed itself in the laboratory, too. As another example, the case of a highly talented physiologist may be quoted. He produced a couple of brilliant papers, but his co-workers were convinced he could have finished them just as easily in at least half the time. It was necessary for this physiologist to interrupt his laboratory work ever and again in order to plunge into involved affairs with women. This proved costly in time and physical strength. He stayed away from the laboratory for days with the characteristic rationalization that it was impossible for a scientist to stick to fixed office hours. Here, the valid principle of independence in scientific investigation was misused to rationalize the living out of one's personal problems. This has to be taken into consideration if one is talking about the personal style of scientific productivity. The judgment of such style questions will always revolve around the following two pivots.

On the one hand, there is the acceptance of individual peculiar features which cannot be separated from the method of working; on the other hand, we must consider whether the relationship between style and performance can still be deemed adequate, and whether, in a particular situation, the team work will not be handicapped by this very style. A genius may expect greater concessions to his personal style of living than a laboratory assistant, at least in terms of the economics of the situation. On the other hand, in science as much as elsewhere, geniuses are the exception. The question whether from the economic point of view a given scientist's structure is an asset or a liability becomes more and more pressing as we deal with an ever increasing number of scientists.

What criteria shall be used to evaluate the working economy of a personality? Psychological tests, which measure certain characteristics relatively reliably, such as persistency, rigidity, authoritarian mindedness, are only of limited use because the conditions of the total personality, which determine productivity in scientific work in different subjects, are still too little known today. Hence, at least for the time being, there remains nothing but practical experience. A decision as to whether there is a visible correlation between personal style and productivity is best made after one has worked with scientists for a prolonged period.

THE DEPRESSIVE PERSONALITY

He risks little with respect to the nature of the problem. For the most part he embarks upon such problems as have been studied sufficiently by others in advance, although, like other scientists, too, he is bent upon producing especially good results; however, he is afraid that his own ideas will not really be accepted or appreciated. This fear leads to defensive measures. Typically, this means that he turns to problems which have already been sufficiently studied and recognized. Provided he rests content with this achievement, he is likely to render very valuable services, and above all, he becomes a competent member of the team. If he is not satisfied and if he feels called upon to carry out independent work, then it will result in a rather keen sensitivity to criticism.

Occasionally, such sensitivity can result in a person's closing himself off from the ideas of others in order not to be influenced. He reads less and less technical literature and no longer discusses his ideas with colleagues. Such reactions, which can be very troublesome for effective teamwork, may be observed in most cases only if the depressive person has made up his mind to work independently. He will leave no measures untried, be they correct or incorrect, to defend his independence.

Altogether, as far as his capacity to communicate within the group is concerned, the depressive personality is likely to become conspicuous due to his passive-expectant attitude. At times this may border on eccentricity. It depends on the nature of the problem and the role occupied by the depressive person whether the effect of this attitude is detrimental to the group effort or not. If one wishes to engage him deeply in group work, he demands much more personal attention than other personalities. Regarding the carrying through and the completion of an assignment, particularly if the work is of an experimental nature, the depressive personality is discouraged rather quickly.

A biologist whose experiments after many years' work did not yield the expected results entered treatment because of depression. At first he did not mention at all his hitherto unsuccessful experiments but talked mainly about his marital difficulties. He said he had become estranged from his wife, he was longing for other women but was afraid to yield to his desire. It was only after some time that he talked about his work in the laboratory, though he introduced it with the significant statement: "What I am telling you now is not connected with my depression. Actually, it is silly to talk to you about it since you are not a biologist and will not be able to help me with my difficulties in the laboratory."

In the context of this description it is interesting to note that he had been engaged in an experiment for many years. During the year preceding the outbreak of the depression, he read less and less technical literature. Increasingly he buried himself in his work; he evaded his colleagues—but he believed the solution of his scientific problem was impending. He was unusually aggressive in talking with colleagues. The depression started when he realized that he had reached a dead-end. His contact with the colleagues improved a few weeks after treatment started. In the course of a conversation he learned of a paper containing references that were important for the further development of his experiments.

Discouragements, to be sure, are known to every scientist, as are situations in which one discovers that a course one has pursued for years does not produce the expected result. This is not the place to deal with the diversity of discouragements occurring during scientific work. All I wish to do while discussing the depressive type is to raise an important question: Does the discouragement originate exclusively in the difficulties of the task? Or does the discouragement derive from other sources, perhaps unknown to the person concerned, which render an objective judgment of his own work impossible? Such sources are frequently the marital situation or, with unmarried people, the problem of marriage. There may be personal problems which the individual concerned cannot admit to himself and from which he will escape into his scientific work. These tensions stemming from the conflict situation may then adversely affect his scientific work.

THE HYSTERIC

He is actually found rarely among truly creative scientists, since, in most cases, he cannot summon the stamina necessary for creative scientific activity. This does not preclude that such personalities occasionally work at scientific institutes. They may make up for the lack of persistency by means of an astonishing capacity for enthusiasm. If this enables them to put up with the hardships of scientific work, then we often encounter the following peculiarities among those who continue their scientific career: They enthusiastically approach a problem but are prone to underestimate the difficulties to be dealt with. With an astonishing independence and unconcern, they often reformulate the problem if they cannot hush up the difficulties; at any rate, they do it much more quickly than their compulsive colleagues. Reverses are easily compensated for by their enthusiasm for a new project. In case of serious disappointments, these will be worked off violently, above all within the immediate family. The wife may be accused of not giving the husband enough peace and quiet for creative work. In short, at home the hysteric behaves like a misunderstood genius and wrecks important interpersonal relations.

In work the hysteric generally keeps aloof from dramatic demonstrations, all the more since nowadays dramatic outbursts are not as effective as, say, fifty years ago. In those days one still believed that such outbursts represented genuine emotion, whereas today even the layman is more likely to react to such demonstrations as phony than to be impressed by them.

Today the hysteric has to live in accordance with a different style. This becomes evident within scientific organizations in different ways. In a team he acts as the driving element; we may call him the energizer of a group. He reflects, as it were, the atmosphere of the group both in a positive and a negative sense. Members of the opposite sex play an important role as far as the communication process is concerned. He is the initiator of group life, he has an immediate appeal and moves quickly, he is also moved quickly, thus inspiring group effort. He is a gifted organizer, and he has no difficulty in expressing himself effectively. However, his knowledge tends to be shallow and unreliable.

In his publications one is impressed by his grasp, by a tendency toward evaluation of his own results, but above all the abundance of his publications is conspicuous. It is out of all proportions to the importance of the subject. Or to formulate it in a different way: the less the hysteric has to contribute, the more he has to talk and to write.

It would be worthwhile to examine some time how many scientific publications are, strictly speaking, superfluous. How many serve more the author's narcissism than the advancement of knowledge! Of course, it is the business of science, too, to acquaint as many people as possible with a result within the shortest possible time. However, there is a difference in whether the process is guided by the subject matter or primarily by the selfish motives of the scientist who is more concerned with being noticed.

As I already tried to indicate, these personalities usually do not persevere in creative scientific work for a long time, with the possible exception of certain women who under certain conditions are apt to do excellent work when strongly guided by a scientific personality they worship in a more or less platonic form. The majority of male hysterics sooner or later turn to jobs which focus on representation, publicity, or they become involved in administration rather than continuing scientific work proper. They are likely to be very useful since they are capable of arousing enthusiasm which in turn may benefit their quiet easily dejected colleagues. Due to their enthusiasm, they are also capable of inspiring many hard-boiled potential financial backers to contribute major sums of money, a capacity which is of vital importance for large-scale scientific planning.

There is an astonishing phenomenon which we encounter again and again when present-day science planning is studied from the psychological point of view: There are many projects for which there is an abundance of money, whereas for others there is little or none, even though they may pursue a worthier objective. This problem, which, by the way, is frequently discussed in the technical literature, cannot be solved in terms of economic, sociological, and political considerations. Rather, it is my opinion, that psychological factors have to be taken into consideration. Hysterics, who can adapt themselves quickly to the most diverse dispositions of their financial backers, who are public-centered and arouse enthusiasm, would certainly represent a group that should be studied in this connection.

Of course, such a person has his drawbacks, too, which may seriously endanger a scientific operation and reliable planning. Above all, the problem of unreliability has to be emphasized. For example, if such a person has climbed to an important position by virtue of adaptability and his overriding need to excel, he can usually be trusted less than if he were still in a position in which he has to struggle and in which he is dependent on others. Promises made today may be forgotten tomorrow. Orders and directions recently announced may soon be countermanded. As a "public-relations man" for science, he is prone to exaggerate, he likes to monopolize attention, thus possibly obstructing a valuable research program.

This tendency of the hysteric may prove to be particularly dangerous in case such a personality becomes a consultant. Clearly, large, relatively expansive, long-term studies play a much more important part in the scientific community today than ever before. Committees of experts are called in to evaluate such projects. They generally hover between two major dangers: If the expert opinion is given by people who are not specialists regarding the project to be appraised, there exists the danger of their being biased due to lack of specialized knowledge. If, on the other hand, such projects are evaluated by expert scientists, problems of rivalry crop up. The hysteric in particular falls prey to irrelevant rivalry problems. He may not realize this himself but, rather, bases his negative judgments on usually pertinent arguments. This is not difficult with most projects. In this he is aided by his gifts of persuasion. Thus, a committee of experts may be steered almost imperceptibly by a hysteric in an untoward direction. It would be worthwhile to investigate how many important projects are suppressed in this way in terms of time, energy, and money. The damages thus done to the advancement of science by uncontrolled hysterics may be incalculable.

It would be erroneous, however, to apply the problems indicated to the hysteric personality exclusively. It is only that with him the struggle for the usurpation of powers is especially obvious. Regarding their reliability as experts, the other personality structures indeed have their characteristic features, too. Perhaps I would be well advised to mention right now that the ability to participate in a committee of experts depends on the degree of neurotic tendencies on the whole. The more neurotic a personality is the more it tends to tip the balance by acting in accordance with personal motives instead of material considerations.

THE SCHIZOID

The schizoid personality is always present among the exceptionally great men and the so-called geniuses, especially in the theoretic-abstract branches of science. He certainly contributed to the misconception held by the general public—but not only there—that genius and madness are somehow interdependent. Here the layman readily "diagnoses" "insanity," where we may merely be dealing with moods and oddities. The detailed studies which were undertaken by Juda[6] at our institute on all artists and scientists of genius of the past two centuries proved that mental disturbance did not occur more frequently among highly talented and highly creative scientists and their families than in other people. Nevertheless, the layman believes that here is a genuine relationship. The truly exceptional discoveries require such intense devotion, concentration, and even frenzy which can hardly be summoned up by a so-called normal personality.

Devotion to a task and concentration are encountered, it is true, with other personality types, too, but then they are motivated by sources other than in the case of the schizoid. With them it is mainly a matter of evading interpersonal relations, of avoiding human closeness and thus being enabled to employ all their energies for one great idea. The schizoid personality believes in keeping people at a distance, and this should be the more successful the greater his accomplishments are. He does not rest content with trivial tasks and "common" problems, which can be carried out by others, too. He wants to accomplish unique feats in order to assure himself of a unique status in the world. While such people often make creative discoveries—the number of schizoid scientists among the discoverers is probably relatively high—they are unsuitable as members of a team. If they co-operate in a group, they are mostly outsiders and may thus endanger the group work.

---

[6] A. Juda, *Hochstegabung: Ihre Erbverhaltnisse sowie ihre Beziehungen zu Psychischen Anomalien* (Munich and Berlin, 1953).

Of course, whether the urge for a singular feat is successful depends on many internal and external factors. The example of really successful schizoids cannot be permitted to delude as to the numerous stranded schizoid personalities. It may happen indeed that at first a schizoid may make sensational discoveries, only to subsequently deteriorate rapidly in his scientific effectiveness. Characteristically this is often noticed very late.

I am familiar with the case of a late scientist who had extraordinary accomplishments in his field and on whom the highest decorations had been conferred. Experts considered him to be a genius. Nobody perceived that once he had reached a certain age his results were no longer correct. At first his results were accepted and other studies were based on them, until after years and at various institutes of the world the experiments of this genius were proved to be wrong.

Just consider how many scientists at how many institutes were needed and how much time and strength were expended to detect the error! The importance of the question raised here is brought home, too, with regard to research economy. It revolves around the problem of authoritarianism. Brown,[7] Eaton,[8] and others point out that the productive scientist tends to resist authority, consequently he could not be authoritarian-minded. But what do we understand by the expression "authoritarian-minded?" Does not every scientist have to depend within certain limits on the correctness of other scientists' results? Is it possible to check on every result? The more an authority has won confidence, as was true of the scientist in my history, the less will any of his findings be questioned.

To me it does not appear justified to dismiss the problem as one of the inevitable risks of any scientific operation. Certain concrete possibilities to solve the problem which, in part, can be carried out already today escape our notice if we resign ourselves by saying: "Well, such is man" or "Belief and trust can be disappointed everywhere." The problem of the age of the scientist is one of the problems I have in mind.

---

[7] *Op. cit.*
[8] *Op. cit.*

Here we proceed from the not unsupported assumption that once a certain age is reached the truly creative accomplishments start to deteriorate, whereas one's authority increases at this period of life. If we wish to make sure that somebody bases his authority on his accomplishments rather than on other factors, we shall be well advised to put him in such a position where he performs administrative or organizational rather than scientific tasks. Of course, in the individual case we never know at which point the creative performance curve decreases and the scientist concerned starts to rely anxiously on his authority. This differs from case to case and certainly from specialty to specialty, too.

Apart from studying the age problem, the sociologists have called our attention to the need for reform of the scientific operation if we want to eliminate an authority-dependent science. Among other things they pointed out that in many scientific operations throughout the world—in Europe perhaps more than in America—the career of a scientist depends on a system still showing patriarchal features. Expressed in general form, they manifest themselves in that the scientist cannot advance if he does not accept the views and doctrines of his superiors or of the most influential authority. Therefore, various efforts are made to bring about greater scientific independence. However worthwhile such attempts may be, they do not suffice to check the bad tradition of an authoritarian-minded science. For authoritarian-mindedness can be encountered even when there is no directly institutionalized dependence as was demonstrated by the example just mentioned.

It seems to me that, here too, the study of the scientist's personality could help us along. We would have to examine which personalities are prone to authoritarian-mindedness and which ones instil in others the same tendency. I can deal with only the latter question in the present context.

I already mentioned that the schizoid personality endeavors to occupy a unique and singular position in the world. This is often the incentive for really great accomplishments in science but occasionally, too, a motivation which overvaluates one's own efficiency. This manifests itself in a mania for recognition and unconditional allegiance which can be enforced in various ways in a scientific operation.

As an example, I wish to mention the important problem of the use of scientific literature. Such scientists often do not know the publications of others and even in case they have read them they have done so only incompletely and frequently with the intention to find their own results confirmed and to depreciate those of others. In this context they rather frequently make use of the mechanism of generalization. A few instances are sufficient for them to pass final judgment. Thus, one scientist on principle may not approve of American authorities, whereas another one may hold the same prejudice about German authorities, or about the publications of a certain group of scientists.

It is true, with such a mechanism, it is easier to find one's way in the steadily growing jungle of highly specialized literature; but it results, too, in that valuable findings are neither seen nor utilized. It would be worthwhile to ascertain how many discoveries throughout the world have been duplicated independently and repeatedly, the only reason being that certain personalities simply ignore the direction of work and the results of other groups.

In the past one frequently attempted to explain such characteristics in terms of inadequate sources of information. Today this explanation is no longer tenable. Even the availability of the best sources of information does not guarantee that a given individual will use them. If it were merely a question of an individual's blindness, he would soon disqualify himself due to his ignorance and thus not cause any damage. However, it is not like this in science. Here, blindness has a preponderantly group character and confines itself to institutes, special fields, theories, and so on. Those groups defend themselves against the intrusion of undesired findings.

The phenomenon of an ideologically controlled science in dictatorial countries is known all over the world. However, today's psychology is not only well acquainted with the official ideologies, which can be imposed from the outside, but it also knows something about the individual's own ideologies, which can have an effect just as dictatorial as any exterior force. Among other things, they are more difficult to perceive because they do not carry along the official label of an ideology.

To give but two examples, let me cite, from my special field, Freud's psychoanalysis and the behaviorists. These discoveries, despite their originality, show distinct traits of an ideologically impregnated science. Due to the complexity of the subject matter, such dangers are more likely to occur in psychology than in natural science, but in principle they occur there, too, if only in a different form. Thus we should examine whether the ever increasing number of publications is somehow connected with certain ideologically determined behaviors of some scientists. Let me suggest the following formula: Anyone who in science needs success in order to maintain his personal equilibrium will arrange for his results to be disseminated within the shortest possible time among as many scientists as possible.

I should like to conclude my presentation of a few personality types with regard to their effects on the scientific operation. I am aware that the description is incomplete, and I cannot indicate but a small fraction of the problems which should be discussed in this context. However, I was not so much interested in giving a "perfect" description of the personality types working in science but in calling attention to the following problems:

We face an urgent task in modern research planning to see to it that the "right" projects are studied, that they are carried out by competent people, and that they are completed with maximal effectiveness. The personality of the scientist has to be studied thoroughly if this task is to be carried out. He is not a special type, rather he has characteristic features in common with all men; only in his case they have different effects in science. In describing these personality factors and their relevance for science planning, I am less concerned with psychiatric nomenclature. What matters is the realization that the multifariousness of personality structures makes a given assignment best for a particular personality type and another for a different type; that even a perfectly planned project can be impeded by one personality type and advanced by another. Wherever these differences will be taken into consideration, research and its applications will be more efficient than where one falsely assumes the existence of standard personality types.

In this connection we should not forget that in science planning, too, it is *man* who ultimately matters. All research projects are intended to advance human welfare. It is man, too, who in his research work wishes to remain a human being. Consequently, the more he can express the main springs of his personality, the more he can be *human* in his work, the better will be his work.

HIERARCHY OR TEAM? CONSIDERATIONS ON THE ORGANIZATION OF R&D CO-OPERATIVES

Horst Rittel

SINCE 1959, the subject of this paper has been discussed in the seminars of the "Studiengruppe fur angewandte Radio- and Strahlenchemie" in Heidelberg. The first considerations were set forth in a joint publication by H. P. Bahrdt, H. Krauch, and the author, see [3] in the Bibliography to this paper. Since then, more experiences with the various forms of co-operation have been acquired, and attempts have been made to elaborate and examine in detail some principles for the division of labor in research and development. The author was in charge of the organizational-theoretical part. Owing to our disappointment with the inefficiency of the strictly hierarchial institutions, we once proposed a purely co-operative team approach as alternative, but since then we have changed our opinion. It became evident that the choice of an adequate pattern of co-operation is complicated, and that "team" and "hierarchy" are not simple alternatives. The problem of adequate forms of co-operation is more complicated. One cannot decide to favor as a general principle one of the two above mentioned forms of organization. One must take into account the characteristics of each specific task. The following remarks represent an interim report on the current studies and are meant to demonstrate some considerations and methodical approaches.

I

It is not suprising that the organization of research and development institutions has been the subject of lively discussion during the last few years. Especially in Europe, the

majority of existing organizations look back upon a respectable history and owe their origins to an epoch during which
science played a part different from that which it plays today.
The new conditions and range of functions, which have arisen
during the last few decades, quite obviously call for novel
organization forms:

1. There is an increasing number of tasks which exceed
by far the competence of any single expert. Even partial
tasks can only be dealt with by permanent co-operation of
experts belonging to different branches of science. We encounter such tasks not only in connection with the development and design of complicated systems (e.g., in planning or
data processing), but distinct subspecializations developed,
too, within conventional branches of science, so that even
problems of basic research require a division of labor between the various specialists.

2. Frequently, research and development is only one
phase in the solution of a comprehensive "real" and "extra-
scientific" problem of economy, production, technological
planning. Today, owing to increasing specifications [23],
there is no longer a clear-cut boundary between the "province of science" and the "real" world of its application. In
many cases, even basic research becomes a part of such an
action problem. The old distinctions between science and
technique, between "theorists" and "practitioners," are
losing their meaning.

3. The institution "science" is playing an increasing
political role. More and more scientists are called upon to
participate in making political decisions. Their job is not
to advise in the traditional sense, but to use scientific
methods to open up political alternatives and to estimate
their consequences. This, too, offers new tasks for research
and development and consequently raises new problems
of its execution.

4. The increasing demand for scientific activity has resulted in a shortage. The lack of scientific manpower, institutions, and facilities causes bottlenecks, with the increasing
demand made on R&D to serve as a tool for "progress" or

even mere survival. Thus originate questions of the efficiency of existing institutions and of principles for the foundations of new ones.

Traditional research institutions, in contrast, were established on quite distinct conditions; that is, they were based upon a concept of science according to which scientific research can ideally be defined as a systematic search for knowledge in conformity with its own well-determined codes and criteria. Accordingly, science has formed a frame of reference *sui generis;* that is, a well-screened province. According to this way of thinking, science receives its impulses and its directions primarily from itself. It provides knowledge which may or may not be applied, application being considered external to the realm of science. This opinion presupposes that the gain of knowledge is identical with progress, and hence worthy of aspiration—a thesis which can be justified so long as the direction of progress is taken as given, and so long as the things worth striving for are self-evident. But precisely these justifications are put in question once science becomes a participant or a tool within the search for the direction of progress.

This changed situation gives rise to a novel "science of science" which deals with scientific activities as scientific subject. The multitude of publications on this sector, designated in U.S. as "R&D planning," indicates the extent of this introspection: How do we organize to deal with those novel problems? What kind of policy is to be adopted concerning the promotion of research and development? What sort of form are the institutions to be given? Here, common but important objections arise: Science is unfit to be planned since primarily its task is to reveal the unknown and the unpredictable, whereas any planning is based on predictable factors. Research cannot be organized since the hunt after the unknown does not fit into a routine program. Research is said to be an activity which requires extreme liberty. It is extremely sensitive to organizational restrictions and the bureaucracy which the latter precipitates. All these questions, therefore, are to be solved by self-regulation, i.e., by the experienced judgment of the expert concerned in the specific situation. This liberty is considered to be the price society has to pay for the gain of knowledge. Self-government and the highest degree of liberty for the researcher when choosing his objects will guarantee the best organization. For who else could do it more expertly?

So far, so good, and everybody will agree. Nevertheless, this argumentation fails to meet our problem. In the first place, the question mentioned need not come from outside of science. It originates precisely from those scientists who are confronted, in the face of new kinds of problems, with the task of "self-organization." Put another way, the existing research institutions are exactly the product of the basic assumption that science is to be free and independent, but their development according to its principle of self-organization has resulted frequently in conditions evidently in contradiction to the proclaimed principles. Whereas, for example, in the traditional industrial organization the prestige of an individual is determined by his power over others, in science "the prestige of an individual depends upon his achievement as judged by his colleagues. His prestige carries with it no power of command" [25].

Nevertheless, a "dual hierarchy" can be observed in many existing research organizations, to wit, the simultaneous existence of a hierarchy of the power of command and a hierarchy of scientific prestige, the latter one frequently emerging as a secondary result. With time, the two hierarchies become identical: The superior scientific rank entails, as a matter of course, a higher administrative position and, inversely, it is only the highly qualified scientists who gets promoted. Apart from the question of qualification (and scientific qualification need not correspond with administrative abilities), this identification often results in the strangest discrepancies, especially when aggravated by the myth that the genuinely creative scientist is unable to co-operate with others or even that co-operation is simply a symptom of mediocrity [25].

The effects of such an attitude on the functioning of science are impressively demonstrated, for example, in an inquiry of sociologists of the University of Göttingen concerning the situation of German university staff [29]. There, assertions like the following are to be found:

> The professors breed a staff of co-operators, at the top of which they themselves are standing. Sometimes there is talk of slaves.
>
> Some have a brilliant way to make others work for them.
>
> It even happens pretty often that somebody ranking higher publishes under his name a work for which he did nothing but suggest the program.
>
> Specialization becomes a tool for professional rivalry. Only oneself is master of a certain method. Everybody is an expert guarding his own small specialty.
>
> Specialization is necessary in order to deal adequately with the expanded range of tasks. One is no longer able to cope with all the tasks because one no longer sees the context of the whole. . . . If in the USA specialists contact each other, work together in a team, and publish jointly, then all this indicates that specialization need not make co-operation impossible.

These are symptoms which certainly cannot be observed in all the branches of science or at all the institutions. There is an abundance of imposing counterexamples. The indications, however, are alarming. Thus, we would be well advised to look for the causes and other organization forms of research. They are not to be interpreted exclusively as consequences of the usual human shortcomings; rather are they to be derived from the discrepancy between the ideology, the nature of the tasks, and the organization form.

> The contemporary social patterns of science, the institutionalized as well as those cemented by tradition, have a venerable history from which much can be learnt and used; however, with regard to the actual tasks of research they are really archaic. In modern society, one will seldom find such a grotesque inconsistency between the form of an institution and its tasks, as is the case with the majority of the existing research institutions. [3]

Corresponding statements can be made regarding development and planning activities. Here, too, we come across the discrepancy between the ideal image of the great creator with brilliant abilities and the reality that the design and development of large and complex systems cannot be accomplished single-handed.

II

Which alternatives are available to conventional hierarchic institutions? Since World War II, the "team," i.e., a group of specialists from different disciplines but with the same target, has been in high esteem, especially among younger scientists. Indeed, the multidisciplinary work-team seems today to be the sole possibility to deal with the comprehensive tasks mentioned. Whenever it is of great consequence to tackle a task from many points of view, it is expedient to mobilize the best specialist available for each point of view. And who else would be in a better position to co-ordinate expertly the partial results than these very specialists working together? All the "good judgment" and enthusiasm, which often induces one to pronounce team-work to be the panacea, are not sufficient to solve the organization problem in R&D; for many questions remain unsolved. It is just because there is no "natural" and established cascade of authority and distribution of responsibility that the tendency toward anarchy and irresponsibility is permanently impending. Everybody is liable to rely upon the other: A cannot deal with his part of the task because he needs for it the results of B which, however, are based on those of C who cannot start before he has the results from A. How can a task be suitably divided in order to avoid such difficulties? Does one need a team-leader or a co-ordinator? With what powers? How is the team to be protected against mistakes of a partner if all are specialists for different aspects and if, in the result, the contributions of the fellow-scientists are interlaced so manifoldly that it is next to impossible to distinguish the individual contributions? It is too easy for a team to turn into a refuge of mediocrity. Or, how is the group to be protected against "too much talk and too little work," because the actual group situation of discussion, mutual reporting, and criticism will demand but a small part of time; in a research team, most of the time by far will be spent in isolated individual work. How does the group provide against the danger of becoming a gathering of "Jacks of all trades" who develop such an intense self-confidence that technical literature or the advice of other experts is hardly considered still necessary? Is it at all possible to work out organizational principles for team-work, or would it be better to leave the team to self-organization as it occurs from case to case; all the more since the influence of personal particularities within a small group is perhaps more determinant than any organizational measure? To quote Shepard [25] in this connection:

> Organizational structure is only one determinant of productivity and creativity. For creativity, organizational structure may matter a good deal less than personnel selection. At the same time creativity is as much a function of the environment as of the individual.

Today there are already many examples of functioning teams. It is unfortunate that they have hardly been analyzed systematically. On the one hand, there is a great number of impressive scientific and technical results which could not have been achieved except by team co-operation; on the other hand, there is many an example that many a team produces "more heat than light." Today there is still no compact theory on the division of "brain-work," or of R&D activity, as has existed in the division of mechanical work for a long time. All we can do with regard to team-work is to formulate a series of rules-of-thumb which are justified more or less by empirical evidence and scientific motivation. For example see [3], [24], [25], [28]:

> A team-like cooperative is only justified if it is required by the nature of the task, especially if the task does not come within the competence of one single discipline or specialization. The group is founded to deal with one specific task and ought to be liquidated once this task is completed. Otherwise individual work is to be preferred.
>
> Team-like cooperation is especially efficient with regard to tasks which are under high extraneous pressure (crash-programs).
>
> At many American institutions a distinction is made between "programs" and "projects" with respect to R&D. Programs stand for

the work "on one sector", e.g., a basic research job is a program, whereas projects deal with the solution of a specified problem in due time with given means. Team-like cooperation is predominantly suitable for projects whereas programs are best carried out by means of parallel individual work.

Each member of such a team ought to have his permanent place in a "home department". Shepard [25, 26] distinguishes between "functional groups", consisting of similar specialists, and "project groups", which are made up of various specialists and deal with one specified task. The functional groups act either as "feeder" for the project groups or their members are "lent" temporarily to a project group. Thus, the functional groups are "pools", i.e., reservoirs of homogeneous specialists. Consequently each one does not only deal with projects but with programs, too. This is important in order to maintain the contact with one's own special field.

The appointment of a project leader proved a success. He is greatly independent with regard to the composition of the project group and its organization, and is responsible for the success of the project. Project leader is not a rank; it is possible that he does not hold this position in the next project. He is not a superior but a "primus inter pares."

Inside the project group, a formalized contact control has to be waived to a large degree. Every one ought to be able to communicate with everybody else if necessary. Nevertheless, regular group meetings ought to be arranged, the intervals between which are determined by balancing the "meeting costs" against the costs caused by the expected deviations of the individual efforts, during each interval, from the "course of procedure" agreed upon at the previous meeting.

At every control meeting, the work for the next phase, i.e., up to the next control meeting, has to be divided so clearly that each group member can achieve his next partial target as independently as possible.

The group advantage due to mutual stimulation to an increased production of ideas is optimal at the beginning of the work. It decreases rapidly with increasing duration of the life of the group.

The dissociation tendencies of a group are reduced if there is a guarantee that the increase in prestige for each member due to his participation in a promising project exceeds that which he would be able to achieve for himself alone.

However, such rules-of-thumb are still far from giving a satisfactory answer to the question of appropriate co-operation patterns for R&D: The alternative "hierarchy or team" is not settled.

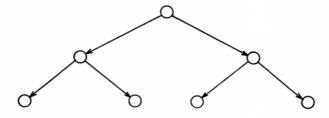

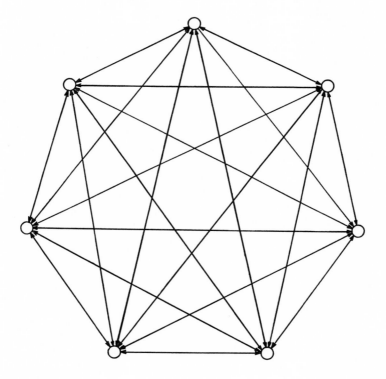

FIG. 1.—Graph presentation of the relationships in "hierarchy" and "team."

III

A graphic representation of organizational structures is given in Fig. 1. Each person is symbolized by a point; their mutual relations to one another are symbolized by arrows connecting the corresponding points. For something customarily labeled as "hierarchy," this results in a tree-like graph, whereas an ideally typical "team" is symbolized by a set of nodes in which each is connected with the others in both directions.

But what is the meaning of these arrows? Which kind of "relation" do they express? The following distinctions seem to be relevant for the analysis of organizations. "$A \rightarrow B$" can signify:

1. A has a communication channel to B; i.e., A can send messages to B.

2. A is bound to send certain information to B.

3. A supervises the activity of B.

4. A is entitled to give directions to B; i.e., A has the authority to program the behavior of B.

5. A has a higher rank than B with respect to an institutionalized system of rank order.

6. B concedes A the higher authority; this means that A is informally acknowledged to be an authority because of expert knowledge, experience, age, rank, or whatever.

7. A is responsible for B; i.e., A has to pay for B's errors.

Further, such relation types can easily be defined: the power of jurisdiction, the power of reward and punishment, the obligation to assistance and advice, relations of friendship, and so on.

A diagram of the kind described can be designed with regard to each one of these aspects for each institution. It is obvious that not all of these graphs are congruent to one another for all the aspects (to some extent the arrows according to [2] show a tendency toward the reverse, "anticongruent" course, as do the arrows according to [4] and [5]). Normally one is likely to receive a different set of relations under each of these aspects. In many an existing institution the aspect of rank (5), for example, will produce a graph different from that shown by aspect (6), the informal authority.

In addition, the graph of the formal officialized channels according to (1) will be different from the graph for the actually existing, "informal" communication channels. There is still another useful distinction. In R&D organizations it is reasonable to mark off "administrative" and "task-orientated" relations against one another. Using the terminology of Simon [27] and Marschak [19], administrative relations are concerned with maintaining the "viability" of the institutions as a whole; they furnish the precondition for the production to be carried through and direct the long-term development of the institution. Task-orientated relations, however, are directed toward events in connection with the treatment of a specific project or program. Sometimes it is neither easy to distinguish between these two types of relations nor reasonable to do so with regard to all the aspects mentioned. It supplies, nevertheless, useful insights into the function of an organization.

These considerations demonstrate that "hierarchy" and "team" are not simple alternatives, for it is possible for one and the same institution to be organized hierarchically with respect to one of the aspects (e.g., the direction-flow [4]) whereas it is team-like regarding another aspect (e.g., the informal communication [1], a not too rare case). The manifoldness of the potential organization forms, and thus the set of alternatives for the solution of our organization problem, is substantially increased by taking into consideration the fact that apart from the hierarchical and team-like marginal cases, a large number of other topologically different graphs are possible. Each of these graphs represents a unique relational structure (theoretically there are as many possibilities as topologically different graphs which can be designed from a given set of nodes). Indeed, many other organizational structures can be observed—as, e.g., the "staff-line system," cliques, and others. In order to mitigate the terminological difficulties which are liable to arise by persisting with the terms used by Marschak [19, 20], for example, we shall avoid in the following discussion the expressions "hierarchy" and "team" to denote the organizational form of an institution. Instead we shall label any group engaged in a joint task as "co-operative."

By first approximation, the organizational form of a co-operative is described by the relation-structure regarding all the aspects mentioned. By second approximation, the behavior of an organization can be described by specifying, further, the kind and frequency of the events under the various aspects. However primitive the description of first order may be, it can serve, nevertheless, to explain the dilemma of many existing R&D institutions. Thus, the typical hierarchy is characterized by a pronounced asymmetry of the relations between the members with regard to all the aspects mentioned; the relation structures showing high congruence and/or anti-congruence for the various aspects; the aggregate number of the connecting arrows is comparatively small; the graphs have a more or less distinct cascade-form. The typical team, however, shows a high symmetry of relations; the aggregate amount of relations reaches nearly the saturation-value, i.e., nearly all possible relations are existing.

The above-quoted conditions in certain research institutes can be analyzed, for example, as follows: In these institutes the administrative relations are formally identified with task-orientated relations; the multi-stage ranking system (5) is at variance with the authority structure (6); the task-dependent communication channels (1) are hierarchically organized and, moreover, inflexibly formalized; in addition, the reporting system (2) is congruent to the rank-order systems (5). In badly functioning teams, however, the authority system is frequently underdeveloped; the same applies to the institutionalized channels (1) and (2); on the other hand, the system of informal channels is very compact and utilized so much that the work suffers from the lack of restrictions of the communication-flow; the "group-temperature" rises due to the lack of institutionalized channels and too egalitarian control.

There are nevertheless strictly hierarchic project organizations which are quite successful. The Manhattan Project for the development of the atomic bomb during the last war was

characterized by a rigidly formalized communication network
(1), identical with the ranking structure. Communication with
a neighbor had to be performed at least via the next common
superior scientist or military person. However, a strong informal and secret communication structure developed which
played an important role in the exchange of task-orientated
information. As Szilard [14] once stated before a congressional
committee, the scientists could not observe the regulations
even if they wished to. The only choice they had was either
to obey and thus severely interrupt their work or infringe
the regulations.

IV

As I have already mentioned above, a theory of the
division of labor for R&D is still lacking. The results of
such a theory are certain to be different from the rules as
they were successfully developed for the division of mechanical labor or for routine "brain-work." One would not be well
advised to attempt to establish strong analogies. A science
of administration for R&D activities is essentially a new problem, which cannot be solved by simply taking over the existing
methods applied in industrial organizations. The organization
problem for R&D can be formulated as follows: Given a task
or a class of tasks which have to be dealt with by the organization, the problem is to devise an organizational structure
(described, for example, by particularizing the formal relation-
structure as mentioned above) for an appropriate set of
experts, subsidiary workers, and facilities such that the task
will be solved in accordance with an evaluation characteristic
in the best possible manner. However, several of the terms
used in this formulation stand for rather complicated circumstances. What is a "task" or a "set of tasks"? What is meant
by "appropriate" or by "evaluation characteristic"? A more
detailed discussion of one aspect of R&D planning should
throw some light into the meaning of these terms. Let us

consider the problem of evaluating the performance of a
co-operative.

The criteria according to which the activity of a R&D
co-operative is evaluated refer first to the result. The value of
the result, however, has to be compared with the expenses;
moreover, the solution of the task is not the only result.
Consequently, the carrying-through of a project ought to be
judged according to the following aspects:

a. The value of the result with regard to the expectations
about the outcome. To what degree is the result assured?
How "far" is it from the ideal or expected result? How
many innovations does it contain? In the case of an industrial development, the market value of the result would
have to be evaluated as well as the influence of the result
on the position of the enterprise in the long run.

b. The direct costs for the solution: wages, salaries,
communication and administration costs, capital cost for
equipment, etc.

c. The time elapsed up to the solution date, for in many
cases the value of a solution depends on the date of its
realization. In these cases "time costs money" though these
costs cannot be accounted in terms of direct costs.

d. The increment in "brain power," i.e., in increased
expert knowledge and skill of the participants. What has
been learned? Or has the experts' capacity deteriorated as
a consequence of the job? All the losses or profits due to
social or psychic conditions have to be entered under this
category.

e. The "opportunity costs": the amount of losses which
were brought about because other projects could not be
embarked upon owing to the choice of the project. Possibly,
the capacities available could have been better utilized elsewhere. It is precisely in the case of R&D activities, the
long-term effect of which is characteristic, that such an
evaluation ought to be attempted.

f. The value of the by-products, i.e., all those results
which have not been the direct purpose of the project but
which were obtained "incidentally" during the activity.

Each of these aspects presents its own difficulties of measurement. Although value theory developed many approaches to an evaluation of some of these quantities during the last few years, we are still short of methods enabling us to balance one with another all the values relating to the various aspects. Given the ideal case, the value of a project would have to be presented on a numerical scale (at least a difference scale). If we succeeded in finding a common measure (e.g., a monetary one) for all the criteria, the net value of a result would be

$$W = a - b - c + d - e + f$$

(the quantities are to be discounted in an appropriate manner). When planning a project in advance, adequate expected values would have to be used. It is easier to make such considerations for industrial R&D activities than for a state or an institute. Similar catalogues are to be worked out concerning the "characteristics of the tasks," "the characteristics of the co-operative's members," "the characteristics of the organization form," "the characteristics of environment and infrastructure."

In the present situation it is hopeless to tackle the problem of an optimal solution or a viable and stable solution of the organization problem. There are dozens of influencing factors, of which the majority are unmeasurable and subject to imponderables and psychological and individual peculiarities. For the time being such analyses serve only to develop an adequate vocabulary and to categorize the existing institutions in preparation for an empirical analysis. At present all we can do is to examine such frames of reference, and then with their help to look for further rules-of-thumb for the organization of R&D institutions.

v

There are still very few research results for our problem (see, e.g., the articles by Shepard [24, 25, 26]). Unfortunately we are short, too, of empirical investigations into the function and efficiency of existing organizations of this type. However, there are a great number of research results concerning the functions of groups in general and, moreover, with regard to problem-solving and target-orientated groups in particular. Social psychology (especially group dynamics) and organization theory have produced a wealth of results the application of which to R&D co-operatives ought to be attempted at least. The majority of these results were empirically corroborated very well, and they provide some evidence about the mechanisms of problem-solving in groups. Nevertheless, one is well advised to apply the results cautiously. Mostly they were obtained under laboratory conditions, with all the usual simplifications and specialized preconditions. In most cases, moreover, a problem which is set to an experimental group does not bear much resemblance to a real problem of research.

Apart from these experimental results, there are several "paradigmatic" considerations. There are simplified "thinking-models" on the functioning of groups. These models are taken as "homomorphic" to "real" groups, and reflect the present state of scientific knowledge about the mechanisms within such groups. In these studies the mutual dependence and the interplay of some essential variables are put together to form a model, which is then investigated while other influencing factors are neutralized (i.e., kept constant). Since in these models empirical knowledge of group behavior is processed and summarized, they can be used as frames of reference for the observation of real non-experimental co-operatives. The possible differences then noticed between the observed behavior and the behavior predicted on the basis of the model may enable us to deduce suggestions for an appropriate revision of definitions and theoretical conceptions.

From among the existing works on normative approaches to group dynamics, the following are especially interesting: models for problem-solving co-operatives [28], group learning [28], some characteristic quantities of a co-operative [6, 13, 27], decision processes and communication [19, 21], models for relation structures in groups. Bibliographies are to be found in [5, 6, 11, 16, 18]. The following arguments bear on similar considerations for R&D co-operatives and attack the problem of suitable division of labor in more detail.

VI

In order to deal with division of labor it is necessary to find out the performance advantages of group work as compared to individual work. In social psychology there is quite a series of results substantiating, in fact, that in many cases of problem-solving, the group performance is superior to that of the aggregate of individual performances of its members. As, e.g., was demonstrated by Hofstätter [12], many of these group advantages are to be attributed to purely statistical causes—analogous to frequent repetition of a measurement to supply a more accurate result than is found from a single measurement. Thus, a group's ability to judge exceeds that of any individual person alone, once the group judgment is adequately composed of individual judgments each independent of the other and as long as each individual judgment contains at least one sparklet of accuracy. However, in spite of this, the thesis that in co-operatives "the total accomplishes more than the aggregate of the parts" cannot be generalized into a principle. As already proven by the experiments of Allport [1], the fact of test persons being merely close together in the same room, without communication, influences their associations and ideas. Among other findings he discovered: A test person in the presence of others produces more associations than when isolated; this intensification effect is strongest at the beginning of the experiment; the objects and circumstances of the environment influence the type of association; and complicated associations are produced less frequently than in isolation.

The mere presence of other persons increases the quantity of the production of ideas but decreases their quality. However, this cannot be generalized either. In a group without restrictions upon communication, an animated discussion is likely to produce better ideas, too, as everybody is ready to confirm on the basis of his own experience.

The influence of the organization form (especially the communication network and the rank order) on the group performance with regard to the problem solution has been investigated (e.g., Kelley [15], Bavelas [4], Festinger [8]). The results of Bavelas are especially worth mentioning in this connection. He entrusts small groups co-operating in a given communication network with the task of solving simple combination problems. The tasks are formulated in such a manner that each participant is supposed to obtain a partial solution. This, however, cannot be achieved except by means of co-operation and agreement with the others. The temptation, therefore, is rather great for one or another of the group to obtain a nearly correct partial solution and to stick to it egoistically, thus thwarting the correct total solution. The effect of the various types of networks on the carrying-through of the task, the formation of authority systems, and the attitude of those concerned with the situation was thereby investigated. Bavelas discovered that an accepted superior came into power most probably at the positions of supreme centrality. Co-operation was brought about more rapidly in highly centralized networks but the "morale" decreased simultaneously. Willingness to take appropriate action on the strength of correct insight diminished, too. This can even result in somebody receiving the order from a superior to "forget" a better insight and therefore act against his better judgment [4]:

> Losses of productive potential (due to the suppression of insight) are probably very common in most working groups, and must be enormous in society at large.
>
> In areas where effective and highly integrated social effort is required, the problem (of adequate intercommunication) is particularly difficult. This is nowhere better illustrated than in scientific work. In many fields, it has become impossible to think in other terms than research teams. These groups, aside from the ordinary problems of communication which attend organization, face a whole new set of problems arising from the current emphasis upon "security." In practice, security is invariably translated into "communication restriction."

Bavelas draws the conclusion that the empirical evidence of his results are "provocative," though, of course, one would have to be wary of generalizing thoughtlessly.

A few results of Kelley and Festinger should also be mentioned:

> The lower the position within the hierarchy of ranks the larger is the production of task irrelevant information. Such communication offers some kind of substitute for poor promotion chances.
>
> The more stringent the hierarchy of ranks the weaker becomes the willingness of members of the higher ranks to criticize each other, especially in the presence of the lower ranks.
>
> The readiness to communicate from "low" to "high" increases as more and more prerogatives are granted to the upper ranks, whereas communication from "high" to "low" decreases.

In R&D co-operatives the occurrence of the type of face-to-face groups frequently presumed in the publications mentioned is comparatively rare. Usually, face-to-face contact occurs between long periods of isolated individual work.

As the next step of this study, the influence of the type of task on the division of labor of such co-operatives will be considered. The analysis will be conducted without reference to personality factors, though a few assumptions will be made on the abilities and capacities of the co-operative's members with regard to the solution of various types of tasks.

VII

"Much of research is search"—i.e., a large part of R&D activities can be understood as "search processes": search for a solution or a method, search for special information, search through a variety of alternatives for one possessing desired properties, systematic trials. A search process is a sequence of trials or experiments the results of which are subjected to evaluation. This sequence takes place in a "search space" determined by the problem. The search space can, for instance, consist of a class of chemical compounds or procedures, a measuring range, a series of possible procedures,

or a number of technical construction principles. The various
search processes can be classified, moreover, without reference to the object searched for: according to the size of
the search space, according to the structure of the search
space, or according to the search strategy pursued in order
to find a solution.

The size of the search space (i.e. its "variety") can be
described by means of the number of possibilities existing in
it or by an entropy measure. With respect to its structure,
we have to distinguish between (1) metrical search spaces
which can be described by a set of metrical parameters (e.g.,
the space delineated by the possible properties of material,
whereby elasticity modulus, tensile strength, melting point,
or like measures are each represented by one dimension);
and (2) topological search spaces whereby the alternatives
are fully or partially ordered according to a principle of the
"greatest similarity." In extreme cases, the alternatives are
not ordered at all (an example of partially ordered search
spaces is given by the variety of procedures available in
analytical chemistry).

The structure of the search spaces is additionally characterized by the quantity of information which the result of
each experiment gives about the proximity to the desired
solution. Sometimes one can assess quantitatively the change
in proximity of the solution owing to any given trial and in
so doing measure the worth of that trial. In other cases, all we
will find out after each trial is whether we have become
"better" or "worse" as compared to the preceding trial. There
are cases, too, in which nothing is known about the search
space except that certain alternatives are contained in it:
after each test it will only be stated whether that test brought
about the solution or was a failure. Finally, the search strategy
indicates how to proceed further in the light of a given result,
and its form depends on the nature of the search space. It can
be systematic; it can be a deliberate "search at random," or it
can be a mixture of both procedures.

In order to recognize that a particular problem is a search
problem and in order to specify the search space, one must

perform certain activities and make certain judgments which cannot easily be understood as search processes. An expert is distinguished, apart from his proficiency in establishing large and adequate search spaces, by his intimate knowledge of the structure of the search space, his ability to estimate safely the "location" of the solution within the search space, and his skill in developing a purposive and economic strategy. The better a region of the search space is explored, or the better the expert, the more highly structured will be the search space.

Let us now consider the problem of division of labor regarding a few specific search processes of the described types. The search space is supposed to be a well-defined set of determinable alternatives, the number of which is very large. One and only one of these possibilities is to be chosen according to unequivocally stated criteria. What are the consequences of division of labor among r persons, i.e., at each step to perform r parallel trials? To begin with, we shall study the following cases in which the trials do not provide any information about the proximity of the solution:

1. Random selection of trials: Every participant selects one possibility. If among these is the one searched for, the process is finished. When this is not the case, however, a new trial is undertaken and the process is repeated.

2. The same as 1 but "with memory": possibilities already tried are excluded from repetition. One "keeps in mind" one's results and stores them as experience.

3. Systematic search: The search space is organized in such a way that its alternatives are labeled, e.g., by number.

It is easily proved that in case 1, the expected value for the number of trials—i.e., the average number T_r of steps within the search procedure—is as follows:

$$T_r = \frac{N}{r}$$

N: number of alternatives within the search space; r: number of persons participating.

In case 2, the variety of the search space decreases with each step by r possibilities. This results when N is very large as compared to r in

$$T_r \approx \frac{N}{2r}$$

The maximum number of steps is given by

$$T_{r \atop \text{max}} \approx \frac{N}{r}$$

With regard to the average and the maximum number of steps, the same result is obtained in case 3 as in 2. These three cases demonstrate that "memory" or "system" reduce the average number of steps by one half, and that "memory" in the case of random procedure is just as helpful as a systematic sequential search.

The relative saving of steps as compared to the number of steps which one person alone needed, and thus the reduction of the process by division of labor, amounts, in case 1, to

$$\frac{T_r}{T_1} \approx \frac{N/r}{N/1} = \frac{1}{r}$$

in cases 2 and 3 to:

$$\frac{T_r}{T_1} \approx \frac{N/2r}{N/2} = \frac{1}{r}$$

The cost of the whole job remains the same whether the labor is divided or not:

$$\frac{C_r}{C_1} = \frac{r c T_r}{c T_1} \approx 1$$

C_r: total cost when r persons are used; C_1: total cost when one person is used; c: cost of one trial.

Thus, in the cases considered, the same properties are found as in the division of mechanical labor. The duration is inversely proportional to the number of participants; the total number of trials is independent of the number of participants; the costs remain unchanged however many persons share the work. Saving of time by division of labor therefore costs nothing.

What about the communication processes necessary to carry out the division of labor? In case 1 no communication is necessary during the search. It merely has to be arranged initially that he who finds the solution conveys at once an "order to stop" to the other participants. This results in altogether $2(r-1)$ messages or—if no initial arrangement is necessary—in only $(r-1)$ messages. In case 2, however, higher communication and "memory" costs result. After each step, each participant has to inform every one of the others which possibility has been tested: this means $r(r-1)$ messages at each step, i.e., on the average, the number during the whole job is:

$$ T_r \cdot r(r-1) \approx \frac{N(r-1)}{2} $$

As soon as more than $r=2$ persons are participating, this number becomes greater than N. Such a communication effort can best be accomplished by a conference subsequent to each step. Then each message has to be communicated only once in order to be received $(r-1)$ times (each hierarchical network would therefore increase the communication expenditure). Finally, in case 3, each participant can be assigned a describable part of the search space inside which he searches independently without any need for communication until he or one of his colleagues has found the solution. Here, too, we have the same number of necessary messages as in case 1, even if the communication expenditure is likely to be considerable at the beginning. In this case, a "once for all" classification of alternatives is obviously useful (e.g., lexicographical ordering, or some other classification system in common use). If the communication costs are high as compared with the test cost, it may occur that a procedure according to 1 is less expensive than according to 2.

The considerations above refer to the case of unrestricted communication. Any restriction of communication (e.g., by means of a hierarchic communication network) admittedly reduces the number of channels, but it rapidly increases the quantity of information to be communicated. The procedure 2 proves to be the most susceptible to this effect; but cases 1 and 3 are relatively undisturbed. The little important, but perhaps expensive, problem of the assignment of work is likely to be solved in the most favorable manner by assigning the function of a co-ordinator to one member of the co-operative.

VIII

We have to deal with a more interesting search task when, because of the result of a trial, one can derive definite information about the position of the solution. The following case is of this type:

4. As in 3, the search space is classified; we assume the possibilities to be numbered serially. In addition, each experiment yields one of the following results: "the solution is achieved," "the solution lies below the result of this experiment," or "the solution lies above the result of this experiment."

Consequently, each experiment provides either the solution or the answer to an alternative. (Much the same effect occurs when, after each experiment that does not yield the answer, one can be sure whether the outcome was better or worse than that of the preceding experiment.) It is easily seen that the best search strategy after an unsuccessful set of experiments is to divide the remaining search space into $r + 1$ intervals containing equal numbers of alternatives and then to assign the alternative at the ith point of division to the ith member of the co-operative.

In this case the maximum number of steps (when N is large, this equals approximately the average number of steps) is given by the following formula:

$$\underset{\text{max}}{T_r} \approx T_r \approx \frac{\log N}{\log (r+1)}$$

Thus the reduction in the number of steps T_r by means of division of labor among r participants as compared to the number of steps needed by an individual is:

$$\frac{T_r}{T_1} \approx \frac{\log 2}{\log (r+1)}$$

In FIG. 2a, this ratio for case 4 is represented, in comparison with the cases 1, 2, and 3, which, as mentioned, are equivalent in this respect. It becomes evident that the gain by division of labor is considerably smaller in the case of 4 than in 1, 2, and 3, or in the case of mechanical labor. If the search costs are compared with those of the other cases in which they are independent of the number of persons, it turns out that they mount up rapidly with an increasing number of participants (FIG. 2a). For a search problem of type 4, a new assignment of tasks has to be undertaken after each step, as each new step is determined by the outcome of all the trials composing the previous one. Only after com-

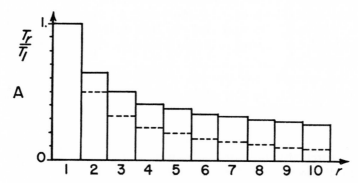

FIG. 2a.—Systematic search. 2b—Comparison of duration of search. $r =$ number of participants; $T_1 =$ duration if task is performed by one person; $T_r =$ duration if task is performed by r persons; $C_1 =$ cost of solution if task is performed by one person; $C_r =$ cost of solution if task is performed by r persons. ———— = systematic search [Type (4)]. - - - - - = physical labor or search [Types (1), (2), or (3)].

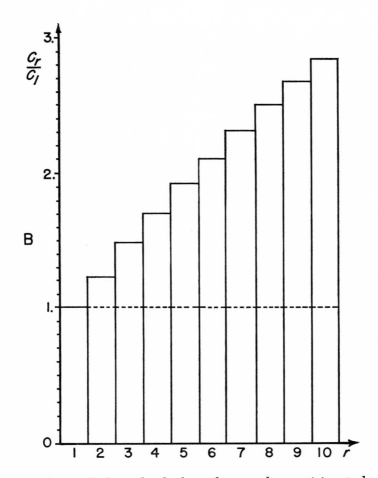

bination of all the individual results can the participants be assigned their next experiments. A communication expenditure equal to that for case 2 is unavoidable. As in 2, however, this communication cost can be economized if after each step a co-ordinator programs the next one.

In this case, division of labor is only profitable if the duration of the search itself involves "cost," i.e., if losses are incurred by the duration of the exploration. This applies, for example, to a situation of competition or to military development. The mathematical reasoning behind all of these conclusions is easily verified, and one could develop more general models at the cost of more complicated mathematics. The aim here, however, is to see whether we can analyze the problem of division of labor in R&D as successfully as it has been done with the organization of industrial labor.

IX

It has been shown that search processes, and consequently many R&D procedures, can be partitioned between several persons with substantial differences in gain. In reality, the majority of problems will fall between the two extremes represented by the ideal forms 1, 2, and 3 taken together (in which cases, nothing is known about the location of the solution in the searchspace) and the form 4 (in which all trials are planned according to a rank-ordered solution space). The problem becomes more complicated if experts on various specialities co-operate with each other, but the characteristics sketched above remain valid to a large extent. It is in this case advisable to distribute the search space according to competences in such a way that each expert is allotted a range within which he can complete several steps as independently as possible, and in which his ability to suggest the location of the solution proves an advantage. This is not always possible, but it is worth striving for.

X

Another class of activities in R&D can better be understood as "problem-solving." In this connection a problem is to be understood as a formulated question to which there are several alternative solution-possibilities. Each expert of the co-operative is assumed to have a certain ability to solve the

problem all alone. Considering the problem in a normative
manner, it may be admissible to substitute for this ability a
probability measure, which might be calculated from the
relative frequency with which the expert concerned is capable
of solving similar problems by himself. Two further factors
affect the probability that the co-operative solves the problem:
the number of participants and the breakdown of the problem
into subproblems.

Given a problem X. Let p_i be the probability that the
person A_i solves the problem all alone. Moreover, let it be
possible to divide the problem X into a sequence of k subproblems $X_1, X_2, \ldots X_k$ which must be solved sequentially.
Thus, X_i can only be tackled if X_{i-1} is solved. The solution of X_k is the solution of the problem X. Let p_{ij} be the
probability that A_i solves the partial problem X_j. Then the
probability that A_i solves the whole problem alone is given by:

$$p_i = p_{i1} \cdot p_{i2} \ldots p_{ik}$$

However, if r individuals $A_1, A_2, \ldots A_r$ are trying in common
to solve the problem, the probability P_r of their solving the
problem together is given by:

$$P_r = \prod_{j=1}^{k} \left[1 - \prod_{i=1}^{r} (1 - p_{ij}) \right]$$

Let us first consider the case that all the A_i have the same
ability to solve the problem and that the steps are equally
difficult, i.e., that all the p_{ij} are equal. Then: $p_{ij} = p^{1/k}$ in
which case p is the probability that any one participant will
solve the whole problem independently. Consequently,

$$P_r = [\, 1 - (1 - p^{1/k})^r]^k$$

This formula was developed by Lorge-Solomon [23]. It shows
that P_r increases with the number k of steps (see FIG. 3).

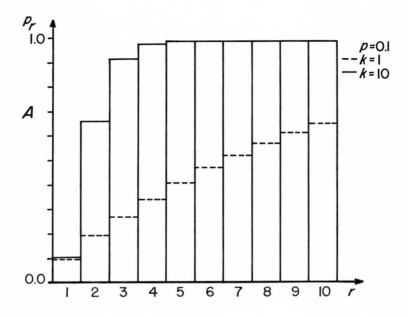

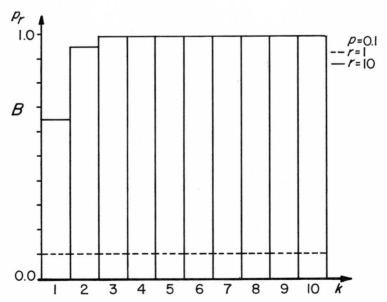

Fig. 3.—Probability of success for group problem-solving. 3a.—Influence of number of participants upon probability of group success. 3b.—Influence of number of steps upon probability of group success. 3c.—Dependence

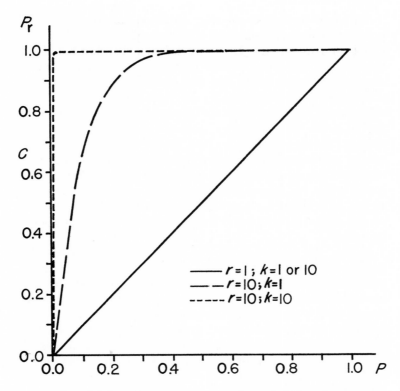

of probability of group success on the probability of success for the individual. $r =$ number of participants; $k =$
number of steps (i.e., number of subdivisions of task);
$p =$ probability of success for an individual; $p_r =$ probability of success for a group of r persons; $p_r = [1 -
(1 - p^{1/k})^r]^k$.

Many experiments have confirmed the validity of this
formula which explains by statistical arguments alone the
superiority of groups over individuals in solving the so-called
eureka problems. At the first glance, the influence of the
number of subproblems is surprising; however, it is evident
that in group situations even poor individual abilities and
small contributions can prove useful for the total solution. In
most cases the values of p_{ij} and those of k, too, cannot easily
be ascertained. But one can empirically determine average
values for the group.

We are interested in the problem of organizational processes which guarantee that the group has an advantage. One tacit assumption of the described model is that individual attempts to solve the partial problems are independent of each other or, at least, that the probabilities of individual solutions are not decreased by the group situation. The same effect could be achieved if the participants tried to solve the partial problems in isolation, provided each participant were able to decide whether he has found the solution of the partial problem or not. If able to so decide, he should communicate the solution as fast as possible to the other participants either by means of a hierarchial network or directly. If the individual A_i, however, cannot decide independently on the value of his partial result, a group judgment should be sought.

In just the same way as one can represent a model for group problem-solving, one can construct a picture of group evaluation and decision-making. If judgment and decision are ceded to a superior expert, be he even the best expert of the co-operative, it is still uneconomic since the accuracy of judgment of the whole expert group statistically exceeds that of any individual. The communication network should be such that everybody is provided with everybody else's intermediate solution. This can be most economically achieved by a meeting.

The optimal group size can be determined in the following way: Let V be the value of the solution, C the costs for achieving the solution, and P_r the probability that the co-operative will achieve the solution, then the expected value for the success of the group effort is $E\ (V_n)_r = P_r V - C$. Whereby $V_n =$ net value; this function E is to be maximized; C is determined by $C = c\ r$ (c is the cost incurred by one expert).

In the simplest case of an undivided problem and equal probabilities, one obtains

$$P_r = 1 - (1-p)^r$$

and

$$E(V_n)_r = V - cr - V(1-p)^r$$

Optimum r is reached when $E(V_n)_{r+1} - E(V_n)_r = 0$
or

$$r_{\text{opt}} = \frac{\ln c - \ln p - \ln V}{\ln (1-p)}$$

For example: if $c = 1$, $V = 10^3$, and $p = 0.5$, *then $r_{\text{opt}} = 9$.*

Trial-and-error processes can be treated in a similar way. By breaking down the whole process of an R&D project into partial tasks—for example, represented by a PERT-like network (for a similar approach, see Eisner [8])—such theories can be applied to chains of problem-solving and trial-and-error processes as they appear within R&D tasks. The influence of such activities on the whole project can be studied as a network to provide data for an adequate division of labor (see FIG. 4). Within this network of activities, the various partial tasks are weighted by their duration and the probability of the various results. Then critical paths with respect to time can be searched for, and the probability of achieving specified final results can be determined. Such networks display the consequences of further subdivision of the task.

In some cases, for such a scheme, an entropy measure can be determined as a measure for the uncertainty of the various potential results. By this means an entropy profile on the project's progress can be drawn to reflect the change in the uncertainty about the success of the project. This profile will be seen to start at maximum and to fall to zero at the completion of the project. Another such a profile can be constructed which reflects the uncertainty about the choice of the next step. In this case the peaks of the profile signify such situations where unrestricted communication should be most useful. During periods of routine work, when there is no doubt about the choice of the next step, this profile goes down to zero. So far, there is no compact theory which could be used to optimize such networks. They are useful, however, to compare the various possibilies for organizing a project.

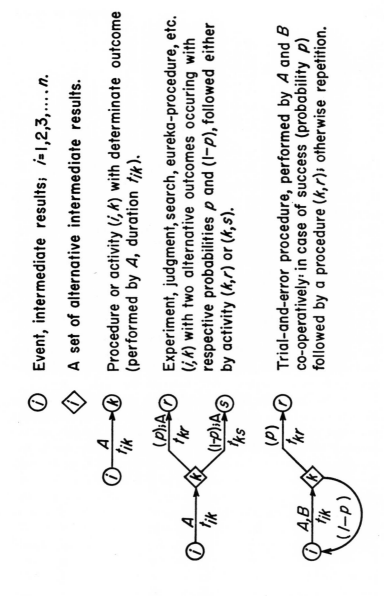

Event, intermediate results; $i=1,2,3,\ldots n.$

A set of alternative intermediate results.

Procedure or activity (i,k) with determinate outcome (performed by A, duration t_{ik}).

Experiment, judgment, search, eureka-procedure, etc. (i,k) with two alternative outcomes occuring with respective probabilities p and $(1-p)$, followed either by activity (k,r) or (k,s).

Trial-and-error procedure, performed by A and B co-operatively: in case of success (probability p) followed by a procedure (k,r); otherwise repetition.

A

FIG. 4.—Flow-graph representation of a problem-solving procedure. 4a.—Explanation of symbols (above). 4b.—Transfer function of a trial-and-error procedure (p. 207). 4c.—Example of the flow in a problem-solving procedure (p. 208).

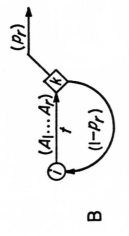

B

r = number of participants.

p = probability of success per run for an individual participant.

p_r = probability of group success per run.

x = delay operator.

Probability of group success: $P_r = 1-(1-p)^r$

Transfer function of procedure: $F(x) = \dfrac{P_r x}{1-(1-P_r)x}$

$$= P_r x + (1-P_r)P_r x^2 + \cdots$$

Mean duration time: $\bar{T} = \dfrac{t}{1-P_r} = \dfrac{t}{(1-p)^r}$

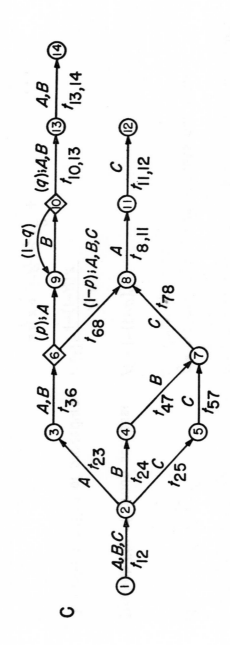

C

XI

To the present point, we have assumed that the problem and its subproblems have already been formulated and given. We have dealt with closed systems of alternatives. To establish such a system, however, is the result of another type of research work. In general, it may be suggested that the more complex the system (i.e., the greater the number of alternatives considered and the better the evaluation of their consequences) the more satisfying and well-founded the solution of the task can be. Using the vocabulary of Ashby [2], the system of alternatives originates from a process "generating variety." During the whole course of a project, but especially at the beginning, new ideas and aspects are flowing into the system. This tends to make the system more complicated and to increase its variety. On the other hand, the activities mentioned earlier aim at the reduction of variety: the task is, therefore, considered to be solved once the variety is eliminated again.

The production of variety is a substantial part of a R&D project. One (very disputed) possibility to understand the production of inspirations and ideas is to view it as an associative process: a certain stimulus initiates a chain of associations which are more or less directional. If N signifies the number of associations within the time t, then the empirically well-supported equation can be formed (C and m being constants [17]):

$$N = C(1 - e^{-mt}).$$

This equation demonstrates that there is a saturation value C for the number of associations produced by a certain stimulus. It can be expected that the exchange of associations between several persons is likely to raise this threshold since each association acts as a new stimulus on the other persons. In this manner, not only C is increased but also the diversity of the associations produced. This diversity is greatest when the individual reservoirs of associations overlap least (i.e., they are specialists from widely different fields). The chance of a good idea is increased even if only because the total number of ideas is increased. A superior intending to supervise this process would act as a filter and tend to reduce the range of ambient ideas to comply with his knowledge and critical abilities. According to Shannon's theorem No. 10, a channel cannot control more variety than it itself is able to produce. Of course, the same organizational principles hold good for the ability of judgment as far as the points of view of several experts are concerned. In such situations a diagram according to FIG. 4 can be useful, for it represents the understanding of the structure of the problem. It can help to generate directed ideas and proposals for alterations. Of course, these presentations are still rather rough and should be formulated as a more rigorous model.

XII

The previous considerations referred predominantly to the influence of co-operation in R&D groups. Now we shall take up the question of the organizational structure for a specific project. For a future analysis the theory of teams by Marschak and Radner promises to become an efficient tool [19, 21].

Marschak considers the co-operative with a common task as a set of participants whose activities have to be co-ordinated and the task directed toward producing change in a certain environment or object. To each participant, A_i, is assigned a set of actions out of which one action has to be selected in each phase of the project. Moreover, a set of observable variables of the study object's behavior is assigned to each

A_i. The organization is described by a communication matrix. Each element A_{ik} of the matrix indicates whether a communication channel from A_i to A_k exists or not. All the A_i are assumed to have the same preference order concerning the state of the object system, and the aim is to try to co-ordinate their behavior in order to fulfil the purpose of the organization (which is, to make a directional change in the state of the object).

Actions, observations, and communications cost money. The net gain of the co-operative's activity is the difference between the value of the achieved solution and the cost of the activity. This net gain is to be maximized by an adequate organization structure, by suitable rules for communication within the group, and by suitable rules by which the actions of the participants are chosen (dependent on the observed state of the object and the information received from the other members of the co-operative).

The simplest case is the so-called three-phase team without memory or ability to learn. For this case, Marschak derives a measure for the value of information and for the value of precision with regard to a given target. The majority of the cases investigated are restricted to the study of problems of decision-making under risk or uncertainty. Although there are as yet no specific applications of this theory to our problem, we shall scrutinize at least a few concepts.

Let us consider a development problem consisting of the design of a system composed of several components O_1, O_2, . . . O_s. These components are connected with each other according to a given network. Each component O_k is to be designed by a specialist A_k. The total system to be designed is supposed to transform a given input into a desired output; consequently, the several components have to be adjusted to each other appropriately. Each specialist designs his component by determining its properties. He uses his special knowledge which refers to the properties of his component. The relation between the communication structure within the co-operative, the assignment of the experts to their respective components, and the connections between the components of the object system can be displayed in a matrix (Fig. 5). Let us assume that the final design is the result of a bargaining process between the experts: A_i proposes values for the parameters of his component; these produce an output from the component O_i which from the point of view of the next specialist A_k is more or less suitable as input of the component O_k. At each phase of the bargaining process, the object system demonstrates a total behavior corresponding more or less to the desired one. The intermediate solutions are subject to modifications until a satisfying solution has been found which meets the requirements of the various experts.

What communication channels inside the co-operative are necessary in order to provide for this bargaining process? For this purpose it is certainly necessary that each expert, A_i, can "complain" about his "input." He needs the opportunity to communicate with those experts determining his inputs, in order to inform them that those inputs render his problem insoluble or lead to an unfavorable solution for his part of the task. From this it follows that the communication flow inside the co-operative has to have exactly the inverse (anti-congruent) course to the flow of effects between the components within the system to be designed. This means that the submatrix I (in Fig. 5a) is just the transposed of the submatrix V. As shown by the examples (in Fig. 5b and Fig. 5c), a hierarchical information flow cannot be justified except in the case of systems the components of which are coupled in parallel and where the total system has only one output. A huge variety of communication networks can result in the other cases, especially when feed-back loops have to be taken into consideration. Of course, the communication between the experts can be transmitted via a superior or supervisor. In this case, however, the number of messages transmitted would amount to twice as much though the number of channels would possibly be reduced. If such a supervisor were to act not only as a relayer of information but also as a controller, he would have to combine the abilities of all the experts. In order to rationalize the bargaining processes, it proves very advantageous to keep open the communication channels in both directions, i.e., not only complaints but direct replies to them should be possible.

	$A_1, A_2, \ldots A_r$	$O_1, O_2, \ldots O_s$	O
$A_1,$ $A_2,$ $\vdots$ $A_r,$	I communication network	II assignment of action	III actions to outside
$O_1,$ $O_2,$ $\vdots$ O_s	IV assignment of observables	V interdependence network within the system to be designed	VI output
O	VII message from outside	VII inputs	IX

(A labels the left group of rows)

FIG. 5.—Representation of a system-design co-operative. 5a.—Composition of a matrix representing the co-operative (above). 5b.—Example of a system-design co-operative (p. 214). 5c.—Example of a system-design co-operative (p. 215). A_i = specialists $(i = 1, 2, \ldots s)$; O_k = components of the system to be designed $(k = 1, 2, \ldots s)$; O = "outer world," environment; 1 = immediate channel; $\bullet$ = no immediate channel.

Block diagram of the system to be designed

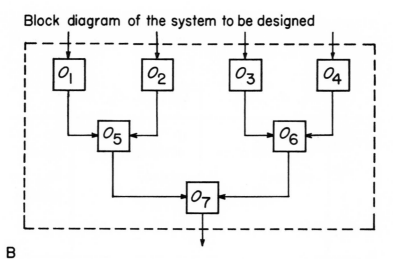

B

Representation of the system-design co-operative

	A_1	A_2	A_3	A_4	A_5	A_6	A_7	O_1	O_2	O_3	O_4	O_5	O_6	O_7	O
A_1	·	·	·	·	·	·	·	1	·	·	·	·	·	·	1
A_2	·	·	·	·	·	·	·	·	1	·	·	·	·	·	1
A_3	·	·	·	·	·	·	·	·	·	1	·	·	·	·	1
A_4	·	·	·	·	·	·	·	·	·	·	1	·	·	·	1
A_5	1	1	·	·	·	·	·	·	·	·	·	1	·	·	·
A_6	·	·	1	1	·	·	·	·	·	·	·	·	1	·	·
A_7	·	·	·	·	1	1	·	·	·	·	·	·	·	1	·
O_1	1	·	·	·	·	·	·	·	·	·	·	1	·	·	·
O_2	·	1	·	·	·	·	·	·	·	·	·	1	·	·	·
O_3	·	·	1	·	·	·	·	·	·	·	·	·	1	·	·
O_4	·	·	·	1	·	·	·	·	·	·	·	·	1	·	·
O_5	·	·	·	·	1	·	·	·	·	·	·	·	·	1	·
O_6	·	·	·	·	·	1	·	·	·	·	·	·	·	1	·
O_7	·	·	·	·	·	·	1	·	·	·	·	·	·	·	·
O	·	·	·	·	·	·	1	1	1	1	1	·	·	·	·

Block diagram of the system to be designed

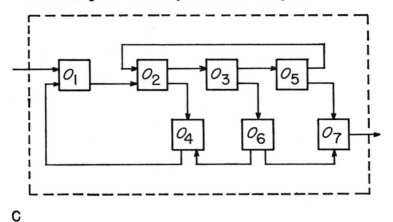

c

Representation of the system-design co-operative

	A_1	A_2	A_3	A_4	A_5	A_6	A_7	O_1	O_2	O_3	O_4	O_5	O_6	O_7	O
A_1	·	·	·	I	·	·	·	I	·	·	·	·	·	·	I
A_2	I	·	·	·	I	·	·	·	I	·	·	·	·	·	·
A_3	·	I	·	·	·	·	·	·	·	I	·	·	·	·	·
A_4	·	I	·	·	·	·	·	·	·	·	I	·	·	·	·
A_5	·	·	I	·	·	·	·	·	·	·	·	I	·	·	·
A_6	·	·	I	I	·	·	·	·	·	·	·	·	I	·	·
A_7	·	·	·	·	I	I	·	·	·	·	·	·	·	I	·
O_1	I	·	·	·	·	·	·	·	I	·	·	·	·	·	·
O_2	·	I	·	·	·	·	·	·	·	I	I	·	·	·	·
O_3	·	·	I	·	·	·	·	·	·	·	·	I	I	·	·
O_4	·	·	·	I	·	·	·	I	·	·	·	·	I	·	·
O_5	·	·	·	·	I	·	·	·	I	·	·	·	·	I	·
O_6	·	·	·	·	·	I	·	·	·	·	·	·	·	I	·
O_7	·	·	·	·	·	·	I	·	·	·	·	·	·	·	I
O	I	·	·	·	·	·	·	I	·	·	·	·	·	·	·

XIII

A whole series of similar considerations could still be made; they would, however, exceed the scope of this presentation. A few further possibilities that might be given thought: the question of the influence of the organizational structure on the role differentiation and authority (e.g., Kelley [15]); the influence of the clarity of formulation of the task (e.g., Raven and Rietsema [22]); the relationships between group targets and individual targets (e.g., Deutsch [7]); the introduction of variables such as "degree of hierarchy" or "complexity of the task" [13]; the setting-up of a model analogous to Simon's group model [27].

Empirical research work on existing R&D institutions and the development of individual projects would be extremely useful. It is only by such observations that the validity and utility of such models can be proved.

What is the use of such considerations? As already mentioned, they represent some ideas at an early stage of investigation. The problem of the division of mental labor raises questions very different from the corresponding problem of the division of physical labor. It is different, too, from the problem of industrial organization. Although there are many results and observations about the organization of R&D co-operatives, there is not yet anything like a theoretical framework. The above considerations are attempts to establish some components of such a frame of reference. They are sufficient to show that R&D co-operatives cannot be organized simply in terms of "hierarchy" or "team," or "project group" vs. "functional group": the variety of organizational patterns is much larger and ought to be adapted to the nature of the task and the properties of the participants. Although the ideas at hand are not very advanced, they do present a conceptual springboard from which we can make more or less empirical attacks on the organizational problems of R&D. The ideas represent what we now know or believe organization to be, and offer a basis for further discussion, ideas, and, above all, specific criticisms.

BIBLIOGRAPHY

1. ALLPORT, F. H. "The Influence of the Group upon Association and Thought," in *Small Groups*, ed. P. A. HARE, E. F. BORGATTA, and R. F. BALES. New York, 1955. Pp. 31–34.

2. ASHBY, W. R. *An Introduction to Cybernetics*. New York and London, 1956.

3. BAHRDT, H. P.; KRAUCH, H.; and RITTEL, H. "Die Wissenschaftliche Arbeit in Gruppen," *Kölner Zeitschrift für Soziologie und Sozialpsychologie*, XII, No. 1 (1960), 1–40.

4. BAVELAS, A. "Communication on Patterns in Task-oriented Groups," in *Group Dynamics*, ed. D. CARTWRIGHT and A. ZANDER. Evanston, Ill. and Elmsford, N. Y., 1960.

5. CARTWRIGHT, D.; and ZANDER, A. (eds.). *Group Dynamics, Research, and Theory*. Vol. III. Evanston, Ill. and Elmsford, N. Y., 1960.

6. COLEMAN, J. S. "The Mathematical Study of Small Groups," in *Mathematical Thinking in the Measurement of Behavior*, ed. H. SOLOMON. Glencoe, Ill., 1960. Pp. 1–149.

7. DEUTSCH, M. "The Effects of Co-operation and Competition upon Group Processes," in *Group Dynamics*. (See entry 5.) Pp. 414–48.

8. EISNER, H. "A General Network Approach to the Planning and Scheduling of a Research Program," *Operations Research*, X, No. 1 (1962), 115–25.

9. FESTINGER, L. "Informal Social Communication," *Psychology Review*, LVII (1950), 271–82.

10. HAIRE, M. (ed.). *Modern Organization Theory*. New York and London, 1959.

11. HARE, P. A.; BORGATTA, E. F.; BALES, R. F. (eds.). *Small Groups*. New York, 1955.

12. HOFSTÄTTER, P. R. *Gruppendynamik*. Hamburg, 1957.

13. ———. *Sozialpsychologie*. Berlin, 1956.

14. JUNGK, R. *Heller als Tausend Sonnen*. Berlin, 1956.

15. KELLEY, H. H. "Communication in Experimentally Created Hierarchies," in *Group Dynamics*. (See entry 5.) Pp. 781–99.

16. ———, and THIBAUT, J. W. "Experimental Studies of Group-Problem-Solving," in *Handbook of Social Psychology*, ed. G. LINDSAY. Vols. II, III. Reading, Mass., and London, 1959. Pp. 735–85.

17. LINDSAY, G. (ed.). *Handbook of Social Psychology*. Vols. II, III. Reading, Mass., and London, 1959.

18. MARCH, L. G., and SIMON, H. *Organizations*. New York, 1958.

19. MARSCHAK, J. "Efficient and Viable Organizational Forms," in *Modern Organization Theory*. (See entry 10.) Pp. 307–20.

20. ———. "Towards an Economic Theory of Organizations and Information," in *Decision Processes*, ed. R. M. THRALL, C. H. COOMBS, and R. L. DAVIS. New York, 1954. Pp. 187 ff.

21. ———, and RADNER, R. "Structural and Operational Communication Problems in Teams," *Econometrics* (July, 1953), p. 485.

22. RAVEN, B. H., and RIETSENA, J. "The Effect of Varied Clarity of Group Goal and Group Path upon the Individual and His Relation to His Group," in *Group Dynamics*. (See entry 5.) Pp. 395–413.

23. ROTHSCHUH, K. E. "Das Verfahren und die Entwicklungsstufen der Scientifikation," *Universitas*, XIV, No. 5 (1939), 521–27.

24. SHEPARD, H. A. "Nine Dilemmas in Industrial Research," *Administrative Science Quarterly*, I, No. 3 (December, 1956) 295–309.

25. ———. "Patterns of Organization for Applied Research and Development," *Journal of Business of the University of Chicago*, XIV, No. 1 (January, 1956), 52–58.

26. ———. "Superiors and Subordinates in Research," *Journal of Business of the University of Chicago*, XIV, No. 14 (October, 1956), 261–67.

27. SIMON, H. A. *Models of Man*. New York, 1957.

28. SOLOMON, H. (ed.). *Mathematical Thinking in the Measurement of Behavior*. Glencoe, Ill. 1960.

29. *Der Spiegel*, XVI, No. 34 (1962), 34.

30. THRALL, R. M.; COOMBS, C. H.; and DAVIS, R. L. (eds.). *Decision Processes*. New York, 1954.

IDEA FLOW AND PROJECT SELECTION IN SEVERAL INDUSTRIAL RESEARCH AND DEVELOPMENT LABORATORIES

*Albert H. Rubenstein and
Richard C. Hannenberg*

IN THIS REPORT we present some preliminary results of a study of the process of idea flow and project selection in industrial research and development laboratories.[1] The study is primarily concerned with the influence of technical, economic, and behavioral factors on idea generation, idea flow in the organization, and project selection.

AN IDEA-FLOW MODEL

Our general concepts about the nature of the idea-flow process are embodied in a schematic model, Fig. 6. The model was based on initial observations of the idea-flow process, and will be refined as necessary during the course of the study. It has been helpful in indicating the factors that should be considered and the places at which they might influence the flow process.

For the purpose of discussing the model, consider a single individual in an R&D department, remembering that several individuals might be involved. The general flow of an idea that will be accepted as a project for technical work will be via the boxes numbered 1, 2, 3, 6, 9, 13, 12, and 11. Boxes 1, 2, and 3 represent the individual acting in three separate capacities: originator, evaluator, and decision-maker, all relative

---

[1] The background of the present study is described in A. H. Rubenstein, "Field Studies of Project Selection Behavior in Industrial Laboratories," in *Applications of Operations Research to Research and Development Management* (New York, 1963).

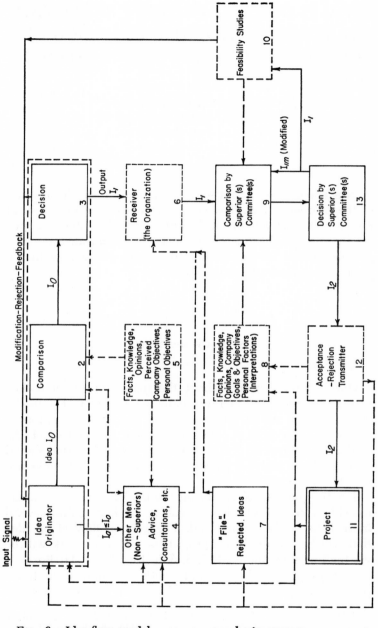

FIG. 6.—Idea-flow model. ⟶ = basic process; —·—·—→ = supplementary; — — —→ = information.

to his own idea. At 6, he passes the idea on to the organization; this would be to any person or persons organizationally responsible for doing something about the idea. Boxes 9 and 13 repeat the evaluation and decision-making stages, this time at the level of the organization; at 12, the idea is being communicated and translated into a project and other information.

A man may do a number of things with his own idea: talk about it to others, consult others, try to convince them that it is a good idea, modify it, reject it, etc. In doing this, he may or may not reveal the complete idea. This interaction on the idea is shown by connections from 1 to 4, 2 to 4, and 4 to 2. As the originator, he may just inform others about the whole idea or parts of it (1–4). Evaluation of the idea might be expressed by others even though advice is not requested (1–4–2), or advice may be obtained as the direct result of a request (2–4–2). On the other hand, the individual may consult only the body of facts, knowledge, personal perceptions, etc. that he has built up (5–2). Also, as shown for convenience by the same number 5 box, the other men consulted have bodies of facts, knowledge, and opinions that they consult (5–4).

Parallel relationships are indicated as occurring in the organization. The company evaluator (evaluators) calls on his body of facts, knowledge, and especially on ideas about company goals and objectives to see if the idea is usable (8–9). In certain instances, the decision might be made that not enough is known about the idea and, therefore, a feasibility study is undertaken (9–10). The information supplied by such a feasibility study enters at 9 from 10 and is really a special case of the relationship between 8 and 9; thus, 10 could be included in 8. On the other hand, an idea may be directly modified at the decision stage, then evaluated before the final decision—the cycle being 13 to 9 via the right-hand path, then back to 13.

The scheme is conceptual, and nothing shown is indicative of implied time lags in the process—e.g., modification coupled with decision-making and a new evaluation might be instantaneous; the validity of the modification having been determined almost directly through the process of comparison prior to modification.

The remaining lines represent feedback relationships and an alternate path for a given idea to enter into the organization. When the organization processes the idea, the results become available for reinforcing or altering its own body of facts, knowledge, and so on; it is available also for influencing the processes of the idea originator and the other man, as shown by the connections from 12 to 8, 12 to 1, and 12 to 4. Since similar relationships would be expected to exist for individuals, a connection from 3 to 5 would be appropriate; if the decision process at 4 had been shown, then also from 4 to 5. These possibilities are considered, but their inclusion tends to confuse the other relationships in the model.

Once project status is reached, there is further opportunity for the results to influence the processes (11–8, 11–1, 11–4). Some of the possible results are that a project is dropped before it is started, is held up indefinitely by being displaced by more important projects, is a failure in some or many aspects, or is a success. The results may have a more profound influence than other occurrences because, as an example, it is easy to refer to a past failure as sufficient reason for not attempting a similar technical project. At another stage, 7, there exists a file of rejected ideas, mental or actual, that might be called on to supply "new" ideas to the process.

While the idea is still internal to the individual, he might modify it or reject it; there is the possibility that he may start it back through the system as shown by the connection from 3 to 1. Also, the feasibility study at 10 may influence the scope of the idea so that the originator may wish to make changes (10–1). An alternate path from 4 to 6 is meant to suggest that the other men have an opportunity to transmit the idea or influence its reception. This might occur with or without the permission of the originator and before or after he has made a decision about it. It is even possible that if the originator told some others about a part of the idea (1–4), or about something general that should be done, these others might subsequently come up with the same idea. Thus, in this manner or by coincidence, two or more men might originate the "same" idea.

Previously, the organization was mentioned in a way which suggested that it is capable of making comparisons and decisions as a single unit. Actually, we are viewing the organizational level first via the interaction of individuals in positions of organizational responsibility and then as a composite unit. In a given case, one or several managerial persons may make a decision about an idea. They may have identical or very different perceptions of company objectives and criteria for approving projects. Each individual also has perceptions about what is expected of him in his organizational role. Thus, the study ultimately concerns itself with the influence of these perceptions at the different levels—researcher, group leader, department head, etc.—on the flow process.

THE IDEA-FLOW QUESTIONNAIRE

Several methods have already been used to explore the relationships described in the model: examination of records, interviews, and questionnaires. The study design also includes observations over time. An "idea-flow questionnaire" has been administered in several laboratories and in a modified pretest form to twelve R&D administrators in twelve firms.

The questionnaire was designed to gain a better understanding of the gross relationships that exist pertinent to the flow of ideas for technical work within the R&D laboratory being studied. It does not delve into questions about *why* something happened, but concentrates on reporting *what* happened to several specific ideas. The questions may be classified into two groups: those that ask about the technical-economic parameters of ideas reported, and those that are related to behavioral factors. Two earlier reports have been made concerning the questionnaire with analysis of some data, one by Avery,[2] and the other by Rubenstein and Avery.[3]

---

[2] R. N. Avery, "Technical Objectives and the Production of Ideas in Industrial Laboratories" (Unpublished paper, School of Industrial Management, Massachusetts Institute of Technology, 1959).

[3] A. H. Rubenstein and R. W. Avery, "Idea Flow in Research and Development," *Proceedings of the National Electronics Conference*, Vol. XIV (October, 1958).

FIG. 7.—IDEA-FLOW QUESTIONNAIRE

Indicate for each idea which *one* of the following categories of R and D work would be undertaken first *if* the idea has become, or were to become, a project or part of a project. *Place only one check (∨) in each column.*

GENERAL GROUP CLASSIFICATION	SPECIFIC CLASSIFICATION	YOUR OWN IDEAS			IDEAS FROM OTHERS		
		A	B	C	X	Y	Z
A. Work Supporting Current Operations*	1. Customer service on current product						
	2. Minor improvement of current product						
	3. Major improvement of current product						
	4. Factory service on current product						
	5. Minor improvement of current process						
	6. Major improvement of current process						
B. Work Leading to Expansion of Present Product Line*	7. Work on new product not currently made here						
	8. Work on radically new product not currently made anywhere						
	9. Applied work leading toward an idea for a new product						
	10. Work on a new process not currently used here						
	11. Work on radically new process not currently used anywhere						
	12. Applied work leading toward an idea for a new process						
	13. Translation of a research discovery into the prototype of a new product or process or part thereof						
C. Work Not Yet Connected to Any Product or Process	14. Exploratory work in a field of current interest						
	15. Exploratory work in a field of potential interest						
	16. Work producing knowledge for its own sake						

* The distinction between "improvement of a current product (or process)" and "work on a new product (or process)" is sometimes difficult to make. Please use this rule: In case of doubt, call the idea an improvement instead of a new product or process.

The concept "idea" is made operational in this study by asking for ideas that contain a suggestion for technical work —the work to be performed by the R&D laboratory of the firm being studied. The idea is considered to be the responder's own if he brought it to the stage at which most persons have a good conception of what has to be done in the way of a project. The customer who says that the company should design a better television set may start an R&D man thinking about the different ways in which it could be improved; but it hardly may be claimed that the customer was the one who had the R&D idea for technical work. With these distinctions in mind, the twelve individuals were each asked to select, for a recent period, his three best ideas (his own criteria to be used) and three of the best ideas of others with whom he is acquainted and to subject each to the series of thirteen questions.

In order to keep the ideas confidential, individuals were not required to reveal the idea. They were asked to make a brief written description of each one under the code letters A, B, C for their own and X, Y, Z for those from others; this is for their reference purposes only. Then they were to answer the questions for the specific idea, but not to submit the written descriptions of the ideas.

Question 1 required classification according to the intended scope of the idea; only one classification out of sixteen is to be chosen per idea. Figure 7 is a reproduction of question 1. The three main classifications are suggestive of the scope and type of work being done by R&D for projects that fall within the brackets.

The categories have been found useful in a wide range of companies and technologies.

Question 2 asked for time horizons where appropriate: (1) the time expected to obtain the first economic results, (2) the time to a "future 'break-even' point, when all R&D expenses and other 'start-up' expenses will have been recovered and the company will begin to show a profit."

Questions 4 and 5 asked how much work and time would be necessary to determine technical feasibility of the idea. Question 3 merely asked how long ago the idea was conceived, while 12 asked what happened to the idea—rejected, accepted, incorporated in an ongoing project, set aside temporarily, or still being considered.

Question 13 was a multiple-check type of question that asked what the expected outcome of the project might be. The possible outcomes include: cost savings; capital investments; benefits to new and old customers; and professional outcomes such as publications of findings, presentation of findings, and patents.

Questions 6, 7, 8, 9, 10, and 11 were concerned with specific patterns of action taken in regard to the ideas. The first two asked the originator whom he consulted about his own idea and whom he tried to convince that his ideas should be used in some way. The four remaining were concerned with the ideas of others (X, Y, and Z). Questions included: who originated the ideas; who transmitted the ideas to the respondent; in what way he responded to the idea—whether he gave consultation, tried to convince others of their value (and who these others were); whether he had responsibility to decide if the idea should or should not be used; whether he used the idea himself; or whether he took no active part concerning the idea.

SOME FINDINGS OF THE FIRST IDEA-FLOW QUESTIONNAIRE

In two companies it was found that research and development departments produce and use ideas that fall into the same categories of work. The differences are ones of emphasis in which the research departments show a concentration in "work not yet connected to any product or process" and the development departments report concentration in "work supporting current operations." These findings are represented in Fig. 7 by classification numbers 14 to 16 for research and numbers 1 to 6 for development. In numbers 7 to 13, the total percentage of ideas was much the same in each department for a given company, 46 to 40 per cent and 55 to 53 per cent. In the classification 1 to 6, the best ideas seem to show a consistent tendency to have shorter time horizons.

The occurrence of a tendency to have different time horizons might be explained by the difference in the nature of the projects once they are in the development department, or by a feeling that all projects must be rushed to completion once they reach the development stage. Thus, in the second explanation, there are implications about the behavior of individuals in the different departments. For example, development personnel may be giving expression to their feelings of being rushed. There also is some question as to why the differences are so small although they are consistent. Is it possible that the development personnel are giving expression to a general feeling that their projects should have longer time horizons?

In the Avery study,[4] data from ten laboratories were analyzed to see if managers might have preferences for certain kinds of ideas. Such preferences might motivate the members of the laboratory to emulate the pattern, especially if further motivated by aspirations to be a manager. It was found that managers in "all laboratories indicated an overwhelming interest in ideas with specifiable economic consequences." Plotting the ideas of managers that had economic consequences by classifications from question 1 vs. the time horizon further indicated a clustered pattern.

Although it was not a part of the purpose to compare laboratories in the above study, it was reported that managers in each laboratory "place some premium upon ideas leading toward new products and processes." Of more concern was the internal correspondence of the patten of the ideas created by members to that of their managers. Each laboratory was divided into three groups: the managers, the middle-level supervisors, and professionals at the bench. In all but one case out of ten, the middle-level supervisors reported more ideas of the type preferred by the manager than did the professionals. However, with only one exception, agreement is not large; supervisors concentrate no more than half of their ideas in the area preferred by managers.

---

[4] *Op. cit.*, n. 2.

As a part of the study, persons were named by others as producing the best ideas. The ideas of those so named were then compared with the ideas of the supervisors as before; now it was found that those named in this way had ideas that were closer matches to the supervisors' preferred ideas in five laboratories. This was not the case for the ideas of the professionals not named. In two cases, not enough data were available; in another, the difference did not appear; it may or may not have appeared in the fourth; and in the last, it was denied.

The foregoing analysis suggests further questions regarding behavioral aspects to be investigated. Might it be true that those named as having the best ideas tend to be the ones perceived as having high personal prestige? How will this be affected if these men overshadow the supervisors in the opinion of newer or less experienced men? Are these the men who help get ideas through channels if the ideas meet their criteria? These are questions that we hope to answer as the study progresses.

A STUDY OF ACCEPTED IDEAS

During the past few months, a field study has been under way in another organization we shall call "Company 20."

Table 6 shows the project portfolio for the R&D department of Company 20 distributed according to the questionnaire classifications. These are the projects that were active at the end of February, 1962. As there are exactly 100 projects listed, the individual classification totals are equal to the percentages of the projects in each class. From this it can be seen that most of the R&D work by project class is in work supporting current operations, 61 per cent compared with 34 per cent and 5 per cent in the other two groups. The median class is 4. A conservative approach to R&D is indicated by the above and is further confirmed by the relationship of class 7 to 8—there are almost twice as many projects on "products not currently made by this company" compared to those "not

TABLE 6

COMPANY 20: ACTIVE PROJECTS, FEBRUARY 28, 1962, CLASSIFIED BY IDEA TYPE AND DISTRIBUTED TO THE PERIOD IN WHICH WORK STARTED

PROJECT CLASSIFICATION	ACTUAL PROJECT COUNT				PER CENT			
	Prior to July, 1961	July to December, 1961	January, February, 1962	Total by Class	Group Total	Prior to July, 1961	July to December, 1961	January, February, 1962
A { 1.	...	2	2	4		...	6.9	9.5
2.	7	5	5	17		14	17.2	23.8
3.	7	5	2	14	61	14	17.2	9.5
4.	14	7	5	26		28	24.1	23.8
5.	...	...	...	...		...	...	...
6.	...	...	...	...		...	...	...
7.	8	4	3	15		16	13.8	14.3
8.	5	1	2	8		10	3.4	9.5
9.	3	1	...	4		6	3.4	...
B { 10.	...	...	...	...		...	...	...
11.	3	2	1	6	34	6	6.9	4.8
12.	...	...	...	...		...	...	...
13.	1	...	...	1		2	...	...
C { 14.	2	2	1	5	5	4	6.9	4.8
15.	...	...	...	...		...	...	...
Total	50	29	21	100	100	100	100	100

currently made anywhere." This company might be described as satisfied with maintaining a position in its current products; as just meeting competition; or as expanding the product line into areas that are safe and proven—especially as far as pay-off on money invested in R&D is concerned.

Table 6 also includes information about the number of projects started vs. a particular time period. Each project listed is included in the total number of active projects. The reason for showing starts for the last half of 1961 and first two months of 1962 is that many of the shorter projects have not been completed as yet. Therefore, the data are representative of all the types of projects being accepted, especially since it is known that a number of projects were dropped to make room for these.

The estimated times to complete the projects in the portfolio of Company 20 vs. the period in which they were started is given in Table 7. There are a total of nineteen more projects in the data for Table 7 than in Table 6; actually, the dis-

TABLE 7

COMPANY 20: DISTRIBUTION OF PROJECTS BY ESTIMATED TIME FOR COMPLETION AND PERIOD IN WHICH WORK STARTED

Estimated Time for Completion (in Months)	Prior to July, 1960	July to Dec., 1960	Jan. to June, 1961	July to Dec., 1961	Jan., Feb., 1962	Total
0–3	0	2	1	9	3	15
4–6	4	5	5	3	3	20
7–9	1	1	5	6	4	17
10–12	7	2	2	2	1	14*
13–18	3	6	2	5	. . .	16
19–24	6	5	1	. . .	. . .	12
25–30	7	. . .	. . .	. . .	. . .	7
31–36	1	. . .	2	. . .	. . .	3
Over 36	12	1	1	1	. . .	15
Total	41	22	19	26	11	119

– – – – – – median classification over time.
*Median for data from approximately a five-year span.

crepancy is even greater. The last six months of 1961 and the first two of 1962 contain thirteen less projects because the estimated time to complete was not available for these. In addition, when possible, all projects that had been active or completed are included. It was not possible to do this in Table 6 because there were projects with numbers but no descriptions; these were completed before the current management group moved in a year before.

Notice the very short time horizon: over half the projects fall into the groups that are expected to take twelve months or less to complete. This is a further substantiation of the conservative nature of the R&D portfolio. It seems that they want to undertake projects that will not take too long to pay off. Another interesting observation is that these projects exhibit a median time horizon that is decreasing as the starting date becomes more current.

Since it was not possible to obtain information on all projects, especially earlier ones, there is a question about the validity of the trend. First of all, it is known that for 1961 a major portion of the projects are included; in the projects not included, there were apparently more projects that were completed in a shorter time than ones taking a longer time. If the balance of projects started in the first half of 1962 could now be included, it is very likely that the median might shift back to the seven to nine month scope. However, a check with management indicates that no unusually large number of long-term projects have been added, so the shift of the median would be limited.

The assistant research manager was asked about the portfolio. He expressed the opinion that the work they are doing has been dominated by accounting and financial interests. These interests seem to be looking for fast payoff from R&D effort. The manager has now classified the manpower effort to see what percentage of the work is spent on research. In July, he found that 51 per cent of his manpower effort was on such projects. The balance of the effort he classified as being for the maintenance of current business—a defensive operation, in his opinion.

The R&D management in this firm wants to start changing this emphasis; they want to be leaders in their field. We hope that we will be able to continue the observations during this period of attempted change. If the observations are continued, it is planned that attitude and value questionnaires will be administered to obtain information about why the behavior did or did not change.

PILOT TEST OF A MODIFIED QUESTIONNAIRE

Twelve men holding managerial R&D positions in different companies agreed to pretest a modified form of the questionnaire. Table 8 gives the position of each man in his company and the type of industry. From this it may be seen that there is a diversity of industries, represented by higher administrative levels in R&D. The instructions were modified: we asked

TABLE 8

MANAGERIAL POSITIONS OF TWELVE MEN WHO PRETESTED THE
MODIFIED QUESTIONNAIRE
(by Company Number)

Company Number	Position	Type of Company
1.	Department Manager	Electronics
2.	Director of R&D	Consumer products
3.	Department Manager	Machinery
4.	Section Manager	Metal products
5.	Department Manager	Electronics
6.	Director of Research	Electronics
7.	Chief Engineer	Instruments
8.	Department Manager	Food
9.	Department Manager	Electronics
10.	Department Manager	Materials
11.	Vice-President, R&D	Instruments
12.	Vice-President, New Products	Chemicals

for eight ideas, to be split between their own and others. The requirement that the ideas be "best" was removed from half of the questionnaires, but they all were asked to submit ideas that they initially considered worthy of project status. In addition, we asked them to try to list several projects that had been rejected and some that had never been formally submitted. From this heterogeneous sample of respondents, ninety-five ideas were obtained. Only six had never been submitted, six had been rejected, and nine had been temporarily put in inventory.

A summary of all the projects reported by project type vs. estimated man months required to complete the project is presented in graphic form in FIG. 8. By looking down a classification column (the sixteen classes from FIG. 7), the distribution of expected outcome from these selected ideas may be gauged. Despite the heterogeneous nature of the data, the trend of the median indicates that more manpower is committed to Group B projects (classes 7 through 13) than to Group A.

The type of projects that these managers have in mind appear to cluster into projects concerned first with improving the product, then on new products not made by their company. However, the emphasis on new products not currently made anywhere must be mentioned since there are fourteen ideas in this class. Another factor to be noticed is the relatively short time horizon for effort input: more than half the projects are estimated to require twelve man months of time or less; ideas in particular classes such as 2 and 3 typically require no more than six man months; and those in 7 and 8, no more than twenty-four.

It would be of interest to know what extra values, if any, an idea needs to have in order to be acceptable as this time horizon is increased. The explanation might help to explain what kind of ideas would be acceptable for Group C projects. Without follow-up interviewing, we cannot explain why these projects have such limited time horizons. One possibility is that the projects are ones requiring only technical feasibility studies before being reclassified. If this is what was reported, then the categories were either misunderstood or the respondents have a special concept of the Group C classes.

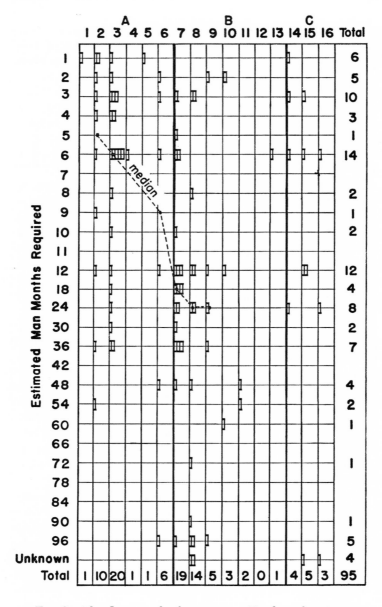

FIG. 8.—Idea-flow: results from pretest. Number of projects in each classification and estimated number of man months to complete each project. Each cell represents one project.

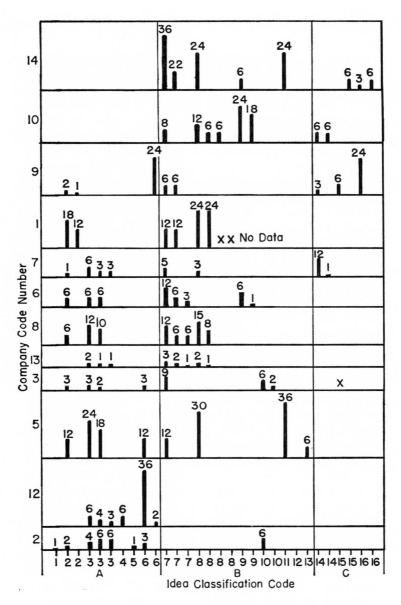

Fig. 9.—Estimated time required to complete R&D projects, by company name and idea-classification code. Each bar represents one project; its height represents estimated time, in months, to complete the project. The number of months appears above each bar.

FIG. 9 is a detailed graphic presentation of the data for his ideas submitted by each manager. Each is recorded by classification vs. estimated time to complete projects. At the top are managers who may have ideas in mind that reflect a more adventuresome spirit, while those toward the bottom may be more conservative. It will be interesting to learn which managers reflect corporate policy or freedom from it.

Further data may enable us to explain the short time horizon expressed by many of the managers on the basis of market objectives. If this is the consideration that is most important, especially to the high-level executive, projects not falling into the preferred pattern suggested by the data would probably be rejected. The pattern does not seem to change in a significant way when the rejected ideas are removed from the graph: the rejected ideas come from several classes and time horizons, so there appears to be no consistent pattern—they were not rejected just because they had longer time horizons or the scope was more advanced.

FIGS. 10 and 11 are included to show the time horizons in a more summarized form. FIG. 10 is the estimate of calendar months and FIG. 11 of man months. In FIG. 10, the median project falls in the six-month time class, indicating, as before, the short time horizon. The frequency with which one-, two-, and three-month projects are mentioned is very high; it appears that no one wants seven- or eleven-month projects. From one year on, time estimates are clustered at eighteen-, twenty-four-, and thirty-six-month points.

If these are the limits of acceptable projects, is it necessary for the estimator to select the "correct" number from the sequence shown—correct to the extent that he knows the "boss" will perceive it as correct? If he said twenty months, would he be criticized for trying to pass off a two-year project as one that would take less time? Is it often the case that the person will avoid making commitments about manpower requirements in order to have flexibility in finishing the project within the estimate?

When the ideas are distributed on a man-month estimate, the results are as shown in FIG. 11. Now the median project estimate would be twelve months if only one man worked on each idea. As previously observed, this is a short horizon.

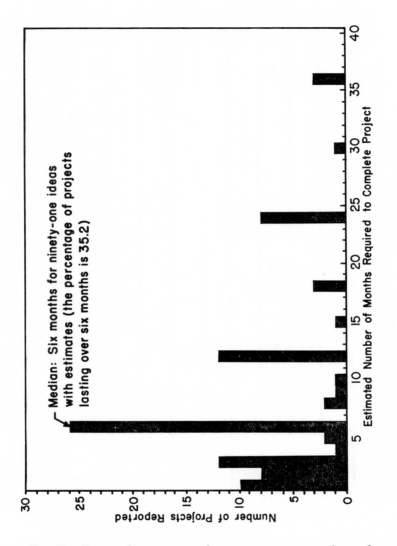

FIG. 10.—Estimated time to complete projects—summary for twelve managers representing companies 1, 2, 3, 5, 6, 7, 8, 9, 10, 12, 13, and 14.

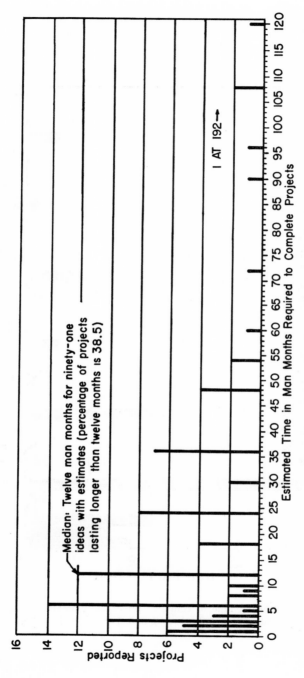

Fig. 11.—Number of ideas received and estimated number of man months required to complete projects—summary for twelve managers. Companies 1, 2, 3, 5, 6, 7, 8, 9, 10, 12, 13, and 14.

The shape is distorted by the large-scale factor for a single project, but it is useful for showing the clustering of ideas at points which are multiples of six months.

Considering that only three projects in FIG. 11 were estimated at thirty-six months and one at thirty months, it is interesting to note that fourteen are now beyond the thirty-six-man-month point. The distribution of manpower on projects in these twelve companies needs more investigation because we are not sure how many projects are concurrently active, nor how much maneuverability the manager has in assigning manpower as various degrees of completion are reached. Going back to FIG. 10, it is seen that classes 6, 7, 8, and 9 are the ones with these long horizons.

One interesting finding of the pretest is that the link from 3 to 6 in the idea-flow diagram is not always used. The idea is not always passed on to the organization even if the originator thinks it would be a good project. Since this question was not asked on this version of the questionnaire, we do not know why the six ideas were not submitted.

A STUDY OF PATTERNS OF CONSULTATION ON IDEAS

In another firm, Company 21, some data concerning the patterns of consultation are available. In this company, over two thousand persons are employed in various capacities in the R&D division within one branch of the company. There are six organizational lines reporting to the R&D manager. Two of these lines are concerned with two major areas of product interest and are headed by higher-level managers; one is broken into two lines, the other into three, each subdivision headed by a manager at the same level as the remaining four division managers who report directly to the R&D manager.

The consultation pattern for two departments is given in Table 9. The results have a bearing on the gross relationships pertinent to the flow model, FIG. 6. The connecting links involved are 2-4 (question 6); 4-2 (question 10), when the individual is playing the role of the "other person"; 4-4 and 4-6 (question 11), when trying to convince others as a non-originator; and 1-4 (questions 8, 9), when the person who

TABLE 9

CONSULTATION PATTERNS IN TWO DEPARTMENTS OF A COMPANY

PERSON CONSULTED	QUESTION 6*		QUESTION 7		QUESTION 8		QUESTION 9		QUESTION 10		QUESTION 11	
	Number of Times	Per Cent	Number of Times	Per Cent	Number of Times	Per Cent	Number of Times	Per Cent	Number of Times	Per Cent	Number of Times	Per Cent
Department 22: Project Management†												
Within department	31	55.3	27	62.8	......	......	28	59.5	......	......	......	......
Not in department, but within branch	2	3.6	11	2.3	......	......	2	4.3	......	......	......	......
Other branches	6	10.7	3	7.0	......	......	1	2.1	......	......	......	......
Customer	3	5.4	......	......	......	......	4	8.5	......	......	......	......
Vendor	......	......	......	......	......	......	......		......	......	......	......
Technical literature	......	......	......	......	......	......	......		......	......	......	......
Consultant	......	......	......	......	......	......	......		......	......	......	......
Other R&D departments	14	25.0	12	27.9	......	......	12	25.5	......	......	......	......
Total	56	100.0	43	100.0	......	......	47	100.0	......	......	......	......
Department 66: Reliability†												
Within department	62	62.0	50	61.7	......	......	40	64.5	......	......	......	......
Not in department, but within branch	11	11.0	10	12.3	......	......	2	3.2	......	......	......	......
Other branches	3	3.0	6	7.4	......	......	1	1.6	......	......	......	......

TABLE 9 (Continued)

Person Consulted	Question 6*		Question 7		Question 8		Question 9		Question 10		Question 11	
	Number of Times	Per Cent	Number of Times	Per Cent	Number of Times	Per Cent	Number of Times	Per Cent	Number of Times	Per Cent	Number of Times	Per Cent
					Department 66: Reliability‡							
Customer	3	3.0	2	2.5	......	......	6	9.7	......	......	......	......
Vendor	1	1.0	......	......	......	......	......	......	......	......	......	......
Technical literature	1	1.0	......	......	......	......	1	1.6	......	......	......	......
Consultant	1	1.0	......	......	......	......	......	......	......	......	......	......
Other R&D departments	18	18.0	13	16.0	......	......	12	19.4	......	......	......	......
Total	100	100.0	81	100.0	......	......	62	100.0	......	......	......	......

* Question 6: "Who was consulted?"

Question 7: "Whom did you try to convince?" } About own ideas

Question 8: "From whom was it heard?"

Question 9: "Who was the originator?" } About ideas of others

Question 10: "Were you consulted?"

Question 11: "Whom did you try to convince?"

† Number of persons in department: 49. Number reporting: 31. Per cent reporting: 63.3.

‡ Number of persons in department: 54. Number reporting: 33. Per cent reporting: 61.1.

transmits the idea is the one who originated it. Very noticeable for the two departments is the fact that individuals
mention their own department members very often when
they consult and/or try to convince others about their own
ideas and give credit to others for originating ideas. Also,
the range in the percentages for these responses is very
narrow, essentially from 55 to 65 per cent, with three not
far from 60 per cent.

The department designated "Reliability" did not give as
much credit to other R&D departments for originating ideas
as the Project Management department did, 19 per cent as
opposed to 25 per cent of the credit mentions. The same
thing holds true for those they consulted or tried to convince
about their own ideas; Project Management went to other
R&D departments about 26 per cent of the time, and Reliability went to others only 17 per cent of the time.

Because the percentages are so close for consulting and
convincing in each case, one may wonder not only if the
same individuals were involved in each case, but whether
the distinction can always be clearly drawn. For Project
Management, identical names were given eight out of fourteen times (57 per cent) for contacts with other R&D departments, and thirteen out of thirty-one times (42 per cent)
for contacts inside the department. The respective figures for
Reliability are twelve out of eighteen (67 per cent) and
thirty-eight out of sixty-two (61 per cent). Thus, it may be
said that it appears important to convince the person consulted, but the narrowness of the range between questions
is not specifically due to repeating the same name on each
question.

Department 66, Reliability, does consult more with others
in the branch that are not in R&D than does Project Management. On the other hand, Project Management consults more
with other branches of the company than does Reliability.
The relationships are much the same for Question 7, those
they try to convince about the usefulness of their ideas. Some
of these differences may be explained directly in terms of
organizational tasks; for example, it is known that products
similar to the ones Reliability is interested in are currently
being produced by the manufacturing division of the branch.

These relationships and the questions concerned with relationships between R&D departments need to be studied in more detail. This will be done by trying to obtain statements from managers about the relationships that should exist, or about reasons why they do exist.

Another frequently used response, but one not mentioned in Table 9, is that of consulting with no one. In Reliability, this answer was given eighteen times compared to one hundred specific answers. Does it mean that they are very self-sufficient, or that the individual who gave the answer is that sure of his knowledge and experience? For the other group, the ratio was twenty-seven to fifty-six. When it came time to convince some one, the ratio for Reliability was twenty-four mentions of "no one" to the eighty-one mentions of trying to convince some one; for Project Management, it was thirty to forty-three. It seems that those in this department need to do more convincing because they have more direct responsibility for projects but less authority than department heads.

One more observation important to the pattern of consulting and convincing is that only a few individuals report engaging in this type of activity outside of their department. For Department 22, Project Management, six men account for the fourteen consultations initiated with other R&D groups; for Department 66, Reliability, nine men account for the eighteen contacts. In trying to convince those in other R&D groups, four men from Department 22 initiated the twelve contacts; and in Department 66, there were nine men for the thirteen contacts. Are these the men who are responsible for getting ideas through? If they are, perhaps they should be contacted by others within their own departments with convincing as the objective. In Department 22, this happens two out of four times, and in Department 66, six out of nine times. More information is needed for the analysis to be complete.

Diagrams of the social interactions of individuals may be plotted from the answers to questions 6, 7, 8, 9, 10, and 11. However, these results are rather one-sided when the number of reports is limited. The interactions obtained by using the data are limited to what one individual says about another for a given idea. Therefore, there is no way of knowing whether or not the second person has perceived the contact or remembers it as important. In the modified version of the questionnaire, we do ask the person to identify the idea with a company number or other means that will allow us to trace it back, if necessary. This identification provides an opportunity to determine whether different persons think the same idea is good, and to know what each says he did about it.

Any number of reasons might exist for one person being named by the other: persons might be friends; for prestige value, the name of a person held in high esteem might be mentioned; the person might actually have consulted with the one named because that person was an expert of wielded influence; it is one person's work-task to consult with the other so the name must be mentioned. On the other hand, a person might name someone in another department, or "no-one" because he is in competition with those in his department and the best way to avoid the direct conflict is to seek outside reference points.

Some of the possibilities involve influence paths. These we are interested in isolating. How will it be possible? Essentially, questionnaire results have been discussed to show that the results obtained begin to isolate the factors. Through relationships between questions and from other organizational data obtained from records and interviews, it is possible to describe some patterns. However, other instruments are needed and are being developed to try to tie down some of the problem areas to which we have alluded.

Comment on Part III Papers

Harold B. Pepinsky

THAT THE FOREGOING PRESENTATIONS are concerned with "research and development organizations" or "institutes" is attested by the frequency with which any or all of these words appear in the three papers. Beyond this tendency for a common use of terms, however, there is little redundancy in content from paper to paper. The dissimilarity itself becomes understandable if one bears in mind that the first participant is a psychoanalytically oriented psychiatrist and psychologist; the second, a mathematician and sociologist; and the third pair of participants are operations researchers whom I infer to be industrial engineers. There is little occasion for surprise in the fact that the psychoanalyst has drawn upon his vast reservoir of face-to-face (or should I say "couch to chair") interviews to construct for us modal types representative of scientific personalities encountered in "research and development organizations." Nor is it surprising that the mathematician has chosen to offer us normative modals of individual and group problem-solving whose deductive consequences have empirical counterparts in everyday life, subject to statement and testable in principle as hypotheses. And our operations researchers again have run true to form in their induction of a "flow chart"—specifically, of a "flow of ideas," which becomes a kind of administrative outline for the collection of data about everyday routines in "research and development organizations."

From what I have said in summary comparison here, it can be inferred that the participants do have in common at least one methodological objective, that of reducing—i.e., simplifying—statements about observable or potentially observable events, which in their turn are assumed to be wholly or partially descriptive of "research and development organization." Thus, each of the participants has attempted to develop, more or less explicitly, for himself a rationale for codifying data and for collecting and treating data so codified. However diverse the participants may be in their rationales and in the uses to which these are to be put, each can lay claim to having been a kind of scientist in his search. And the diversity itself is healthy, I think.

Space does not permit me to be more than superficially critical in discussing these papers. In Dr. Matussek's case, I trust he will not be offended if it is suggested that his personality syndromes, while of undeniable personal use to him as a psychiatrist, are still too sketchy to be reliably communicated to other persons. Greater attention to their internal consistency is also needed if their deductive implications are to be more clearly stated. And we may hope that he will be able to tell us more about his categories through subsequently co-ordinated empirical work on their construct and predictive validities. But let us not do him the indignity of concluding that his work to date has not been empirical. What he has done in building inferences out of his intensive and extensive contacts with individuals has been a far more exhaustively empirical task than many a computer-programmed mountain of superficial observations.

Herr Rittel, as a mathematician, can best be criticized by other mathematicians. As far as I can follow his argument, his logic is not easily assailed. And I like the way in which he has harnessed it to empirical circumstances. Yet, I think, his models apply largely to problems whose solutions are trivial and to be achieved in determinable step functions. Hence, although his models may help to account for particular everyday routines, their application may be limited even in the case of "development" activities. Moreover, there appear to be as yet unresolved difficulties that lie ahead in defining and measuring empirical events. Let me illustrate by asking, for example, when a message is a message, a system is a system, a component is a component, or a task is a task, and in whose view—or I should like to know when a task is completed—to say nothing of "successfully"—and in whose view. For that matter, when is a problem solved "efficiently" and in whose view? I think these and other defini-

tional issues—and their ambiguous resolutions—have plagued
many a normative study of "research and development" activity. Nevertheless, Herr Rittel's models are intuitively and
aesthetically appealing, and I admire his capacity for this
kind of reductionism. He has been frank in stating that his
ideas are exploratory, and I judge that he would be the first
to welcome further a carefully reported empirical search that
is co-ordinate with his normative formulations and that could
lead to revisions of them.

Drs. Rubinstein and Hannenberg have made a clear and
orderly attack upon the problem of "idea flow." Their methods
are explicit, and the empirical data yielded by them are neatly
quantified and impressively displayed. And the authors are
modest in drawing inferences from the results of their labors
to date. Nevertheless, it is possible that they—and we—may
be led to feel a satisfaction with this report of research in
progress that is as yet premature. Instead, one may be impelled
to ask what it is that Rubenstein and Hannenberg want to
know—and why. Perhaps this is because their work is so
descriptively rich that its possible formal definition and
structure have been obscured. These things are not made
apparent to us; and because they are not, it becomes difficult
to assess what kind of progress has been made in the research
to date. Although other questions may be raised, I have limited myself now to asking what seems to be a central one.
Still I do not wish to rest here in commenting upon the last
paper. It is always easier to criticize someone else's labor
than to accomplish constructive work of one's own. Rubinstein and Hannenberg surely have understated the difficulties
involved in accomplishing research of this sort, and they have
submitted their procedures and some of their findings to a
jury of their peers. If their effort is vulnerable to criticism,
it is precisely because—of all the participants—these last two
have given us tangible evidence of their empirical accomplishment.

In conclusion, I am not sure whether any of the participants
has clearly made up his mind whether to act as scientist who
is seeking to discover knowledge or as technologist who
serves as consultant to management in its attempts to manipu-
late human behavior, so as to effect the kinds of changes in

human outputs that management thinks it wants. If the latter strategy is the preferred one of the two (there is no reconciling of the strategies of scientist and remunerated sage, in my view), our participants need to think about whether their task is to make possible further bureaucratic restrictions upon human behavior or to permit its freer play by amplifying the intelligence that is assumed to lie behind it. Such an "amplification of human intelligence" has been advocated by a British scientist as an ideal strategic objective for cybernetic systems in our society. I like the phrase; it has a ringing quality to it, even if I do not understand what it means. Be that as it may, the intent of inquiry into this ambiguous area of "research and development" that is "organized" needs to be more thoughtfully contemplated and explicitly stated than it has been here; otherwise, there remain large ethical and methodological problems which are easily and expediently glossed over.

IV

PUBLIC POLICY

SCIENCE AND INNOVATION

A *Special Address by*
J. Herbert Hollomon

THE DISCUSSIONS at this conference raise basic problems that we and our government must face in the use of science and technology in striving for national goals. Everyone has become aware that science and technology—as well as money—will determine the rate at which we explore space. Our progress in coping with cancer is limited more by our ability to apply science to medicine than by the funds available for the purpose. We must continually top the advances of potential enemies through new technological ability that derives from new science if we are to continue to defend our nation. In all of these things, it is clear that we are limited by the advances of science, but it is altogether too easy to forget that science and technology, acting through the agencies of invention and innovation, also provide the basis for the high standard of living that we regard as ours by right of birth. This high standard of living, however, comes to us through the process of the use of science and technology to improve the productivity of our workers and to generate the new products and processes that enrich our lives.

The great importance and direct application of science to the national purposes of health, defense, and space exploration have produced great changes in the institutions of science and technology and the way that government relates to it.

Federal support of industrial research in the United States has increased over the last decade from 30 to 40 per cent of all such expenditures to a present level of 65 to 70 per cent. Presently, there are about 350,000 people in industry who perform research and development. But of these, only about 120,000 are supported by industry for civilian industrial purposes. The remainder are supported by federal programs that have to do primarily with military preparedness, weapons systems, atomic energy, and the rapidly increasing space effort. This increased government support for research and development performed by industry has not only changed the character of industrial research and development, but also has changed the factors which influence its cost. The cost-plus-fixed-fee contract arrangements by which we conduct much of our military research and development tends to make for inefficiency and higher costs. These special contractual arrangements usually require physical and organizational separation of government-supported "research and development" from the privately supported. This separation makes it difficult for one to benefit the other and for techniques and discoveries in one area to spill over to the other. The great demand for technically-trained people for these national programs has tended to raise their relative salaries, particularly of the newly trained junior men who are needed in large numbers as technical assistants.

Furthermore, the growing complexity of science and technology deriving in large measure from the advances in military and space technology raises the costs of the tools that are used, making it less possible for the smaller industrial unit to be able to support these activities.

Another problem of growing importance is that of achieving a rapid and adequate dissemination of technical knowledge. The huge investment in research and development has tended to be concentrated in relatively few companies and in relatively few industries. Thus, there is considerable difficulty in spreading knowledge of the advances of technology from these industries and companies to the rest of society. Three hundred companies perform more than 80 per cent of all research and development. Five of sixteen industrial sectors perform more than half of it, and more than half is concentrated in three states. The opportunities afforded by new science are not uniformly distributed throughout the nation.

If no special efforts are applied to prevent it, the large federal programs can prejudice our educational system toward the special sophisticated technical work which uniquely serves these space and military activities. These programs, limited as they are by scientific advance, operate at the forefront of man's scientific capability. They stretch the technical arts to the limit. If our research and, consequently, our education are directed only toward these special requirements, then they may not produce some other kinds of knowledge that are important to us, or the trained people who appreciate the needs of the civilian economy. The institutions and the special requirements that have to do with the application of new techniques, new technology, and its spread throughout industry at large may not be readily available.

This process of harnessing science and technology for the space and military programs is not the same as that which is usually the case for the civilian economy. The sequence— new science from research, application of new science, development, prototype manufacturing, and sales—is not the usual way that innovation occurs. The majority of new processes which increase our ability to turn out products and services efficiently, broaden our economic life, and widen our variety of choice takes place as a result of a process that involves the recognition of a *need*, by people who are knowledgeable about science and technology. Usually such innovations await only this recognition, not the latest scientific achievement.

The sequence—perceived need, invention, innovation (limited by political, social, or economic forces), and diffusion or adaptation (determined by the organizational character and incentives of industry)—is the one most often met in the regular civilian economy. As a matter of fact, the studies by Jewkes, and many other case studies of innovation conducted largely by members of this audience, indicate that new technological developments most commonly use old science. These improvements are limited by an appreciation of need, and the availability of the sort of people who appreciate the market, yet know science and the capability of technology. I am reminded of an interesting observation made sometime ago, by one who is present at this conference, to the effect that the development of the automobile did not await new technology but rather awaited the improvement of the income level of people to buy a peculiar, individual, transportation package.

The use of invention, through innovation, in order to bring about economic benefit often awaits the development of financing needed to underwrite the displacement of old practice by new, or the development of a new distribution system, or a change in basic business practice. Innovation is resisted, and sometimes can only come about through the invasion of a firm or industry into the operating terrain of another. Innovation, in short, is often limited by factors that are economic or sociological rather than scientific.

Science is, nonetheless, the resource from which new technology derives, and science is crucial to it. The use of science, particularly for economic purposes, depends upon institutions and attitudes that are different from those necessary for the creation of science. The use of science and the development of new technology is a process that takes place outside of laboratories—the work places of science—but inside plants and in the market. New developments frequently do require new details of knowledge that can be produced by scientific techniques. Science of this kind is not the stimulus to innovation but the servant. Further, the advances in military and space technology may or may not be widely used outside their own realms. To be used they must economically fulfil a need, and the adaptation must be carried forth by people knowledgeable of that need. *Invention* must take place in order for the adaptation to be possible, but *innovation* must be justified on practical grounds. No simple system of information dissemination and no promotional activities can by themselves make this transfer possible. The technical advances deriving from vast programs in defense and space add substantially to the resources available to those who invent, innovate, and adapt for civilian economic purposes. But they are no substitute for invention, innovation, and adaptation.

Today the United States is much more affected by economic developments elsewhere in the world than at any other time in its history. Our European and Japanese competition is installing labor-saving machinery that sometimes out-performs our own. The rapid growth of the European Common Market has deprived us of our monopoly on the advantages of scale which comes from our large domestic market. With decreasing trade barriers, increasing standardization of products, free mobility of labor, and ready financial resources, western Europe will now enjoy the advantages of mass production. Increasingly, Japan and Europe compete with us in the technical quality of the goods they produce, even when their total labor costs for some of these goods are as great or greater than our own. The balance-of-payments problem demands our effective utilization of science and technology through invention and innovation. We must produce more goods that can compete in world markets. This means we must counter the increasing sophistication and ability of those with whom we are in competition.

The Soviet Union, organized to simulate the features of a giant corporation, is committed to advancing through the effective use of science and technology. It concentrates its resources on narrow objectives, and invests enormously in technical education and research. Since it follows the technical lead of the industry of the West, the Soviet Union does not have to bear some of the high costs of the original technological developments. It, too, can produce for a mass market, built upon our successes of the past. The economic growth of Europe and Russia—both building their industries afresh—will continue to present a challenge to us to do more about invention and innovation than we are doing now.

If we are to continue to enjoy a growing economy through improvements in productivity and through new products that enrich our lives, special effort must be made to create conditions more conducive to invention, innovation, and the adaptation of new technology. These efforts must involve attention to the education of engineers in a way that will stimulate them to become inventors, to the incentives of business to innovate, and to new institutions to make the possibilities of technology more apparent and more available to all industry throughout the country.

In order for this conscious effort to be effective in our kind of society, it must be understood and developed by individuals acting freely, both politically and economically. All of us— business leaders, economists, leaders in science and technology —need to recognize and understand that the application of technical resources to the civilian economy is an important national consideration, and it is not now being well done. This recognition may serve more in the defense of our way of life than a military program or winning the race in space. This recognition still leaves us the task of creating new institutions in America for these special purposes of invention, innovation, and adaptation. We should insure the more rapid creation of a system of incentives that will lead to the more economical use of scientists and engineers for whatever national objectives we undertake. Surely in the military sphere this means eliminating those incentives that encourage stockpiling of technical people and escalation of costs. In the civilian sector, it at least requires upgrading the technical information services to the point where it is more economical to make use of what is available than to repeat the work.

We need to create a means for encouraging associations of companies and industries to do technical work that benefits them as a group when it is too costly and wasteful to carry on the work separately. Such associations should leave to the individual firm the incentives and initiatives of prosecuting the development of new products and process on a proprietory basis. Associations are particularly important in industries that are not very profitable, such as the textile industry; in industries that are fragmented and unable to underwrite adequate technological development, such as the building and construction industry; or industries in which the technological developments are extraordinarily costly, such as the aircraft and air-transport industry. We must act upon our recognition that innovations depend on better use of science and technology by businessmen and industrialists who appreciate the opportunities offered by the market. We need to create an extension of our educational system to provide these people with the knowledge and awareness that is so important. The vast technical resources developed by our sophisticated industries and universities in the space and military effort must be made available throughout the country, and people must be educated to use them more efficiently. An industrial analogue of agricultural extension education is required, and it is the responsibility of government, both local and federal, and the universities and industry to establish it. In Europe we created productivity centers after the war to spur the rate of economic development. We spend huge sums on technical assistance to less developed countries. But in our own country we have not yet created the institutions for the rapid education and the rapid spread of those who must adapt science to practical use. We also need to establish new institutions associated with the technical schools and universities of America that act as clinics for the solving of basic technical problems of importance to industry. These clinics would create the link between the university and industry that is so very much needed in the modern technical society. They would put the professor in contact with the real problems of industry as well as with the forefront of man's scientific knowledge.

Finally, we need to support technical activities in the university that are connected with the process of invention and innovation, with engineering and design, as well as with basic science, physical science, and the science of engineering. We need to support activities at universities that relate to the technology that is of importance to transportation, to building and construction, to the development of an urban society. The universities should be concerned with how science is put to use; we need to support both science and the art of using science. We should like to have a technical-education system that would permit our inventors and innovators to be more "scientific." Nonetheless, we want these individuals to *practice* as inventors and innovators, not to concern themselves wholly with engineering research. In engineering, as in medicine, some of our best practitioners must devote themselves to clinical problems rather than research. There are today no national programs that provide for this sort of activity in our university system.

My suggestion, then, is that those of us that concern ourselves with science and innovation must help to create the institutions that are needed. I know of no other commitment that can so alter this nation's prospects or those of the people of all the world.

CLASSIFICATION OF SOCIAL COSTS
AND SOCIAL BENEFITS IN RESEARCH
AND DEVELOPMENT

Bruno Fritsch, Helmut Krauch,
and Richard A. Tybout

THE CONCEPT of social cost encompasses all parts of costs
encountered by an economy, whether the economy is market-
directed (decentralized) or government-directed (centralized)
or some combination of these two extremes, as indeed are all
real world economies. The classic Pigovian case of non-market
costs arising from smoky chimneys[1] illustrates the possible
divergency of social from private costs in a market-directed
economy. In principle, all social costs are relevant for a cen-
trally directed economic order, though the range of costs actually taken into account in such an order may be narrower
than for decentralized economies. The object in dealing with
social costs in either situation is to take account of all dis-
utilities created by a line of activity, whether the activity be
production, research and development, military preparedness,
or whatever.

Exactly how social costs and social benefits are to be measured remains for analysis elsewhere. The present paper is
concerned only with a qualitative classification. The theory
of welfare economics introduces relevant considerations for
a first step toward quantitative measurement, but only insofar
as Paretian efficiency is concerned. The various enigmas implicit in the development of a social-welfare function condition
the application of the present classifications, as they do all
other policy aspects of economics.

Another limitation should be noted. Considerable uncertainty generally attends the estimation of costs and benefits

---

[1] A. C. Pigou, *The Economics of Welfare* (4th ed.; London, 1932),
Part II, chap. ix. A considerable number of other examples of diver-
gences between individual and social values can be found in the same
reference.

for R&D projects. Cost uncertainties arise almost by definition from the fact that explorations of the unknown are the essence of the R&D job. Even more so, benefits are the product of speculative deduction. Expected results are seldom achieved; and if achieved, their value for specific applications can hardly be foreseen accurately. The problem of anticipating benefits is made still more difficult, if that is possible, by the significance of new R&D information for the discovery of still additional information. Future science depends on past science. Nevertheless, the task of somehow obtaining social cost and benefit estimates is logically required by the goal of social efficiency in the process of allocating inputs to R&D. Whether this process is done well or poorly will be shown by after-the-fact evaluations of costs and benefits, i.e., the accuracy with which such costs and benefits were anticipated *and* the breadth with which they were defined. It is to this last topic that we now turn our attention.

THE MODEL

The model is based on a sectorialization of costs and benefits, the sectors (or subsectors) being treated as decision-making units. At the level of generality relevant herein, the model is equally applicable to either a capitalist or a socialist state, provided that decision-making is at least as decentralized as indicated by the definition of the sectors. Four sections are considered: Private households, denoted by an H; the business sector, B; the government sector, G; and the foreign section, F. The B sector has two subsectors, one corresponding to the usual business activities and the other including all private research and development activities. The first subsector may be denoted as "non-R&D," the second as "R&D." The G sector is divided into two subsectors: one corresponding to the "usual" activities of the government, the other including all governmental R&D activities.

Each of these sectors and subsectors consists of a large number of elements. We restrict the combinations between these elements to combination of a two rank type involving single units (s) and many units (m). The number of units included in m may vary from 2 to n, the total number available. Thus, there are a total of twelve possible subsectors including independent decision-making units. Combinations may run from one subsector to any other subsector or, as will become clear in later discussion, may be intrasectoral, i.e., wholly within one sector. The way of defining these sectors and their subdivision into "single" and "many" components is the essence of the present approach.

PRIVATE HOUSEHOLDS

  1. Single
  2. Many

BUSINESS SECTOR

Non-R&D

  3. Single
  4. Many

R&D

  5. Single
  6. Many

GOVERNMENT SECTOR

Non-R&D

  7. Single
  8. Many

R&D

  9. Single
  10. Many

FOREIGN SECTOR

  11. Single
  12. Many

All costs occurring in one sector in the course of an action by another sector are denoted by a and all benefits on the side of the passive, receiving sector are denoted by β. The causing active factors are denoted by a if they render detrimental effects, and with b if they render advantages to the acting sector; a and b denote causes, a and β effects, being directly linked to the respective causes. There are four types of relations:

$$a = a\,(a) \ldots (1)$$
$$\beta = \beta\,(a) \ldots (2)$$
$$a = a\,(b) \ldots (3)$$
$$\beta = \beta\,(b) \ldots (4)$$

In a classical general-equilibrium model where all effects work through the market, functional relations (2) and (3) are the only ones encountered and these take the form $a = b$ (production) and $\beta = a$ (sales) at the margin. All quantities are measured in real terms and, in the preceding sentence, at market value. When measurement is in psychic value, somehow expressed on a common ratio scale, and when non-market effects are considered, all four relations are possible with three ranks for each (a or $b \gtreqless a$ or β). To illustrate the verbal meaning of the latter cases, let the business non-R&D sector be designated by the subscript b and the household sector by the subscript h, and let the second subscripts s and m refer to "single" and "many," respectively. Then the Pigovian case of external effects of smoky chimneys is represented by the relation $a_{bm} > b_{hm}$. The subscript m is interpreted to represent a summation over all relevant households and businesses. Similarly if d refers to the business R&D sector, the dissemination of R&D knowledge from one firm to all others is represented by $\beta_{dm} > b_{ds}$. A strike or other form of involuntary unemployment would result in $a_{hm} = a(a_{bm})$.

It will be noted that some actions taken independently by decision-makers are treated as originating in the "many" subsectors. Two examples appear in the preceding paragraph, identified as a or b with a second subscript m. For some purposes, one could imagine that all independent actions have independent effects. This, however, sometimes results in devious sophistry, such as in the effort to impute an identified quantity of smoke to a particular smoky chimney or an identified quantity of smog to a particular motor vehicle. The quality of independence in decision-making cannot be used as a criterion for distinguishing the "single" from the "many" subsectors even for the originators of an action having non-market effects.

On the other hand, it is probably best to treat market transactions involving individual goods, as opposed to collective goods (see discussion below), as originating in and received by the "single" subsectors. Then, for example, a financial transaction involving two households is an intrasectoral transaction in sector 1. The alternative would be to distinguish among types of economic transactions according to the number of buyers and sellers in various markets. the only intrasectoral transactions involving "single" subsectors would then be those in which there is a bilateral monopoly. This approach is rejected because the emphasis here is not on market structure, but instead on a broader classification of market and non-market relationships. Accordingly pure market transactions take place wholly among "single" subsectors. All other kinds of relationships, including, of course, market relationships with some degree of externality, involve at least one of the "many" subsectors.

The total possible effects among the twelve subsectors can be calculated as follows: There are twelve kinds of relationships for each line of causation, composed of three possible rankings for each of the four possible relations noted in equations (1) through (4). Second, each of the decision-making units s can affect every other decision-making unit singly s or in a group m, and groups of decision-making units m can affect other decision-making units singly s or in groups m. Taking account of all inter- and intrasectoral affects, there are then 12 times 12, or 144 possible lines of causation. Finally, multiply 144 by 12 (kinds of relationships) to get 1,728 possible cases. There is, of course, no assurance that meaningful examples can be found for all 1,728 of these possible cases, but a systematic survey of the possibilities should produce heretofore unrecognized cases.

APPLICATION OF THE MODEL

At the same time that the model is suitable for extending externality classifications of welfare economics, it also permits a comprehensive description of R&D effects. The concept of social benefit has special relevance for R&D activities. The product of R&D is information. Arrow has shown that information possesses extraordinary qualities as an economic commodity.[2] Prominent among these are its inappropriability. New facts regarding a production process or a product are by no intrinsic quality necessarily limited to the utility they have for their originators. Knowledge falls in the category of a public good, the distinguishing feature of which is that consumption by one individual in no way precludes consumption by others.[3] Like the enjoyment of a work of art, the receipt of knowledge in no way limits the ability of others to receive the same knowledge. The situation is to be contrasted with consumption of private goods, which inherently requires the appropriation and removal of the same goods from the market and hence from the reach of other consumers.

A distinction must be made, however, between the inherent qualities of knowledge as a commodity and the properties of new knowledge (as produced by R&D) which result in various degrees of appropriation. The acquisition of sole patent rights, by definition, creates the legal basis for appropriation. Patents are intended as both an incentive for the private financing of R&D and as a bribe for the public disclosure of new knowledge. Their efficacy in achieving these last

---

[2] Kenneth J. Arrow, "Economic Welfare and the Allocation of Resources for Invention" in National Bureau of Economic Research, *The Rate and Direction of Inventive Activity* (Princeton, N.J., 1962). See also Richard A. Tybout, "Government and Invention," *Centennial Review*, Vol. V (Fall, 1961).

[3] Paul A. Samuelson, "The Pure Theory of Public Expenditures," *Review of Economics and Statistics*, XXXVI (November, 1954), 387–89 and "Diagrammatic Exposition of a Theory of Public Expenditure," *ibid.*, XXXVII (November, 1955), 350–56.

two ends must be weighed against the social benefits foregone
by the appropriability quality patents create. It is not the
purpose of the present work to comment on this issue, but
only to note that inappropriability is a general quality creating cross-relationships among all sectors except as restricted
by the institutional environment. Still other causes for inappropriability arise out of limited cognition, or the ability of
potential users of new knowledge to understand it. Complete
cognition includes the subtle quality known as "know-how"
over which the information originator usually retains an
initial advantage as compared with those who would appropriate the information.[4]

The model is best suited for reporting the effects of different institutional arrangements. For example, consider patent
policies of the government for publicly financed R&D. Let
the subscript g refer to the non-R&D government sector and
r to the government R&D sector. At one extreme, there is
the policy of retaining all patent rights in the public sphere,
subject to non-exclusive royalty-free licensing of all domestic
users. The relevant relationships would be:

1. $\beta_{bm} = \beta(b_{rs})$ for business production uses of the
   patents.

2. $\beta_{gm} = \beta(b_{rs})$ for government non-R&D uses of the
   patents.

3. $\beta_{dm} = \beta(b_{rs})$ for business R&D uses of the patents.
   (Science produces science.)

4. $\beta_{rm} = \beta(b_{rs})$ for government R&D uses of the patents.

Where household or foreign users are in prospect, these could
be added to the list. The other extreme in government policy
is to assign the patent to a private person or business firm engaged in the R&D work under contract, retaining for the
government only non-exclusive royalty-free rights. Then the
relationships would be:

---

[4] For a case study of the relative importance of know-how as compared with explicit reported new knowledge, see Richard A. Tybout,
The Reactor Supply Industry ("Ohio State University Bureau of Business Research Monographs," No. 97 [Columbus, 1960]).

1. $\beta_{rm} = \beta(b_{ds})$ for government exercise of its right to use the patents for its own R&D projects elsewhere.

2. $\beta_{gm} = \beta(b_{ds})$ for government exercise of its right to use the patents for its own non-R&D activities.

Whether other businesses, households, or the foreign sector would also benefit depends on the patent-licensing policies of the firm.[5] If the patent were assigned to an individual instead of a business firm, the action would result in the subscript d being replaced by the subscript h and presumably licensing of business uses of the patent would occur, resulting in the relevant additional relationships. At the same time that the foregoing beneficial effects are recorded, it is desirable to express all other outcomes of the R&D process, which might include adverse effects a, for example from radioactive contamination affecting households, business, other government activities and the foreign sector.

Whether new information is of value to its recipient is a further matter. One can never tell in advance what will come of an invention or a discovery, even less so at the start of a research and development project. The effects of uncertainty were noted at an earlier point herein.[6] In addition, there is the possibility that the economic environment might not be propitious for introducing an invention. The extensive literature on innovation attests to the complexity of the problem. One can only get clues from the model as to the deductive possibilities in a given institutional environment.

Finally, there are the possibilities of derived effects. The category of public goods, to which new knowledge belongs, has been described only in terms of direct consumption of outputs. Direct benefits so received are to be contrasted with derived benefits of, for example, the Veblenesque variety in which one's own utilities (benefits) are adversely affected by the conspicuous consumption of a neighbor. The neighbor, in

---

[5] Kenneth J. Arrow, *op. cit.*, pp. 619–22, gives an analysis of the incentive to invent taking account of royalty fees in a competitive and a monopolistic industry structure.

[6] Institutional imperfections in uncertainty bearing and other characteristics of invention give a logical base for government finance of R&D. See *ibid.*

Veblen's analysis, is engaged in direct consumption (of a Rolls-Royce or whatever); one's own feelings (envy or whatever) are derived from witnessing the same consumption. A comparable example among public goods is seen in education. Education is a public good in the sense that it is inappropriable. At the same time, derived benefits can be obtained from the education of others, and it is probably primarily for this last reason that we have compulsory public education up to a given age level.

Derived effects can be incorporated in the model without changing the previous designations, merely by allowing the relationships to refer to the sum total of direct plus derived effects. On the other hand, there are probably advantages in separating the consideration of direct and derived effects, both from a descriptive and normative standpoint.[7] A convenient method of so doing is to recognize derived effects as a second-stage functional relationship. Thus, the derived benefits of education as seen by one individual follow from the receipt of education of all others: $\beta_{hs} = \beta'[\beta_{hm}] = \beta'[\beta(a_{gm})]$. The distinction between functional relations is indicated by using the prime and the square brackets for derived effects. (An a is used rather than a b to indicate that the flow of the education is service out of the government.) It is possible, of course, for derived effects to result from private goods with no direct non-market effects, as in the case of "keeping up with the Joneses." Consistency of notation then suggests that this last case be expressed as: $a_{hm} = a'[b_{hs}]$.

Derived effects of invention are as diverse as the applications of new knowledge itself. Where improvements of public health are expected, a cost-benefit analysis of R&D projects must take account of both the public commodity and the derived characteristics of new knowledge. Where particular private goods are the object of R&D, a normative public calculation should scan all possibilities suggested by the model, comparing the private benefit-cost results with the

[7] The same distinction between direct and derived effects lies behind the welfare economics emphasis on "own" consumption as contrasted with a positive relation of social preferences to individual preferences. See, for example, J. C. Harsanyi, "Cardinal Welfare, Individualistic Ethics, and Interpersonal Comparisons of Utility," *Journal of Political Economy* (1955), pp. 309–21.

public results. Where the expected output of R&D includes
returns to education (as is often the case), direct and derived
effects both come into play. The model provides a systematic
check list of possible effects.

One can only speculate as to whether explicit consideration
of all ramifications will influence public policy for the use of
the inventions referred to in Rachael Carson's *Silent Spring*.[8]
The significance of radioactive fallout (a by-product effect)
has been sufficient to govern the very calculation of whether
or not to test atomic weapons. On the other hand, there is no
assurance that the transistor or the TH microwave relay
would have been developed at all had the communications
industry been composed of firms with a narrower view of
benefits than the Bell Laboratories. The implication of many
cross-effects between sectors and subsectors is that the decision-making unit within a single sector may not take account
of all relevant consequences. The role of public policy for invention has expanded mightily in the last two decades.[9] There
is every reason to ask for a comparable increase in the systematic study of the social costs and benefits of R&D.

---

[8] Houghton-Miffllin, 1962. The President's Science Advisory Committee subsequently vindicated the substance of Miss Carson's most important conclusions. Reported in *Christian Science Monitor,* May 21,
1963, p. 16.

[9] For useful comparisons, see Jesse W. Markham, "Inventive Activity:
Government Controls and the Legal Environment," in *The Rate and
Direction of Inventive Activity.*

APPROPRIATE GOVERNMENT AND PRIVATE RESEARCH ROLES IN A MIXED ECONOMY*

Irving H. Siegel

THIS PAPER notes some of the problems confronting public and private research policy and indicates various directions of remedial action. It cannot pretend, within the available space, to describe exhaustively the content and complexities of the chosen topic.

A few remarks on terminology are desirable at the outset. The title refers to a "mixed economy," which is characterized by a rich diversity of personal values and preferences and by a wide diffusion of responsibility for economic and political decision and action. Despite the relentless historical expansion of the scope and scale of government (especially federal) authority in our country, private individuals and groups insist upon and still retain significant opportunity to pursue independently determined objectives. The sum of all the loosely co-ordinated (and even inconsistent) behaviors observed in the public and private sectors is not necessarily equivalent to the orderly, rational, "superorganic" assignment of available resources according to a definite pattern of social priorities. This distinction between an aggregate and an architectonic unity (in Kant's language) is a matter of some importance in the discussion that follows. Another term in the title, "research," is used as an abbreviation that normally includes "development" and sometimes, as in the federal military case, "test" and "evaluation," too. Similarly, the words "science" and "scientific" are often used here broadly to embrace "engineering" and "technology." Finally, the word "technical" is employed as a rough synonym for "scientific" and "engineering."[1]

---

* The views expressed here are not to be attributed to any organization with which the author is or has been associated.

[1] On this paragraph and many matters considered below, see two other recent papers by the author: "The Role of Scientific Research in

I

The enduring inspiration for policy is the difference between the way things are and the way they "ought" to be, between this most possible of all worlds and the best possible one according to some theory that "ought" to command a broad consensus. Difficulties arise in defining this difference; in formulating corrective measures to narrow the gap; in achieving agreement on preferred specific goals and desirable instruments; and, of course, in the actual conduct of programs intended to reduce the difference. Science and research do not belong to a privileged class of activities exempt from familiar forms of human frailty, disappointment, and error. In this section we look more closely at the difficulties of defining and reaching ideal solutions to the problems of allocating and using resources for research. Regrettably, the linearity of writing and speech prevents the simultaneous deposition, with all their linkages still intact, of the many interrelated ideas that contend for priority in presentation.

The difficulties impeding determination and achievement of the optimum magnitude and mix of the composite national research program over time may be subsumed under these heads:

1. Indistinctness of the boundaries of the universe of discourse, which interpenetrates with other related universes.

2. Indefiniteness and incomplete quantifiability of the composite research goal for a dynamic, pluralistic society.

3. Limitations of human knowledge, especially with respect to the future (which is the critical dimension for resarch reckoning and decision-making), at both the "macro" and "micro" levels.

Stimulating Economic Progress," *American Economic Review* (May, 1960), pp. 340–345; and "Scientific Discovery, Invention, and the Cultural Environment," *Patent, Trademark, and Copyright Journal of Research and Education* (Fall, 1960), pp. 233–48.

4. The challenge of foreign military, political, and economic initiatives, which may be hard to appraise and meet as well as to anticipate.

5. Interference of inflexibilities, priority conflicts, and disproportionalities with the rational reassignment of resources already committed.

6. Incomplete sway of, and insufficient reliance upon, impersonal market mechanisms and the conventional money calculus for research–non-research allocations, for intra-firm and interproject choices, and for balancing of the current-future, public-private, military-civilian, basic-applied, and individual-social research requirements of a mixed free economy.

7. Weaknesses of advisory mechanisms and authoritative committees for attainment of a desired national dynamic equilibrium.

These items are not independent, but they should suffice for our purposes of packaging and communication. In the remaining paragraphs of this section, something is said about each of them.

First, we consider the difficulty of delineating the very universe of discourse. The faces, edges, and vertices of research do not stand out clearly. On one side, research shades into production—as in the procurement of new military weapons required in small quantities. On the other sides, research shades into education—in industry again, in government, and at the graduate-school level. Even though we may agree with the statement (in "Special Analysis G" of the 1963 federal budget) that "the primary aim" in the conduct of research activities "is either to develop new knowledge or to apply existing knowledge to new uses," we must also recognize that the projects actually undertaken provide new occasions to learn what someone else, somewhere, at some other time, has already discovered. Generalized "Man" already has a store of all sorts of knowledge which many a "man" in particularized form is being paid to acquire or find out afresh in a public or private laboratory. The diffusion and mastery, under the guise of creating it, of knowledge already won from nature may be a necessary (even a planned) step toward the production of genuine novelty. In any case, much 'of what we call research is just education, whether or not it also eventuates in a significantly "original" end product. Indeed, the act of inquiry or its result is sometimes given a derogatory name like "duplication" or "waste" in discussions of, say, the avoidability of scientific re-investigation through the provision of better systems for storage, exchange, and distribution of existing information.[2]

For a society such as ours, the desired net outcome of public and private decisions and actions with respect to research is not simply stateable, nor is it readily expressible in a summary statistical measure. The equation, in some sense, of personal and group aims which are diverse, unstable, competitive, and impermanent in priority rating is a familiar standing challenge to economic reckoning; and it is even more formidable when process or lead times are long and the intended products are contingent. A plausible measure of the desired net resultant of research activity would seem to be the discounted expected net addition to the gross national product (and, in the ideal case, the maximum net addition derivable from the utilized resources). But only in form is this an operational criterion, in view of the routine treatment accorded research in national income accounts, the uncertainty (in any case) of future research returns and of their economic value, and the indefiniteness of a suitable interest rate for discounting. Other complications arise when time comparisons of research outputs or inputs are made; indeed, the usual index-number problems that are commonly ignored[3] assume added significance because research is directed primarily toward change in the assortment, quality, and relative cost of physical products.

[2] See, for example, Senate Comm. on Government Operations, *Coordination of Information on Current Federal Research and Development Projects in the Field of Electronics*, 87th Cong., 1st Sess. (1961); or statements released on the same general subject by Senator Humphrey, chairman of the Subcommittee on Reorganization and International Organizations, during 1962.

[3] See I. H. Siegel, "On the Design of Consistent Output and Input Indexes for Productivity Measurement," in *Output, Input, and Productivity Measurement* (Princeton, N.J., 1961), pp. 23–41.

The reference already made to uncertainty concerning the realization and value of research results points to a major obstacle to sound resource use. Knowledge is the complement of ignorance, which, happily, is far less than absolute; and human optimism requires insistence upon the extent of the former. Activities like research are usually supported in the belief that they will have positive pay-offs, and the forecasters themselves try to make their forecasts come true. There is a strong disposition to interpret ambiguous insightful statements about the technological outlook as near misses or as good tries, but the record for prediction by passive observers of specific technical events, circumstances, consequences, and dates of occurrence is hardly encouraging. Dormant patents, new processes and products that fail to become commercially established or to fulfil their early promise, an occasional collapse of market confidence in various "growth" stocks—these illustrate the hazards faced by non-neutral forecasters.[4]

On the "macro" level, the difficulties of anticipating history have been argued energetically at least since Hegel and Marx. Karl Popper, the philosopher, is so impressed with the incapacity of a society to foretell, by scientifically respectable means, the prospective condition of its own applicable knowledge that he assigns decisive weight to this argument in his attack on "historicism": "If there is such a thing as growing human knowledge, then we cannot anticipate today what we can only know tomorrow."[5] Bertrand Russell's "paradox of types" is recalled by this statement, which leaves the door of the future open to surprise despite the best laid plans. Even if the future is fully determined, the inevitability of whatever happens can be convincingly traced only in retrospect.

Foreign challenges, both military and peaceful, threaten to impose increasingly serious constraints on domestic research planning—and on our freedom to allocate resources in general. Often unpredicted, or disregarded as remote possibilities, or

---

[4] See, for example, I. H. Siegel, "Technological Change and Long-Run Forecasting," *Journal of Business* (July, 1953), pp. 141–56.

[5] K. R. Popper, *The Poverty of Historicism* (Boston, 1957), pp. ix-xi.

dismissed as "just propaganda" on expert advice, they may suddenly demand urgent attention nevertheless. The response to a belatedly acknowledged major threat may entail a significant redirection or intensification of public and private research effort. Extensive and drastic revisions may gravely harm existing programs, accomplish less than expected (or produce results more slowly), inspire an unwarranted retrospective downgrading of past achievements, and exaggerate emergent doubts concerning the national style (especially its traditional and worthy emphasis on the enhancement of consumer welfare).

In a few short years, we have even witnessed impressive foreign competitive gains, backed by research, in a wide variety of civilian fields, such as automobiles, steel, drugs, other chemicals, and transistor radios and television sets.[6] In additional areas of technology, such as supersonic jet-aircraft development, the national prospect is also getting cloudy.[7] With respect to military technology, the outlook is far from cheerful—on the basis, for example, of newspaper reports respecting the size and number of thermonuclear weapons tested by an unfriendly power. Above all, it is a foreign initiative, not the vision of an American pioneer or the dynamic of our marketplace, that now drives us prematurely toward the moon; and this "race," which is not of our choosing, involves high stakes in national prestige, great expense in money and manpower, and hazard to other important research undertakings. This same foreign initiative requires us to hope for major by-products that would give more positive economic meaning to the main achievement, even if we are "first" in the "race." [8]

---

[6] Concern has been expressed by the President's Science Advisor (according to *New York Times,* August 1, 1962) that emphasis on military and space research may be weakening our competitive posture in international markets. He cited the production of the first all-transistor television set in Japan rather than the United States.

[7] *Wall Street Journal,* September 20, 1962.

[8] On this sentence and the preceding one see, for example, *New York Times,* August 4, 1962; and *Wall Street Journal,* September 12, 1962; and House Comm. on Science and Astronautics, *The Practical Values of Space Exploration,* H. R. Doc. No. 1276, 87th Cong., 1st Sess. (1961).

Another source of failure to equalize net benefits of alternative research (and non-research) outlays is the resistance of committed resources in the absence of crisis to flow into new areas of opportunity. To undo and to redo are sometimes harder than to do in the first place. Reassignment may be impeded by inertia, the opposition of vested interests, or the unavailability of required complementary skills and material resources. A "going concern" that is not really going anywhere imposes little burden on management, but the redefinition of objectives or the reconstitution of the concern is demanding. A significant change may require troublesome policy decisions and entail other high "costs of bothering about marginal cost."

Much that has already been said documents the point that market signals are not sufficiently pervasive and persuasive to constitute a comprehensive "field of force" for effecting a taut equilibrium in resource allocation. At various levels of decision-making, the technological alternatives worthy of economic notice are not appreciated by all concerned, nor are they completely known; and the options that will not become known until tomorrow must also lie outside the reach of a calculation of expected net returns. In any event, costs already incurred are easier to estimate than the present values of future contingent returns—especially for speculative projects, long-term programs, and basic research. In industry, where research has been a fashionable darling since World War II, there is a strong temptation to pursue her without serious intentions while other company activities finance the affair.[9] Within any organization, the apportionment of a given research fund among competing projects may vary arbitrarily without early market protest, rejection, or reprisal. Conventions of cost accounting (respecting, say, the distribution of joint costs among projects) may also escape decisive confrontation by market tests. The same is true of psycho-

[9] See M. Nelles, "Has Research Been Oversold?", *Industrial Research* (March, 1962), pp. 17–20. The author notes that "it is unpopular to question the value of research," which can, however, be "an insidious undetected leech on profits and progress." This article gains in interest when considered in conjunction with the May, 1962, deflation of stock prices.

logical and other personal "costs" that impede change and of the contending viewpoints represented within a corporate management. In such activities as research, furthermore, there are abundant opportunities, disclosed by writings on welfare economics and monopolistic competition, for divergence between social and private measurements. We should also recall that an *ex post* catalogue of actions of the members of a mixed free economy is not the same thing as the scheme of a Laplacian mind for achieving a grand optimum.

A difficulty especially pertinent to the evaluation of complex military systems is the elusiveness of the appropriate concept of "effectiveness," which is needed for identifying technical equivalents and comparing them economically.[10] In organizations with many articulated parts and layers, the pursuit of obvious "local" concepts of effectiveness need not advance the master aim of the organization as a whole. An experienced student of military resource assignment has recently pointed to the shortcomings of "piecemeal logistics research" and observed that, "unfortunately, logistics research that suboptimizes can be worse than useless, too." [11]

Administrative allocation of research resources under expert guidance is also far from foolproof. Men of knowledge, too, lack sufficiently complete or dependable information to help them determine which scientific trends will reach what state tomorrow—with, without, or despite their invervention. They vary, like other men, in personality, temperament, and degree of acceptance of the modal values of society. They may suffer from pride, prejudice, and parochialism of profession. Some are so indifferent to the requirements of budgetary control as to invite an occasional congressional reminder concerning "the moral obligations of the scientist as a trustee

---

[10] In the authoritative book by C. J. Hitch and R. N. McKean, *The Economics of Defense in the Nuclear Age* (Santa Monica, 1960), the following statement appears near the beginning (pp. 361–62) of a lengthy mathematical appendix on maximization: "The problem of finding a good criterion or measure [of effectiveness] is very important in its own right. Many analyses of defense problems founder on this issue. However, for present purposes, we must assume that the criterion problem has been solved."

[11] S. Enke, "Logistics: Some Obiter Dicta," *Bulletin of the Operations Research Society of America* (Fall, 1962), p. B–68.

of public funds." [12] They frequently disagree with each other on researchable matters, such as the alleged carcinogenic properties of cigarettes, the perils of radiation to man on earth and in space, and the danger of chemical pesticides to the ecological balance. They may range far beyond their specialized competence in giving advice, in making partisan choices, in trying their hand at the "marginalism of policy," and in "planning" for others. (The conflict between Sir Henry Tizard and Lord Cherwell in England, as reflected in C. P. Snow's *Science and Government* and Lord Birkenhead's *The Prof in Two Worlds*, dramatizes some of the issues embedded in the preceding sentences.)

When scientists are included in prestigious decision-making boards or hold top positions in government bureaus, universities, foundations, or companies, they usually have to keep a tight rein on their technical judgment, for better or worse; and, like other executives, they typically take conservative, measured steps. "Pillars of society" do not usually "rock the boat." New fields, novel approaches, offbeat scholars, and little known institutions may have too hard a time securing effective or timely research sponsorship from authoritative interlocking directorates; and visible hardware may find readier favor than ideas.[13]

---

[12] See editorial on "Whose Responsibility?" in *Science* (October 5, 1962), p. 7.

[13] In a talk on "The Impact of Large-Scale Science on the U.S.A." on May 4, 1961, A. M. Weinberg, head of the Oak Ridge National Laboratory, complained that "the line between spending money and spending thought is blurring": "Now that money is relatively plentiful but thought is still scarce, there is a natural rush to spend dollars rather than thought—to order a 10^7 nuclear reactor instead of devising a crucial experiment with the reactors at hand."

This seems to be a good time for historians of science to begin a watch on the support given to molecular biology and related fields, where important breakthroughs have occurred and the development and application of instruments on the same scale as high-energy particle accelerators seem to promise large payoffs. (See R. S. Ledley and L. B. Lusted, "Biochemical Electronics; Potentialities and Problems," *Science* (January 19, 1962), pp. 198–201; and J. R. Platt, "National Laboratories for Biology?", *ibid.* (June 8, 1962), pp. 859–61.) Apparently, the stage has been set for an impressive effort to treat *life* quantitatively, like *materials, energy,* and *information.*

II

From the foregoing, we should conclude that reality must remain a crude model for dreams—at least in our mixed free economy. (In a controlled economy, a closer correspondence is realizable, but there the dreams are those of the central planners, which are likely to be the nightmares of ordinary citizens.) The gap between "is" and "ought" disappoints; yet it offers constructive lessons and guides for, as well as the challenge to, policy. Below the peak of unattainable perfection stretches the long upland of opportunity for improvement. If we cannot maximize, then policy should aim to majorize or pluralize; if we cannot optimize, the object should be to meliorize.

In the rest of this paper, we suggest some of the lines along which improvements in the public and private use of research resources may reasonably be sought. No attempt is made at exhaustiveness, no claim is made to originality, no access to "inside" information is pretended. We aim, above all, to present our own opinions rather than to criticize the policies and programs with which these views may be at variance. Good reasons always exist for "the way things are," at least from the standpoint of officials who are "in the know"; but the less expert citizen and the uncommitted intellectual are also right to doubt that "whatever is, is right." In any case, the main object here, as already stated, is not so much to contradict or to press reform as to exercise an essential freedom to be academic.

Hortatory language is unavoidable in the pages that follow. This is, after all, the language of policy prescription, so no apology is required. Nevertheless, a discerning reader may be left with the uncomfortable feeling that a proposed solution is just a restatement of the problem. This feeling should also be aroused when the language is not hortatory but offers no operational handles for accomplishing the benefits claimed to be attainable. Note, for example, these three self-canceling sentences in an item already cited:

> A few experienced analysts—despite considerable progress in recent years within the Department of Defense—can still indicate ways in which another billion dollars worth of resources a year might be saved. The real difficulty is implementation—despite real cooperation and motivation by the operating agencies—arising from the inevitable magnitude of these organizations. Fundamental improvements always take time when they involve millions of people who use ten million different kinds of parts in a thousand different locations.[14]

It is necessary to add that, as small participants in the widely diffused decision-making processes so highly prized in our mixed free economy, we may feel chagrined and frustrated to find ourselves in the very audiences to which our exhortations are addressed. An apt observation made by a senator at a hearing on research budgets comes to mind:

> I tell you, we are the greatest students of projections. Every office in America has piles of studies of what ought to be done. I had some in here the other day. Whenever we do not know what to do, we have another study.
> But the problem is in a free society—after you have made the survey, how do you implement it? How do you put it to work? [15]

The preceding section of the paper offers clues to priorities, as well as hints of directions, for allocational improvement. These clues apply particularly to government roles. Since the federal government supplies well over half of the vast funds spent annually for support of research in our country, these roles will be considered first.

The focus of government research interest has been national defense, and it is prudent to expect this concern, suitably interpreted, to remain the critical and dominant one during, say, the next decade. Indeed, survival with sovereignty and with political and cultural continuity seems to be the basic inescapable "national purpose" upon which all the other more

---

[14] S. Enke, *loc. cit.*

[15] Senator Humphrey, in Senate Comm. on Government Operations, *Hearings on Federal Budgeting for Research and Development,* 87th Cong., 1st Sess., Pt. 1, 191 (1961).

positive objectives that are often proclaimed for us are implicitly founded. The requirement for determined exercise of the constitutional responsibility of the federal government for defense is obvious and non-deferable, and this responsibility is also unique and non-delegable. We have to assume persistence of the national will for defense despite additional setbacks in world theaters and in international forums as our self-declared enemies continue to stand Clausewitz on his head and pursue " 'peace' as the extension of war by diplomacy and limited violence." [16] We also have to assume that, since unlimited hostilities could mean bilateral homicide, the United States and its allies will, like the principal putative enemy, seek to "win" without war; and this aim means for us "to remain neither red nor dead but, in various significant senses, to keep ahead."

Both military and non-military initiatives are vital for potentially successful defense. Long lead times for U.S.–originated weapon systems, difficulties of anticipating costs and performance, the irrelevance of cost-effectiveness criteria if such systems cannot actually be used as envisaged, and the long cycle times required for matching or countering enemy-originated systems—these facts demand a tiptoe, rather than flatfoot, posture. Besides, since our technical resources are limited, we should structure enemy alternatives according to our own military plans and capabilities and require the proliferation of enemy responses to our own feints and challenges. Furthermore, our productive superiority in general suggests that we should also take non-military initiatives to force the multiplication, and to increase the priority of, civilian wants and opportunities in unfriendly economies. Instead of entering "races" we could well lose, we should force contests entailing the dispersal of military capacity and the diffusion of internal political power in such economies—e.g., contests involving expansion of consumer goods production, reduction of average annual hours of work, and enlargement of civil liberties. The psychological and social research needed for defining and executing favorable non-military initiatives should be taken into account in the deliberations of such groups as

---

[16] I. H. Siegel, *Soviet Labor Productivity* (Chevy Chase, Md., 1952), p. 69.

the behavioral sciences subpanel of the President's Science Advisory Committee and in the programs of the public and private organizations to which these groups address their recommendations.[17]

Not only in the research programs of the military services but also in those of other government agencies should opportunities be sought for decisive upgrading of the nation's defense potential. Thus, the federal research commitments respecting space, atomic energy, health, agriculture, and so forth should continually be re-examined with reference to the insistent demands of national security. Special attention should be given to the need for developing and supporting non-military initiatives (at home as well as abroad) that would bolster military security.

It is important to state explicitly that rehabilitation of the defense motive, that imaginative and deliberate implementation of this blurred master purpose, should not entail a parochial restriction of government research, a reduction of government support, or any greater invasion of traditional civilian precincts by military personnel than has already occurred. The concept of defense adopted here is very broad; indeed, the scope allowed for non-military initiatives is boundless, and even military prowess in the narrow sense has to rest on deep inquiries into nature as well as on projects having obvious combat or logistic value, requiring short cycle times, and promising early payoffs. Our stress on successful defense would, of course, entail redirection, revaluation, reinterpretation, and relabeling. It would require selection, reorientation, formal or informal priority assignments, co-ordination, integration. It would demand resolute leadership. It would mean that, when viewed in a true light, a drab Cinderella (say, agricultural research to increase crop yields further—but in underdeveloped lands) could become more attractive than a glamorous siren (say, one that beckons to a rendezvous somewhere in outer space or in an atomic reactor).

---

[17] See the subpanel's report on "Strengthening the Behavioral Sciences," *Science* (April 20, 1962), pp. 233–41; and I. H. Siegel, "Industrial and Human Resources in U.S. Strategy," in *National Security: Political, Military, and Economic Strategies in the Decade Ahead* (New York, 1963), pp. 939–61.

The legitimacy and propriety of government participation in non-defense research cannot be gainsaid, but the security objective is paramount, and a confrontation of defense and non-defense alternatives is desirable for improving the allocation of resources. Constitutional and statutory authority may be cited—and is—for every activity that is publicly financed. Within the limits discussed in the preceding section, the people and their political representatives seek some sort of net benefit from research as well as from other undertakings. The federal interest may be justified economically on grounds of peculiar competence to finance worthy activities that seem speculative and risky, that cannot at first command wide popular understanding, that require a large initial or continuing investment, and that have to be administered impersonally, faithfully, and evenly over time. But, however worthy, the alleged or expected contributions to defense, to economic strength for meeting foreign competition and providing high-level employment, and to welfare advancement in all directions have to be compared and rated. Many federal projects could, without prejudice to current or foreseeable defense requirements or other national objectives, be terminated, deferred, or transferred to non-defense or non-federal jurisdictions.

Two principles might be invoked to improve the balance between government research requirements and the supply of technical personnel. First, when new programs are proposed, the modification, shift, or extension of existing programs intended to accomplish related purposes should be considered. Where pertinent, an analysis should be made of past failure to obtain the desired new results under older programs. Second, new government research programs that entail significant additional demands for technical personnel might well be accompanied by direct or supporting government proposals for enlargement of the relevant labor supply. Further remarks on manpower will be made below.

Effective utilization of research services by the federal government constitutes a true Laplacian problem; and efforts at solution require the installation of a Laplacian governor, however crude and imperfect. These efforts should lead to substantial improvement, however short of optimization the result would be, in the allocation of our nation's technical resources. A broad-gauged policy board responsible to the President, working with and through existing government agencies and also through responsive subsidiary organizations, should serve as a "high command" for government science. This supreme board and its adjuncts do not have to be combined into a new cabinet agency for the execution of obvious essential functions. It should represent the defense conscience, but do so with proper sophistication. It should, for example, pay due regard to non-defense needs, their interrelations with defense, the implications of changing technology and changing foreign economic capabilities, the main functions of universities, the merits and limitations of commercial and non-profit research firms, the advantages and drawbacks of cost-plus and incentive contracts, the attitudes of the scientific community, the values of antitrust, the relevance of tax and patent policies, the objectives of the Employment Act of 1946, etc. This proposal recognizes that many bodies have been established to perform co-ordinating tasks, at least since the Civil War; and that the growth of federal research support since World War II makes movement toward rational control increasingly urgent.

Because the executive and legislative powers of the federal government are separated in our mixed free economy, the policy board just described cannot realistically be expected to serve the Congress as well as the President. A second board—of legislators aided by staff scientists and advisory panels—is required to co-ordinate congressional deliberations and decisions on the manifold, diffused technical programs included in the national budget. The competitive coexistence of the two boards should upgrade the quality of the allocations determinable by either alone.

The purposes of a joint, comprehensive, congressional mechanism cannot be effectively performed by the Senate Committee on Labor and Public Welfare, the House Committee on Science and Astronautics, and the many other groups now working on different legislative fronts. A published retrospective appraisal of the Eighty-seventh Congress with respect to scientific matters points to the imbalance of "enthusiasm and insight," the inadequacy of organization and

staff for meeting the challenge of the times, and the conse-
quent ability of "the more politically active agencies . . .
to pursue their own interests without reference to overall
national needs." The concluding sentence of this review
acknowledges the opportunity for improving allocation even
though legislators now happen to look with favor upon
research (especially medical, which may even be "financially
overfed"):[18]

> Congressional lack of understanding and the archaic legislative ma-
> chinery have curiously worked to the advantage of the nation's
> scientists, but it is not difficult to recognize that a good deal of
> luck has been at work here and it would be better for everyone
> involved if Congress were both generous and intelligent about science.

Other kinds of fractionization of political power should
be taken into account in the interest of more effective utilization of technical resources. Thus, the traditional interplay of
different nations could doubtless be selectively intensified or
redirected to mutual advantage in fundamental as well as
applied research. State and local governments, too, have responsibilities in technical resource allocation, and they occupy
strategic positions in the enlargement of the specialized
manpower supply through education and training. Greater
compatibility of federal objectives with those of subordinate
political jurisdictions should be sought, without the degradation of local autonomy.

More explicit emphasis on successful defense, broadly
defined, should be matched by greater emphasis on adaptation
of the technological "fallout" to civilian purposes. The more
efficacious a program is for civilian recapture, the greater is
the offset to the original defense cost and the more favorable
is the longer-range evaluation of the whole cycle of resource
use. Once it is agreed that a high-grade defense purpose is
to be served—for example, by missiles, rockets, and satellites
made with specially engineered materials—it also becomes
logical to consider the profitable production of pots and pans
from the same "unobtainium." On the whole, society seems
to have more to gain than to lose from liberal patent rules

---

[18] *Science* (October 19, 1962), pp. 417–18.

encouraging this sort of transfer of new knowledge and skills to new markets.

Another conservation measure to improve the use of relatively scarce technical resources is the development of superior systems for abstracting, storing, indexing, retrieving, and distributing research findings. The mechanization of patent search and of foreign language translation could, if satisfactorily accomplished, also free otherwise committed resources. All such systems clarify the opportunity for deliberate choice, discussed in the preceding section, between the creation of new knowledge and the acquisition of existing knowledge (education). They may save valuable calendar time, as well as man-hours and facility costs, for the military services, government contractors, and other sponsors and performers of laboratory tasks. A library search should be cheaper than, and be made at least as attractive as, a quest for roughly equivalent information through the unwitting duplication of earlier experiments.

Since the future holds technological and other surprises and since our nation's self-declared enemies have a dynamism of their own, it seems most desirable to increase the proportion of technically trained manpower in the labor force. The mere redistribution of a "sense of shortage" by shift from one specialty to another is not so wholesome as raising the educational level of an increasing percentage of our youths.[19] This preferred alternative would increase our capacity and flexibility for undertaking military and non-military initiatives. Educated people represent "research on the hoof"; they are adaptable to a great variety of technical tasks that cannot yet be specified. The crest of the postwar population wave now advances toward the colleges, and the number of youths reaching eighteen years of age will soon rise very dramatically. The higher schools should be made more ready to welcome them than the labor market is likely to be. State universities will apparently play an outstanding role in absorbing these youngsters and in helping raise the economic prestige of

---

[19] See the author's article "Scientific Discovery, Invention, and the Cultural Environment," and his paper on "The Influence of Government on the Demand for Scientists and Engineers," *Scientific Manpower: 1958* (Washington, D.C., 1959), pp. 54–59.

teaching. All echelons of government can also help to enlarge the technical manpower supply by efforts to reduce dropout rates in the primary, secondary, and higher schools, and by further action to improve teacher qualifications and salaries.

The quality of a mixed free economy depends in part on the willingness of private persons and groups to pursue "enlightened self-interest," to seek private gain through creation of social benefits within the constraints of nature, knowledge, custom, and law. By their competitive decisions and actions, they help to shape the meaning of the "public interest," a concept that cannot safely be left to any government official or business monopolist for unilateral definition. The multiplicity of private objectives and their difference in turn from aims proclaimed for government programs provide a basis for constructive interaction.[20]

In the conduct of research, private firms should strive for profit, directly and indirectly (e.g., through reduction of their own costs), within some realistic time frame. Private research should, in general, be expected to yield a positive net return, although any computation of this return is subject to doubt, and any one project may fail. Surely, gain need not result from *un*calculated risks; research does not automatically lead to the growth of productivity, markets, and profits, as is commonly assumed or asserted, although a good assortment of projects will enhance potentials for all three. If the costs to a firm of learning new techniques and unlearning old ones are regarded as prohibitive, if current operations are profitable, and if continuing viability appears a reasonable prospect, then the adoption of a formal company research program for fashion's sake would seem superfluous—even wasteful. Furthermore, no firm need recognize an obligation to engage in "basic" research for the benefit of "society" unless there is also a clear private advantage. Knowledge does not really constitute a social "fund" that is degraded through use and that requires replenishment by users; and these comments do not

---

[20] On this paragraph, see two articles by L. J. Harris and I. H. Siegel in *Patent, Trademark, and Copyright Journal of Research and Education:* "Positive Competition and the Patent System" (Spring, 1959), pp. 21–32; and "Evolving Court Opinion on Patent Licensing: An Interaction of Positive Competition and the Law" (Summer, 1961), pp. 103–13.

disparage the importance of new knowledge as a condition of economic and technological progress.

Since we live in a world in which tolls *are* charged for bridges (and may be collected for construction of additional bridges until all fall down), a firm would do well to keep its *private* accounts in order and serve society through the maintenance of production, employment, and solvency. It should be particularly alert to legal opportunities to appropriate the benefits of public undertakings in education, research, and other realms; and, where cost burdens are legally diffusible, to carry them fully or voluntarily would seem unwise as well as gratuitous. A company that seeks to assure its profitability along a technological dimension should recognize opportunities for improvement of "know-how" in relatively inexpensive ways—e.g., by hire of employees trained in other firms as well as in schools, upgrading of staff through selected contract work, entry into patent-licensing and other arrangements concerning "industrial property," canvass of trade and technical literature, study of existing patents, survey of government reports on publicly financed research (such as those released by the Office of Technical Services, U. S. Department of Commerce), adaptation of various military research results to civilian ends, and acquisition of patents as by-products of activity on government research and production contracts. A firm that is publicly censured for receiving so-called patent give-aways should be publicly complimented when successful commercialization enlarges the social "takeaway" in the form of progressive taxation.

Small firms that seek a technological route to growth should take cognizance of the many government aids already provided. In addition to the aids mentioned or suggested above are those specifically embodied in small-business legislation and in complementary regulations of the Defense Department, NASA, etc. Two examples are: the legal research "pools" envisaged in Section 9 of the Small Business Act of 1958; and the small-business investment corporations authorized in another law of the same year to assist in equity financing and to make long-term loans.

The most significant opportunities to improve the utilization of research resources in the private sector reside in the larger firms that conduct most of the laboratory work. In the pursuit of profit, they are best situated to contribute directly to defense; they also are well situated to promote domestic and foreign market expansion, to develop or innovate major cost-saving processes, and to give technical assistance to suppliers and subcontractors. They have extensive stocks of patents and other intangible property that may be economically exploitable. It is in their interest to stimulate creative employee effort on the job.[21] They may have a sufficiently long time horizon and a sufficiently diverse assortment of product lines to consider fundamental research worth undertaking. Their longer-term manpower needs may also properly encourage the upgrading of employee skills through on-the-job training, university attendance of personnel, and release of time for teaching in local schools.

In short, a firm performs its characteristic social function through operating profitably and planning for profitable continuity; and, in performing this essential function, it should take due account of costs and expected returns in the realm of research as well as in, for example, material-processing. The government's prime concern for successful defense should be communicated to the private sector through contract incentives hedged by appropriate safeguards. As a firm proceeds forward into the open-ended future, it should continually make re-adjustments in its plans in accordance with, among other things, the growth and diversification of its stock of knowledge and the skills of its staff, as well as its reassessment of alternative near-term and longer-term future courses. The leadership of a firm should equip itself to insist, like the lass in the Scottish ballad, that it knows where it is going—while it also concedes that only the Dear Lord really knows toward what end.

---

[21] See I. H. Siegel, "On Individual and Joint Patent Production," *ibid.* (Summer, 1962), pp. 241–60.

THE ALLOCATION OF RESEARCH AND DEVELOPMENT RESOURCES: SOME PROBLEMS OF PUBLIC POLICY

Richard R. Nelson

IN THIS PAPER I shall discuss some of the problems and opportunities for public policy in the allocation of our scientific and technical resources and try to suggest some of the implications of traditional economic analysis which can, and should, be brought to bear on policy-making in this vital area. In particular, I shall discuss the effects of different allocations, the type of criteria that are relevant to choosing among alternative allocations, the role of the market and of public policy in assuring that the actual allocation is as close as possible to optimal, and, in general terms, some of the ways in which public policy could be improved.

ALLOCATION MAKES A DIFFERENCE

One of the major contributions that economic analysis can make in the discussion of science policy is to point out that there is an allocation problem; allocation makes a difference. Often the discussion of the need for more R&D funds for one purpose or another tends to ignore that the human and material resources which comprise our scientific and technical capability are scarce and valuable. Less than one and a half million scientists and engineers carry the major burden of the application and advancement of science and technology. The supply of these resources is not very elastic in the short run. If they are utilized in one job, they cannot be used in another.

Only about one-third of the working time of the scientists and engineers of the United States is spent in R&D. Two-thirds is spent in teaching, management, operations, and other functions. There are some important and complicated problems of public policy involved in the allocation of scientists and engineers among these functions. There is the closely connected, and extremely important, set of problems relating to how to increase the supply of scientists and engineers. But in this paper the concern will be predominantly with the allocation within the research and development function.

The fact that there is a real problem of choice has been somewhat blurred by over-reaction to the fact that the benefits from R&D often diffuse far beyond the area of intended application. It is true that the areas of potential practical application of the results of a basic research project are uncertain, that research on plastics can lead to better paints, and that the civilian economy sometimes can make considerable advantage of the by-products of military or space R&D. This fact is extremely important and its implications will be considered later. But certain kinds of R&D are not all that uncertain and obviously the particular R&D projects to which the talents of scientists and engineers are applied most certainly influence the type of payoffs society can expect from their work. If R&D is aimed at creating information needed to build a better rocket engine, it is likely to do just that and precious little else.

Perhaps the best evidence that the allocation of R&D resources really matters is provided by the Minasian[1] and Terleckyj[2] studies. The Minasian study found that, within an industry, there was a significant correlation (.70) between R&D spending by a firm and subsequent productivity growth.

The Terleckyj study found that between industries there was a significant correlation (.62) between R&D spending (and scientists and engineers employed) by the industry and its productivity growth. The correlations are not spectacularly high, but they are significant. While the historical record

---

[1] J. Minasian, "The Economics of Research and Development," in National Bureau of Economic Research, *Direction of Inventive Activity* (Princeton, N. J., 1962).

[2] N. Terleckyj, "Sources of Productivity Growth" (Unpublished Ph.D. thesis, Princeton University, 1961), cited in J. Kendrik, *Productivity Trends in the U.S.*

is clear that many of the most important technical advances affecting the productivity of an industry originate from research done in other industries, or in universities, or in government laboratories, or by individuals working alone, apparently where the research is done (a good indication of what practical problems the research is designed to illuminate) does matter.

It is interesting that much of the discussion of the likely economic impact of our defense and space R&D efforts has tended to ignore that the allocation of R&D resources among sectors and industries strongly affects the sectoral composition of technological progress. There seems to be a widespread belief that the rapid growth of space and defense R&D will revolutionize the civilian economy. Actually, if their allocation effects are considered, it would seem likely that our military and space R&D programs may be holding down the pace of technological advance in the civilian economy.

While between 1954 and 1961 total R&D spending tripled, the rate of growth of R&D financed by the DOD, AEC, and NASA was almost twice the rate of growth of other R&D. In industry, the number of total R&D scientists and engineers financed by government agencies (over 95 per cent by DOD, AEC, and NASA) increased from 36 per cent to 55 per cent of the total. While the number of total scientists and engineers engaged in R&D in industry grew at approximately a 10 per cent annual rate, the number financed by private industry out of their own funds and, presumably, involved principally on civilian programs grew at only one-third that rate.[3]

The limited data suggest that, in small part at least, the very rapid growth of demand for scientists and engineers for defense and space R&D was met by a more rapidly growing supply.[4] However, a large share of the increase in scientists and engineers in defense and space R&D was achieved

---

[3]These figures are obtained by assuming that if the government finances x per cent of the R&D done in an industry, x per cent of the scientists and engineers are working on the government's problems. There are many difficulties with this assumption, but it is not clear whether it is an overestimate or an underestimate. The data are from the National Science Foundation.

[4] For example, between 1954 and 1960 the number of college degrees in engineering, mathematics, and physical science increased from 13 per cent to 17 per cent of the total.

through the bidding away of talent from civilian industry. Between 1957 and 1960, beginning salaries of engineers increased 19 per cent. There is considerable feeling among R&D laboratory directors that defense and space companies are snapping up the lion's share of the really good graduates. If anything, the market should get tighter over the next few years. The projected increase in space R&D alone is likely to absorb one-third to one-half of the expected increase in the number of available scientists and engineers.

The Terleckyj study suggests that R&D performed to advance the nation's space and defense programs contributes far less to the advance of productivity in civilian industry than R&D concerned more directly with civilian problems. Further, the bulk of military R&D is not of the sort we would expect to generate knowledge of much relevance to civilian problems.

The degree of general purpose relevance of the results of R&D tends to be relatively great toward the basic research and technical experimentation end of the R&D spectrum. Toward the applied research and product development end of the spectrum, the results of R&D tend to be principally of relevance to the particular problems and hardware configurations which are the focus of the work. Of the DOD's total R&D budget, almost 90 per cent is for hardware development, less than 5 per cent for basic research. With NASA and the AEC the percentage of development expenditures to total R&D expenditure is significantly smaller; but for the three agencies taken together, more than 75 per cent of their total R&D spending was aimed at creating information relevant to a specific end item, and probably created very little knowledge of general purpose to the economy as a whole.

The civilian economy does gain some by-product advantage from the research and development financed by the DOD and NASA. But military and space research and development increasingly are exploring areas far away from those of clear relevance to the civilian economy. While it is very difficult to measure the degree of civilian relevance of defense R&D programs, clearly research on mildew resistant fabrics for military use in the tropics is much more likely to have obvious civilian applications than research on nose cones. A very large percentage of the civilian applications of military R&D

listed in the Operations Research Office study[5] are of the "mildew resistant cloth" type, and this type of research probably is a much smaller percentage of military R&D today than before the missile age.

However, while direct product adaptation is not likely to be particularly important, the long-range benefits to the civilian economy from some of the sophisticated defense and space R&D programs may turn out to be substantial. Whole new technologies, of great potential civilian utility, are being opened. However, the translation to civilian uses will not be easy. Considerable further R&D will be needed. Yet the military and space programs are drawing away the lion's share of the people who are capable of doing the work of adapting the new technologies to civilian use.

The purpose of the preceding discussion was not to argue that we are spending too much on defense and space R&D. We may be spending too much or we may be spending too little. Nor is this to argue that our defense R&D programs are hindering economic growth by drawing R&D resources away from the civilian economy. By creating the knowledge which enables the capital and labor engaged in defense work to meet defense needs more effectively, defense R&D contributes to increased productivity in defense industries.[6] This has permitted a given quantity of resources engaged in defense work to produce a greater defense capability, and has reduced the quantity of resources needed to produce a given level of defense capability. Obviously, technical change in the defense industries has contributed to economic growth. But it is clear that to the extent more R&D resources applied to the civilian sector would have contributed to the creation of better products and processes, the opportunity costs of defense and space R&D probably are lower productivity, higher costs, and poorer products in the civilian sector. Allocation has made a difference.

---

[5] Striner, Sherman, and Karadbil, *Defense Spending and the American Economy* (Washington, D.C., 1959).

[6] That growth measured in terms of the gross national product does not account this "productivity" improvement adequately is another matter.

SOCIAL CRITERIA FOR R&D ALLOCATION

Economic analysis also can contribute to an evaluation of R&D allocation by suggesting what are the relevant criteria. An optimal allocation in terms of economic analysis means an allocation such that resources cannot be transferred from one use to another in such a way as to increase welfare. Economic analysis must point out that some R&D (or a considerable amount of R&D) going on in a particular area is not sufficient evidence that enough is going on. The relevant question is: Are the marginal returns from increasing R&D in that area greater or smaller than the marginal returns from the R&D resources in other uses?

In order to deal with this question at all effectively, there must be a relatively clear understanding of the types of returns that society can expect from R&D.

The output of R&D is information; information as to what results when certain chemical compounds are mixed together; information that a virus causes a certain disease; information that a particular theoretical model explains quite well the properties of metals; information as to the properties of a particular metal at high temperatures; information whether or not a metal will fail when used for a particular engine part under specified laboratory conditions; information that a particular engine design will work.

Research and development has economic value because the information it creates permits people to do things better, and sometimes to do things that they did not know how to do before. Put another way, the information created by R&D expands the perceived choice set and enables better informed choices to be made within the set. The information created by R&D throws light on the most fruitful next series of researches in a certain field of chemistry, or whether or not it is worthwhile to try to find a vaccine to prevent a particular disease, whether or not a particular engine should be designed and what metal should be used for a part, whether or not to produce the engine for practical use.

There is no simple way to evaluate the benefits society can expect from the knowledge created by different kinds of R&D aimed at illuminating different kinds of problems and questions. The importance of the added national prestige we may obtain if we allocate more R&D resources to finding out how to get to the moon, the value of obtaining better information on the causes of cancer, and the value of obtaining information which will permit the development of a silent home air conditioner somehow must be compared.

Often it is possible to translate the value of the likely fruits of new information into dollar terms, as when there is a good market for the product involved, or where there are alternative (non-R&D) ways to achieve the objective which would be taken if the R&D project were not undertaken. The economist should stress that, where possible and relevant, these dollar value comparisons should be made. But he must also point out that for some of the kinds of benefits new knowledge can yield, the market is very thin and imperfect.

Yet the fact that the market is thin and imperfect, and that therefore it is difficult to attach a dollar value to the information created by a particular research and development project, is no reason for assigning it a low value. It is extremely difficult to place a dollar value on a successful cure for cancer. Surely the total value would dwarf any measurable contribution to economic product resulting from the increased size and vigor of the work force. It would reflect a distressing confusion of means with ends if basic scientific research had to be justified solely in terms of future economic product. Surely we want a stronger economy in part because then we will have greater room for undertaking cultural pursuits, of which basic research is one.

Returning to the question of whether or not we are allocating too large a quantity of our R&D resources to defense, clearly it is impossible to place a dollar value on the additional defense capability a particular defense R&D project is likely to yield. Economic calculations, however, are applicable to choices among alternative military R&D projects which are likely to have the same effect on defense capability. And economic calculations are applicable to decisions as to whether to increase defense capabilities by R&D or by spending more on existing weapons systems (developing Minuteman rather than building more Atlas missiles). Indeed, economic analysis might suggest that to the extent R&D resources are underpriced on the civilian market relative to the values they produce, a military R&D project must be significantly less costly than the non-R&D alternative which can do the same job before it is socially desirable to choose the military R&D alternative.[7] However, the market can provide very little guidance with respect to the level of military security we should strive for.

While it often is extremely difficult to do so, the attempt to measure and compare the gains to society from better understanding, better information, of the sort which is likely to result from R&D is the proper approach to making R&D allocation judgments. Essentially, R&D must be evaluated in terms of the kind of information it is likely to produce, the increased ability to solve certain problems or make certain decisions which will result from that information, and the value to society of solving the problem or making the decision better. If we focus on R&D likely to lead to technological progress (to more efficient production techniques and better products), we must ask the questions: where is R&D most likely to lead to technological advance and where are technological advances likely to be of most value to society in terms of resources saved or wants better met.[8]

---

[7] This assumes, of course, that the external economies from civilian R&D are likely to exceed the external economies from military R&D. To the extent that the military R&D project is aimed at a particular weapon system far removed from civilian analysis, this is likely to be the case.

[8] As a footnote, it might be added that solving the unemployment problem of sick industries is not a proper criterion. The reasons are obvious. And the data confirm the theory. While R&D growth and productivity growth are related (as Terleckyj's data show), and the productivity growth and output growth are highly correlated, there is little relation between productivity growth and employment growth. (Another way of saying this is that the elasticity of demand is, on the average, equal to one.) If we eliminate the Korean and post-Korean years where the correlation between defense employment (which increased substantially) and R&D spending in the defense industries results in an extremely misleading correlation between R&D and employment growth. Kendrick's data show that productivity advance in an industry and employment increase in that industry have only a very low positive correlation. For the 1899–1953 period, the coefficient of correlation was only +.32. However, rapid growth of output and

THE MECHANISM OF ALLOCATION—PUBLIC POLICY
AND THE MARKET

What are the mechanisms which guide the allocation of R&D resources? How can these mechanisms be controlled so that they will allocate R&D resources to the areas where the social returns are greatest? These are questions on which economic analysis can shed some light.

In the United States we have established a reasonably well-working division of labor and responsibility between public and private agencies, between agencies whose goals are the general welfare and organizations whose goals are those of the controlling individuals.

In general, the federal government must take direct responsibility for seeing to it that for these areas of our political economy where it has major decision-making responsibilities, the investment in R&D is of adequate size and quality, given the returns and the costs. While defense, space, and the development of atomic energy dwarf quantitatively the other governmental R&D programs which are conducted out of a responsibility to manage efficiently a "public function," there are many other areas as well. The government has major responsibility for research to improve weather forecasting, public health, public roads, schools, hospitals, and other urban facilities, to name just a few. This does not mean that the government must do all of the work in its own facilities or that it must finance all, or any, of the work. But since public agencies have direct responsibility for managing these areas of our political economy efficiently, they have an implied responsibility for seeing that the appropriate R&D is done, in one way or another.

In addition, fundamental scientific knowledge itself can, and should, be considered a public good; for the total benefits which accrue from a fundamental advance in knowledge far exceed those which can be traded on a free market. In

---

declining relative price of an industry's product were quite strongly related to rapid productivity growth. The coefficients of correlation are +.69 and —.87, respectively.

recent years, the federal government has acted to sponser basic research generally and has established major programs in certain key areas, such as peacetime atomic energy and space technology, on the grounds that the advances which might result would be very important and sufficiently widespread in their impact to be treated as public goods.[9]

These are the traditional areas of governmental responsibility for R&D: R&D relevant to the public sector, and fundamental research. For research and development aimed at advancing technology in the private sector, the United States has, with limited exceptions, relied on the workings of the market.

However, both the character of the research and development activity and of the commodity it produces—information —tend to make the market work imperfectly. Since it often is difficult to know, in advance, just what practical problems the information generated by a particular R&D project will shed light on, and since the range of illuminated practical problems may be extremely wide, an organization with a relatively narrow range of interests may be able to use, itself, only a fraction of the potential value from the information created by the R&D it sponsors. Since information is a very difficult commodity for which to establish property rights, many organizations other than the one which sponsors the R&D may be able to benefit, without compensating the organization which paid for the work.

These characteristics—uncertainty, widespread potential use, and inappropriability—usually are not particularly serious for R&D on product improvement and new product development. A business firm, feeling the needs of the economy as expressed through the market and stimulated to meet these needs by the lure of profit and the spur of competition, can engage in this kind of R&D reasonably sure that, if successful, it will be well rewarded. The information created by this type of work is likely to be directly relevant to the firm's problems. The firm is likely to be able to make private property of the information through a suitably written patent. And this patent is quite likely to enable the firm to share in

---

[9] For a discussion of these points, see R. Nelson, "The Simple Economics of Basic Scientific Research," *Journal of Political Economy* (1959).

any economic benefits created by the information for activities outside the range of the firm's market interests.

However, there are good reasons to believe that market incentives tend to cause business firms to spend much less than is socially desirable on research and experimental development exploring advanced concepts and designs. This work is risky—in most cases the information created will not be sufficient in itself to permit the design of a marketable product or process but rather will suggest additional R&D, or may prove a blind alley. In all save the largest and most secure firms, the time horizons are too short and the possibilities of spreading the risk too limited to give a firm strong incentives to do much of this kind of work. But society's interests are very long run and for society as a whole risks are spread over a very large number of projects. This difficulty is compounded by the tendency of many (though certainly not all) business firms to think in terms of their existing products line instead of the functions these products serve, woven cloth instead of clothing materials, brick instead of building materials. Thinking in terms of limited market horizons is not necessarily irrational. Often it is a very rational reaction to the facts that the firm has technological competence, market experience, and organization in certain fields and not in others, and that the costs of learning to deal with new technologies and invading new markets may be considerable. Thus there is a bias toward marginally improving old ways rather than experimenting with radically new ways of meeting needs. Yet society scarcely has a vested interest in existing product lines and ways of satisfying needs. The very rapid development of military technology, where the incentives have caused us to devote a considerable effort toward developing and testing new concepts and designs, suggests that the returns might be very great if there were considerably more R&D aimed at creating and testing prototypes of radically new civilian products and processes.

Our enterprise system also tends to fail badly in situations where one company takes the risks and covers the costs but many companies share widely in the benefits. The whole areas of process improvements not subject to patenting (a major source of productivity growth), of testing and evaluation techniques, and of analysis of materials and methods are cases in point. Research on standards, and user safety, also is unlikely to yield a private firm profits commensurate with the benefits to society.

Another problem area is R&D which cuts across the market interests of firms and industries. For example, the analysis and development of integrated production systems is not easily forthcoming where there is no equipment supplier who produces a full range of equipment for a particular production sequence. This problem, as well as those discussed above, is likely to be particularly serious in industries comprised principally of small firms. Small firms often find too little use for highly trained engineers to hire them and often are unable to attract and hold them even when an effort is made. They thereby tend to be cut off from keeping up with the innovations of others as well as from innovating themselves.

These problems of allocation of research and development resources resulting from the properties of the R&D process and of the commodity produced, information, have as their counterpart some serious problems with respect to the dissemination of information. Not only is it true that often the information created by research and development in one organization is of significant value primarily to another organization, but often the two organizations, one which has the information and the other which can use it, are not aware of this fact.

It is clear that many business firms have far less than full information as to the technological possibilities open to them.[10] This problem is not so serious for technical information which is clothed in an industrial product, a machine, a material. The companies which produce the product or machine have a strong incentive to advertise the new develop-

---

[10] While the technical information services in the United States, public and private, have expanded tremendously in recent years, so has the production of new technical and scientific information. Further, the problem of classifying new scientific and technical information in a form convenient for the many and diverse potential benefiters has intensified as a growing share of R&D, of possible benefit to the commercial sector of the economy, is performed in connection with defense, the AEC, and under NASA contracts with firms with little interest in civilian markets. At present we have only begun to experiment with policies and institutions designed to evaluate results of defense and space research for their civilian applicability, and the task of providing potential users with the new information in an understandable form grows increasingly complex as the scientific component of technology increases.

ment; for, in a very real sense, they have been able to make private property out of the information their R&D has created, and thus are able to sell that property on the market.

But for new information which is not so embodied in a product, the market generates very little incentive for dissemination of that information. As Kenneth Arrow has pointed out,[11] the value of information is not known to the potential purchaser until he knows what the information is, but then he has, in effect, acquired it (or a significant part of it) without cost. The producer of the information loses his control of the information the minute he transmits it. Often the alternative to ability to make private property of information is industrial secrecy. Further, even when the information is readily available in the scientific or technical literature, a firm without a strong technical staff often is unable to understand or use the information.

Thus the same problems which suggest that the federal government should take an active role in support of certain kinds of R&D also suggest that the federal government should take an active role in the dissemination of the information that R&D creates.

SOME GENERAL CONCLUSIONS ON NEEDED CHANGES

As long as our research and development resources are limited, we never shall be able to do all the things it would be nice to do. Over the long run, our total research and development capabilities will depend on the number of new scientists and engineers provided by an educational system. But over the shorter run, it is doubtful that public policy will be able to affect strongly, one way or another, the rate at which the supply of scientists and engineers is increasing. Thus, at the same time that we are proceeding with policy in the field of education, the shorter-run problem will be to encourage the most efficient and effective allocation of a given time path of supply.

[11] See his "Welfare Economics and Incentive Activity" in National Bureau of Economic Research, *The Rate and Direction of Incentive Activity* (Princeton, N.J., 1962).

We will have to face some very important decisions. We will not be able to increase very significantly the scientific and technical resources allocated to one area of technology without a parallel decision, explicit or implicit, not to advance another as rapidly as we might like. In particular, it should be noted—or better, stressed—that the decision to allocate a large and rapidly growing quantity of scientists and engineers to the NASA program seriously constrains the expansion we can achieve in the more mundane areas of civilian technology.

Focusing then on what appear to be desirable reallocations, there are several things that can be done to increase the value that society gains from its research and development resources:

First, aside from the fields of defense and space, it is likely that we are relying too much on the workings of private incentives as stimulated by the market to generate R&D relevant to the public sector. Very little is being spent, for example, on research to improve urban transportation systems, or educational technology. While it is not obvious that more research in these areas would yield considerable results, it is clear that the government is only beginning to look into the question carefully. But if the government does not take responsibility in these areas, no one else will. The Bureau of the Budget and the Federal Council for Science and Technology should, each year, be responsible for evaluating the quantity and quality of research going on that is of relevance to the needs of the public sector.

Second, the federal government has not as yet recognized adequately the role that it must play in helping to allocate private sector R&D effectively in those instances where the market does not work well. This does not mean that the federal government should get into the business of developing new products and processes for the civilian economy, save in very unusual circumstances in which private organizations are too small or weak to do a job (as in agriculture). But it does mean that the federal government should support, conduct, or provide special incentives for R&D of the sort which creates information of widespread use to industry but which cannot be readily traded on the market and for the expansion of the system which disseminates that information.

Federal activities in support of agricultural technology suggest a wide spectrum of policy possibilities.[12] The Department of Agriculture conducts some research in its own facilities and, through Hatch Act and other funds, supports research at the agricultural experimenting stations of colleges and universities. TVA has contributed to productivity growth in agriculture by research and development work in fertilizer, an industry which traditionally has not supported much R&D out of private funds. The federal-state co-operative extension service has acted to accelerate the diffusion of the results of research in a form particularly well suited to the needs of farming. The Department of Agriculture itself publishes considerable information. The Griliches [13] study of hybrid corn and other agricultural advances suggests that we, as a nation, have benefited greatly from this work.

The suggestion here is not that the federal government apply to industry exactly the programs in support of technology it has applied to the problem of agriculture. Rather, it is that there are many possible programs, and the agricultural programs provide some basis of relevant experience. The British experience in the government-aided industry research institutes provides another possible approach, the German technical and scientific institutes still another.

Obviously a developing program of support of research and technical information services for the civilian economy—both private and public sectors—should be pragmatic, experimental, and flexible so that we can learn as we go along. The type of relevant programs are likely to differ from sector to sector. However, the experience with programs in support of civilian technology suggests that the programs should be defined broadly enough so as to avoid industry and product-line provincialism and political pressure and to attract scientists and engineers of varied backgrounds. At the same time, it is essential that there be good lines of communication with those who will utilize the results of research.

---

[12] For an excellent discussion see V. Ruttan, "Research on the Economics of Technological Change in Agriculture," *Journal of Farm Economics* (1960).

[13] Z. Griliches, "Research Costs and Social Returns," *Journal of Political Economy* (1958).

To the extent that R&D resources are underallocated to research concepts and designs, to process research not likely to lead to a patent, and to other work where the benefits diffuse widely, it is in the public interest that there be a re-allocation in this direction. One possibility would be to provide government grants on contracts for work of this sort to the engineering experimentation stations of the universities or to other university-affiliated facilities doing research on problems of civilian technology.

A second, and complementary, possibility, would be to provide a tax credit, or matching dollars, for industry funds contributed to co-operative research associations or to other non-profit research institutions (including universities). To assure that firms would not have incentive to finance under this arrangement product development work and other R&D that they would have done otherwise in their own facilities, all results would be published and any resulting patents available for non-exclusive licensing to any American business firm. Several of these institutions presently are doing outstanding work. But in many cases the research is mundane (particularly in the industry association), and in others the work is of little use to industry (particularly in the other non-profits). The incentives provided by a tax credit or matching funds mechanism would provide these institutions with more funds and, by providing a strong interest for industry, help to orient the work toward real problems. However, to relieve the institutions from industry pressure to work on short-run problems, some other mechanisms, like government grants and contracts, are needed.

The recent appointment of an assistant secretary for science and technology at the Department of Commerce should provide a natural focus for a considerable extension of programs in support of civilian technology. A considerable portion of the budget for these programs could be contracted or granted to various non-profit organizations. The success of these programs would depend on the imagination and competence which went into selecting the research areas and organizations. Experience suggests that a strengthening of the in-house R&D competence of the federal government is a pre-requisite for obtaining this competence.

To provide a major part of the needed in-house competence, the National Bureau of Standards might significantly expand its role. A set of broadly oriented research groups might be associated with the Bureau, the mission of each group defined in terms of a broad functional area, like materials, transportation, and housing. The research objective of these groups would be to explore the technological problems and opportunities of its area including experimentation with radically new ways of doing things.

It is clear that effective and imaginative support of non-government research and the strengthening of in-house R&D competence are complementary objectives. The proper division of research between in-house and contract certainly would differ from case to case, and will have to be worked out through actual experience. The objectives of the over-all program would be to generate information as to the technological possibilities open to industry by exploring the feasibility and technical problems of advanced concepts and designs and of ways to increase productivity. Development of new products from this information would remain the responsibility of private enterprise. The major question relating to the value of the program is: Will the quality and relevance of the work supplied by the program be greater than the quality and relevance of the work the same resources would have done in the laboratories of private companies? The analysis of the preceding section suggests that it indeed should have a higher marginal value. But this will not be the case unless the program is well conceived and managed, the non-profit laboratories are competent and imaginative, and the information created by the research is relevant to industry, and industry is well informed of the research results.

As a complementary program in support of civilian technology, the Office of Technical Services (OTS) could develop much more effective program. One of the recent proposals of the Department of Commerce is for a pilot program of support of engineering extension services at the engineering colleges. The objective of the program is the strengthening of the scientific and technical competence of management and supervisory personnel in small and medium-sized firms and to bring to their attention the technological possibilities open to them. At the local level the extension program would be complemented by an expanded program of applied research on technical problems of relevance to the industry of the state or region. The program would include both experimentation and demonstration under pilot-plant conditions at the experimentation stations or in co-operating firms.

The extension centers would be able to call on the OTS for studies and reports on problems which have general applicability or which they are unable to solve in their own facilities. OTS would contract for these reports with the organizations presently associated with OTS in the foreign-aid technical-information program. One of the major benefits of this program would be a feedback to the government of information as to the important technical problems facing American industry.

Of course, the Department of Commerce will not, and should not, have sole responsibility in the civilian technology area. The Departments of Health, Education, and Welfare, and Agriculture, the HHFA, and other government agencies clearly should continue to have prime responsibility within their own areas.

As the government's role in civilian research expands, there will be some difficult problems of co-ordination which the Bureau of the Budget and the Federal Council for Science and Technology will have to deal with.

Third, it is of major importance that the federal government, principally the Bureau of the Budget and the Office of Science and Technology, be more aware of, and concerned with, the effects of its actions on the allocation of R&D and the effects of changes in the allocation on the achievement of various national objectives. The federal government is, after all, a semi-monopolist in the field of R&D, supporting nearly 65 per cent of the total work done in this country.

In general, we economists should be delighted when a monopolist, be it a private firm or the government, does not behave as one. But in the case of R&D, there is reason to believe that the nation might be better off if the government acted more in awareness of its monopolistic position and of the fact that it takes real resources, not money, to perform R&D. Indeed, the federal government often behaves in the field of R&D as if the right hand knoweth not what the left is doing, with the results that it cannot plan effectively and that it has difficulty in carrying out its mission efficiently. There sometimes seems to be little awareness that a sharply increased NASA research budget will, for example, reduce the quantity of real R&D resources a given defense budget will hire by bidding up salaries of scientists and engineers.

Yet if this fact is not considered explicitly, defense R&D plans and the budgets which are supposed to implement them may not match. While considerable attention has been paid to the fact that the effectiveness, from the point of view of the nation, of defense R&D is dependent in part upon the competence of the small group of scientists and engineers within the federal establishment who are responsible for analyzing and monitoring the contract programs, only recently has there been clear awareness that the government's difficulty in hiring such people results, in large part, from bidding against itself.

It is not the "bidding against itself" aspect which should cause concern nor the resulting increase in salaries of scientists and engineers. Rather, it is the lack of awareness and resulting frustration of plans. In order to manage public sector R&D efficiently, the government must do a better job than it has up to now of assessing the impact of its R&D programs upon the total allocation of R&D resources.

The government must look at R&D allocation as a whole, private sector as well as public sector. Without arguing that the decision to invest so heavily in the moon race was a mistake, it can be said that there is strong evidence that the value of alternative uses for R&D resources, particularly private sector uses, were not considered. The development of effective policy with respect to the allocation of scientific and technical resources requires that natural and social scientists join in a continuing effort to appraise priorities based on economic need and technical promise against the existing allocation of resources.

V

MILITARY RESEARCH AND DEVELOPMENT

POLICY ISSUES INVOLVED IN THE CONDUCT OF MILITARY DEVELOPMENT PROGRAMS*

Burton H. Klein

THE MAIN PURPOSE of this paper is to discuss some of the issues involved in the conduct of military research and development. But before turning to policy matters, it may be a good idea to spend some time asking ourselves, "What is the essential nature of this activity?" Unless those who are interested in policy matters can come to some agreement on the kinds of uncertainties that underlie R&D decisions and, therefore, on the environment in which these decisions have to be made, discussion of policy matters hardly can be very fruitful.

While we can agree that the nature of an activity ought to be taken into account in devising policies for its effective conduct, it unfortunately is not easy to characterize this activity—"military development"—in a meaningful way. To be sure, development can be defined in terms such as "the identification, modification, and combination of feasible components and devices to provide a distinctly new application practical in terms of performance, reliability, and cost." But such a definition does not provide much of a flavor as to what development is all about.

The one characteristic that is most common to military development projects, I have no doubt, is the sharp changes in the attitudes taken toward their outcome as they progress through various stages toward completion. The point was illustrated in a talk given by General Clifton Von Kann, Director of Army Aviation:

> Let's examine the typical peaks of joy and valleys of depression in the life of an ordinary helicopter.
> First, the highest peak. It is hot out of the design concept stage and into the cocktail brochure. It will never be as good again. It is

* Any views expressed in this paper are those of the author. They should not be interpreted as reflecting the views of the RAND Corporation or the official opinion or policy of any of its governmental or private research sponsors.

the finest thing since Coca-Cola and is a panacea for any problem you care to mention.

Then comes the first valley. The engine that was to power this dream ship is found to be made of metal, weighs a few pounds, and burns fuel. The original concept did not take this into consideration. Obviously, performances will suffer.

Next peak—the mock-up. Now we can show something. You can just see by looking at it that here is a real machine. Potential customers seem to come from everywhere to take a look, make a few sage remarks, and leave the impression that they're ready to buy a few thousand.

Valley—slippage. If the target date for first flight were met, it would mean taking off without rotor blades or engine installed. Careful engineering department types are mad at sales-happy promotion types in front office for setting such an impossible goal. Front office types are mad at foot-dragging, super-meticulous engineers who want to turn this stage into a lifetime project.

Peak—first flight. There will always be a great number of people who do not understand why a helicopter flies. This includes many helicopter engineers. So naturally they are elated and fascinated when a new one actually gets airborne.

Then the lowest valley. Sometimes in the testing stage, just as real production is being geared up, there is bound to be full panic. It may stem from anything—paint peeling near the exhaust—seat covers not holding up—the horrible realization that the engine life is not eternal—anything can trigger it. But the conclusion is always the same. "Let's stop this thing now and not throw good money after bad!"

The next peak is perhaps not very high in the terms of absolute altitude, but looking back into the very low valley we have just left, it is very impressive and gratifying. A couple of our potential owners have actually bought a few articles and are trying them out. Preliminary reports indicate a few "bugs" but generally they are satisfied and pleased. There is every indication that they will order more and that the helicopters will join the ranks of the accepted standard family.

The only thing I find wrong with General Von Kann's story is that it ends a little bit too abruptly—he fails to mention the trough that often comes after the operational organization in question has bought a few of the articles and has tried them out. Sometimes this is the lowest valley in the entire scenario, and assuming that a very large development program ends as of the time a new capability is initially introduced into operational use can lead to some very mistaken ideas as to how long it actually took to complete a program and how much money was actually involved.

General Von Kann's illustration also brings out another much more significant characteristic of military development projects: not only were the attitudes taken toward his helicopter constantly changing, but so was the helicopter itself. Though the tendency depends somewhat on the ambitiousness of the advances being sought, all of the evidence I have examined strongly suggests that it is seldom indeed that the differences between the system as it was initially conceived and as it emerges from development are only of a minor sort. For example, the congressional hearings on the missile programs show that almost all the major subsystems now being used in the Atlas missiles are of a different kind from those initially planned. Moreover, the differences are considerably greater than such as exist between, say, Boeing's 707 and Douglas' DC-8. The Atlas is not, of course, a unique example among missile systems. Others also have displayed a strong tendency to end up with technological ingredients not initially intended for them. In fact, a reasonable operational definition of a missile system would be that it is a system mainly made up of components and subsystems initially developed for other missile systems.

That pronounced changes in characteristics occur even when the advances sought are not so ambitious as they have been in some of our missile programs is indicated by a study we did at RAND of six fighter plane development projects. All of these planes were designed for some particular mission— all-weather interception or ground support, for example. All of the aircraft manufacturers based their airframe design on some particular engine design furnished by one of the engine manufacturers. In almost all of these cases, there were also programs for developing specialized electronic as well as other kinds of equipment. To what extent did these plans materialize? Four out of the six planes ended up with different engines; three with different electronic systems. In order to make them satisfactory flying machines, five of the airframes had to be extensively modified; three of the fighters came out of development essentially different airplanes. Of the six airplanes, three ended up by having quite different operational roles from what was originally planned for them. Only one of the airplanes possessed the same technological ingredients and had the same kind of operational role that had originally been planned for it. This plane, however, will have a much less important role than it was intended to have, in part because another fighter, whose development was started for a very different kind of role, has already provided quite as good a capability.

Many more such examples could be cited to illustrate changes in the course of development. The question remains as to why such changes are experienced.

I

One of the main causes for change during development, we are often told, is the compulsion that engineers have for squeezing the last ounce of performance out of their systems. If anyone wants to study this tendency, a good place to look, I suggest, is the space business. Here, almost every space vehicle is specially tailored to take utmost advantage of its inherent payload lifting capability right through the development process, sometimes up to and including the day of launch. With regard to most of the military development projects I have looked into, however, I notice no substantial propensity to add refinements for performance after the system is in active development. In military programs the tendency to ask for everything usually gets so adequately expressed in the initial planning and design work that in development there is no longer a question as to whether further performance-oriented improvements ought to be added. One of the main problems in military development, then, and one of the main reasons for modifications, is simply that of getting a system into tolerable working order. To do that, often some performance has to be given up.

A frequently claimed cause of changes in configuration that occur after development starts is that the initial planning was poorly done—for if it wasn't, why, then, the many changes? If there is anything in this allegation, one might expect to find a high degree of correlation between those projects that received the most attention in the initial planning stage of development and those that turned out to be most successful. But all the evidence that I have examined indicates that the correlation, if anything, is negative. For example, in the field of radar development, those radars that were most meticulously designed were almost invariably those radars that took the longest time to get into tolerable working order and whose development cost the most; measured either in terms of time or dollars, the differences were of the order of 2 or 3 to 1.

To continue along this line of thought, consider a radar known as side-looking radar, and more specifically one that operates at a very short wave-length, say, .86 centimeters. The main virtue of this kind of radar over the conventional scanning radar is that it provides fantastically good resolution, almost approaching that of photographs. Scientists were aware that such a radar could provide much better resolution during World War II. It was known that exploitation of the shorter wave-length bands would result in improved resolution; it was also known resolution could be improved by using larger antennas. And, as a matter of fact, there were some experimental attempts during the war to develop a radar which utilized, instead of the conventional scanning antenna, long antennas mounted on the side of an airplane—hence the term "side-looking radar."

Why then didn't the staff at the Radiation Laboratory go ahead and build a practical device that would exploit the potentialities of side-looking, very-short-wave radar? Let's ask first why they didn't develop a side-looking radar with the short wave-length characteristic of present-day side-looking radars. The answer is this: While it was believed that such a radar would have very good resolution, it also was believed— on the basis of experimental evidence—that such a radar would have extremely limited range. An experimental 1.25 centimeter radar had been developed toward the end of the war which, though it gave quite remarkable resolution, had a range of only several miles. From this it was generally concluded that a radar with a wave length less than 2.0 cm would have no military utility.

Had it not been for some experiments conducted by British scientists this probably would have remained the general conclusion for some time. What their experiments proved was that the choice of 1.25 centimeters as a radar frequency was a very unfortunate choice indeed, for at frequencies slightly higher (1.8 centimeters) and slightly lower (.86 centimeters), atmospheric attenuation was far less serious than at 1.25 centimeters and other neighboring frequencies. In other words, these experiments proved that the function was not a monotonic one. Thus, although a good deal was known about radar at the time, and although a good deal more than routine engineering talent was devoted to the selection of the 1.25 centimeter frequency, a side-looking radar such as we have today wasn't built during the war simply because the necessary knowledge did not exist.

The same is true in trying to predict the performance of a particular configuration of a missile, a rocket engine, airplane, or almost any other development project. Contrary to all the allegations that have been made, I don't think that the lack of larger rocket engines has been entirely responsible for holding up our space program. What has been at least as responsible is all that has had to be discovered about making a variety of components and subsystems perform reliably.

In one sense, the radar example just quoted is not typical of the problems that come up in development; that is, whereas in the case of short wave-length radar, the "windows" came out in the form of "peaks," it is more usual for them to come out as "troughs." No matter how many factors are taken into account in the design study, there will invariably be some reactions not taken into account, and sometimes they may be very important. Because such reactions are not taken into account, radars can turn out to have very bad antenna patterns, airplanes can be prone to structural fatigue, and space vehicles to blowing up.

It is true, of course, that none of these kinds of problems is insurmountable—true, that, given enough time and effort, any system can be developed to have more or less the performance characteristics originally predicted for it. In other words, one can be fairly sure that at some finite cost, or in some finite period of time, something more or less like the specified article can be developed. The only hitch is that it might take eight years instead of the originally forecast three years, and development might well cost five or ten times as much to achieve rigidly prescribed performance and input characteristics in the final product. Even in those cases in which there is a wide measure of agreement among experts, their advice may not always turn out to be good advice or their experiences relevant.

The last sentence is illustrated by the case of a radar whose design was laid down during the last part of the war, and whose development became a very high priority matter right after the war. It was generally agreed that this radar would take no longer than two or three years to develop. The advances that it incorporated were regarded as being less ambitious than those incorporated in the wartime radars; and the same organization that had developed several radars during the war to the point of an airborne reliability of greater than 90 per cent in less than two years worked on this new radar. But a host of unanticipated problems came up, and it was much longer than the entire length of World War II before the new radar was made into a reasonably reliable instrument.

To turn to a different field: Some years ago it was believed that ramjet engines were simple devices; and even though no large ramjet engines had ever been developed, no more than a simple scaling job seemed to be involved. On this premise the Navaho missile project was started. Needless to say, the development of large ramjet engines is now considered anything but a simple, straightforward undertaking.

Or consider the case of titanium, which, contrary to all the prophesies, has not been extensively used in airplanes and missiles. The fortunate aspect of titanium is that although its weight-saving characteristics have not proved nearly as useful as was initially contemplated, its non-corrosive qualities will lead to a series of applications that hardly anyone foresaw—from marine vessels to ordinary kitchen utensils.

One final example of the experts' consensus being slightly off the mark: Immediately after World War II, it was widely believed that the turboprop engine would be far better for bomber aircraft and transport airplane applications than the ordinary jet engine, and that the development of such an engine would not be a much more difficult task than the development of an ordinary jet because, after all, the differences between the two engines were only some gears, a propeller, and a few other "simple" items. Because it was believed that the turboprop offered the only way of getting the required range, the B-52 was initially designed as a turboprop airplane. Actually, the development of the turboprop engine took years longer than it was generally supposed to take, in part because the propeller mechanism turned out to be a nasty bottleneck. On the other hand, progress in reducing the fuel consumption of the jets was much more rapid than many experts though it would be. Fortunately before development work got actively underway, a jet had been substituted.

Note that each of these examples, in its way, illustrates (1) rather substantial changes in a system between its inception and the time it could be called a useful device, and (2) that substantial revisions in delivery time and costs are commonly required. In other words, development is a business in which errors of 30 or 40 per cent can hardly be regarded as errors.

It is true, of course, that if military planners had been willing to settle for the kinds of advances that have typified commercial projects, the outcome of military development projects would be far more predictable than it has been. All that I am pointing out is that highly predictable kinds of advances and highly rapid advances are not the same thing.

The next question is, When in the development process can reasonably accurate estimates of performance, total cost and delivery time be made?

At the beginning of a development project, there is a tendency to plan as though the future course of events were known with great certainty, although a large number of unexpected events occurred in every previous program with which the planners were connected. Arguments will go on almost endlessly about details of the design that have nothing whatsoever to do with the fundamental technological problems. In estimating the procurement cost, extreme care is taken to make sure that no item, however small, is left out of account—for example, the cost of the fence that is to enclose the missile site is estimated down to a gnat's eyelash. Kill probabilities are spoken of in terms such as 83 per cent, missile accuracies in numbers more precise than measurement techniques can provide. The development schedules are so meticulously worked out as to imply that development itself is no more than a routine process of confirming them. I often wonder how *I myself* can become so absorbed in a study involving some new kinds of missiles, say, that the computations become the reality, and all that's happened to past estimates becomes as unreal as something that might have happened two hundred years ago.

Sharp improvements in estimates begin to occur only after the missile, radar, or engine is in test. This is not to say that after an aircraft engine has been first put on the test stand, or after the first three shots of a new missile, estimates of cost, performance, and development can be accurate within a margin of error of 2 per cent. On the contrary, some terrible mistakes have been made by concluding on the basis of the first few tests that an end product was practically developed. On the other hand, it is often true that some impressive facts are learned as the result of the initial tests. For example, we at RAND tried to find out why the predictions that Pratt and Whitney made for its engines almost invariably turned out to be better than the predictions made by the other engine companies. One of the reasons, we discovered, is that unlike the other companies, Pratt and Whitney almost always had a preliminary model of the engine in test before they made the prediction. Earlier, I talked about side-looking radar. When an experimental .86 centimeter side-looking radar finally was put into development, it took just ninety days to get it ready to be tested, and the cost of finding out what resolution it actually would provide came to some three million dollars. As it turned out, this was actually a much smaller amount than the government had spent on past studies.

Some time ago, we looked into the accuracy of the estimates of production costs for a number of missiles and aircraft as a function of the phase of development the system had reached when the estimates were made. What we found was that when half of the development time has elapsed in a missile or aircraft development program, estimates could be made with twice the confidence as at the beginning of the program. What it cost to get this improvement in the estimates will ordinarily be a good deal less than half of the total development cost, since the amount spent in the first half of the development period is ordinarily a good deal less than half of the total development cost.

I might point out that the evidence that I have cited reflects, among other things, the kinds of development practices that were used in the programs we studied. I myself am convinced that if the major aim in the programs had been to find out as quickly and cheaply as possible what would be involved in getting a satisfactory capability, the improvement in the estimates would have been much more rapid. In a few of the programs, this was the major aim. But in the vast majority of others, it wasn't.

So far I have been talking about the conditions under which new weapon systems are supplied. One of the two main points I have been trying to make is that initial estimates of a system's performance, reliability, and cost are subject to very large errors—errors that can be substantially eliminated only by developing systems that incorporate more modest advances than have typified military development projects. The other is that there are ways of reducing the risks in relying on initial estimates. Short of making a major decision to develop an entire system, there are commonly many kinds of tests and experiments which, if conducted, will result in decided improvements in the estimates. In short, whether or not it is so regarded, development is essentially a process of learning.

Now let us turn to the demand uncertainties that underlie development decisions. These are quite as important as the supply uncertainties, although my discussion of them will be much briefer and much more in the way of generalizations.

One of the factors that is important in determining the demand for particular weapon systems is the rate of progress in related technologies. The extraordinary progress that has been made in reducing the weight of fission and fusion weapons, for example, has had a very considerable influence on determining the preferred kinds of missiles. Progress that was made some years ago in overcoming the problems associated with large solid-fuel motors also has had a good deal of influence. Development of vertical take-off airplanes could have a good deal to do with the kinds of naval forces we will have in the future. But though developments in related fields may be very important in determining the demand for particular kinds of systems, predicting the course of these technologies is subject to the same kinds of difficulties I already have discussed. If progress in related fields had been better foreseen, some major decisions on the development and production of weapon systems would have been very different from what they were.

Another factor of obvious importance in making decisions on weapon systems is a knowledge of the demands imposed by our actual or potential enemies—of what Russia, for example, is up to in her own military programs. Once having determined who our enemies are now or might be (and a brief glance at the alliances of World War II will reveal that this in itself is not always easy), it would be nice if we could plan our own military procurement programs so that the actions we took were not sensitive to those taken by them. To a certain extent we do this, but to carry this idea very far would require a much higher level of military spending than we now have. Within anything like the current budget level, the programs for our strategic forces have to be premised on some kind of projection of Russian capabilities. We cannot hope to build enough flexibility into our own forces so that their effectiveness is not affected by whatever course of action other nations may take.

However, it should not be necessary for me to belabor the point that there is a very wide range of uncertainties, indeed, in projecting opposing forces over a period of five, ten, or fifteen years. Besides the ordinary kinds of problems involved in making intelligence estimates and intelligence projections, there are, in the case of Russia, some very special problems. Contrary to what is often assumed, the Russians, in fact, do not give the impression of a highly rational set of decision-makers carefully using the country's resources to maximize

some well-thought-out set of objectives. The strategic notions
in back of their planning are at best often very difficult to
understand, as are many of their weapon-systems choices.

All things considered, it is clear that the factors influencing
the demand for new weapon systems are no easier to predict
than those influencing the conditions on which they will be
supplied.

II

There are two main implications of the foregoing for R&D
policy decisions.

First, I think it is important that the government should be
devoting a very significant proportion of its R&D expenditures
to research and development activities falling outside the
major weapon-systems programs. I have in mind here expenditures, not only on basic research, but also on those activities
directed to experimenting with new techniques and to obtaining measurements. I stress experimental activities because one
of the most important prerequisites to rapid technological
progress is a very considerable willingness to try out new
ideas. Very seldom indeed have studies alone led to the decision to go ahead with the development of a major technological advance. In fact, in many cases the effect of
conducting long, drawn-out "scientific" investigations has been
to dampen enthusiasm for trying out a really good idea.

Beginning in the late 1920's, for example, almost every
study that was made of the jet engine came to dimmer conclusions on the feasibility and value of a jet engine than the
study preceding it. Shortly before World War II, a study
group composed of some very distinguished American scientists proved more conclusively than anyone had before that
the idea didn't make any sense. Shortly thereafter, the British
let us in on their wartime secrets, and one of the U. S.
engine companies that had earlier debunked the idea became
the leader in developing the jet engine in this country. An

experimental engine had been developed in Britain only because a British investment company decided a jet-powered airplane would have an enormous advantage for carrying airmail. It is of interest to note that the amount the company risked in demonstrating the feasibility of the jet engine came to something like twenty or twenty-five thousand dollars. This, essentially, is the amount scientific committees spent nearly ten years arguing about.

I do not regard the only purpose of a large program in basic research and exploratory development to be the discovery of strange new techniques. As I tried to point out earlier, the strategic uncertainties facing this country are so large that it would be extremely costly indeed to insure ourselves against all reasonable contingencies in our weapon systems programs. A much less expensive method of buying flexibility—of buying a capability to adapt our weapons programs to the actual strategic situation quickly—is to develop a large menu of technology. In saying this I am not suggesting that we should attempt to carry the development of components so far that weapon systems could be assembled from previously developed components with no technical risks involved. It is true that experimental projects often have been carried too far—that too much money has been spent on them before deciding which, if any, systems will use them. But one of the often-suggested cures for that problem—making decisions on the basis of paper studies—is not a well-advised cure.

If one of the main purposes of these research and development activities is to insure against strategic uncertainties, a very significant part of the research effort should *not* be directed to work which is ordinarily regarded as extending the frontiers of technology. In fact, I personally believe that this country is not doing nearly enough R&D work on kinds of techniques that do not get into the headlines. Even though the less exotic techniques often promise to be of very considerable military value, it's hard to drum up enthusiasm for them.

A second major implication of the nature of military R&D, which experience strongly suggests—at least to me—concerns the kind of strategy that should be pursued in weapon-systems programs. What it suggests is that the approach taken in systems-development projects should be a frankly experimental approach. Initially the requirements for the system should be stated in very broad terms, and considerable emphasis should be placed on keeping the system very flexible until the major technological difficulties have been resolved. To expedite their resolution, equipment should be put to test as rapidly as possible. Decisions on the best set of compromises should not be made until there is some basis for making them; specifically, these decisions should not be made until a preliminary version of the system is in test.

I would also urge that parallel approaches be taken in attempting to overcome difficult technological problems. Part of the reason for this is implicit in what I have already said. Carrying, say, three-component development projects into the initial stages of development is often likely to cost a good deal less in terms of both time and money than selecting the wrong approach initially and proceeding into a full-scale development program on the basis of that approach. Another part of the reason is that the return from putting more and more engineers on the same project or subproject is apt to be rapidly diminishing. Typically, the success of any particular subproject will depend almost entirely on a relatively few individuals. Give these individuals more and more people to supervise and all that you will have accomplished is to substitute complexity for ingenuity. Once you have three hundred instead of fifty engineers on a fighter-plane project, for example, a devilishly complicated device is the price that you have to pay in order to allow all those people to express themselves.

Finally, I want to say something about the obstacles in getting R&D policies more oriented toward the directions I have indicated. The one that has been given most publicity is the extensive review process that projects must go through before they are approved. Committees often impose elaborate requirements on weapon systems long before such requirements should be imposed; and in the course of satisfying all the committee members, systems are often made more complex than they need to be. Committees also constitute an enormous obstacle when it comes to getting action on any really new ideas.

But we all know that all this reviewing is not going to be stopped, or even substantially curtailed. I think that a good deal could be accomplished, however, by making the reviewing process reflect the kind of decision being reviewed. The kind of review that is appropriate before a weapon-system project is started is very different from the kind required when development has been carried far enough that detailed considerations are really worth arguing about. And the kind of review that is appropriate for experimental projects not likely to cost more than a few million dollars is certainly very different from that appropriate for major systems projects likely to cost hundreds of millions. But the way the decision-making machinery works at present low- and high-cost risks are often regarded in the same way.

A second major obstacle to getting policies that will make for more rapid progress in R&D is, I think, the widespread belief that in minimizing the total amount of time required to get a system ready for operational use, production problems are likely to prove a more serious constraint than research and development problems. The belief that production problems are likely to be the dominant problems leads to the initiation of large-scale production preparation early in a development program, even at the expense of minimizing the program's flexibility. Moreover, initiating programs in this way is so costly that the number of options that can be carried into development is substantially smaller than it could be if the programs were initiated on a different basis.

As I have said, this belief is very widely accepted; I myself, however, have seen very little evidence that production problems are a serious constraint on the time required to get a system into operational use. An examination that we made of some twenty development programs failed to disclose that those begun on the basis of very large production preparations furnished operational systems sooner than those that were not so begun. Moreover, I don't know of a single program in which the dominant problems turned out to be production, not technical problems.

But there is a more fundamental objection to making minimal procurement lead times a dominant objective in research and development policies. It is simply that given the uncertainties that exist both in the supply and in the demand conditions, such a policy will not lead to an efficient allocation of the research and development budget. If the military research and development programs had been entirely concentrated on those systems that were regarded as the favorite choices ten years ago, we would not be in a very good strategic position today.

There is, in addition, a more deep-rooted obstacle in the tendency present not only in the Defense Department but also, I suspect, in all large organizations to overestimate the costs of flexibility and to underestimate its benefits.

At least two kinds of flexibility are relevant here. First, there is the type of flexibility that is built into military forces so they can handle a wide range of contingencies—Type I flexibility if you will. There are many matters likely to remain just as uncertain after the forces are built—for example, how a war might get started—as they are today; and Type I flexibility buys insurance against the kinds of uncertainties that are likely to remain uncertainties. It is the type of flexibility that Stigler had in mind as he wrote his famous article on what kind of a plant to build when the demand for a product is very uncertain.

Type II flexibility, on the other hand, attempts to reduce the uncertainties confronting the decision-maker by buying information on competing development alternatives. It is premised on the assumption that some of our resources can be used to reduce these uncertainties before military forces are actually procured and put on the line, that the greater knowledge attained by comparing development alternatives will contribute directly to widening the range of alternatives available and to reducing the number of uncertainties confronting those responsible for using our Type I flexibility. Recently, increasing attention has been focussed on measures that would result in more Type I flexibility, but I have the feeling that still far too little attention is being given to flexibility in the development process itself.

The reasons that far too little Type II flexibility is purchased—aside from a development philosophy which results in large technical as well as financial commitments very early in the game—are, as I have suggested, that its costs are typi-

cally overestimated (in time as well as in dollars), and that its
benefits are typically underestimated. While lower-echelon
organizations sometimes underestimate the costs of program
changes, my observations indicate that upper echelons almost
invariably overestimate them. Often the costs of making any
changes in a particular configuration are made to seem astronomical, even before a single piece of metal has been bent.
The benefits of flexibility are underestimated typically because the range of contingencies the decision-makers regard
as reasonable is much smaller than the range that should be
taken into account. Whether or not large size itself makes the
tendency inevitable, I suggest that large organizations are
commonly highly intolerant of ambiguity.

Finally, another major obstacle to the conditions that would
make for more rapid progress in our military capabilities is
our system of incentives. In the past, the method used for
rewarding defense contractors has made the reward more or
less independent of their performance. At the present time,
incentive contracts are being substituted for cost-plus contracts in an attempt to rectify this situation. But I wonder
whether the incentives embodied in these contracts will be
strong enough to make a real difference in contractors'
behavior. If the government wants to impose a much stronger
system of incentives, it should insist that prototype models
be built before full-scale development contracts are awarded,
and that production contracts will not be let until the system
in question is well in hand. In other words, I suggest that
winning or losing a 500 million dollar contract might prove
a stronger incentive to most contractors than a possible variation of from 4 to 10 per cent in the profit rate of that contract.

Quite as serious a problem as that of the sellers' incentives
is the lack of a much better system of incentives on the
buyers' side of the market. Long-established rules of the game
within the Defense Department often lead to types of behavior which the uninformed may find hard to understand.
I don't mean to imply that these rules are unique to Defense,
for they prevail in many other public organizations and
agencies and are not unknown within the business and academic worlds. Each new proposal for an R&D program will,
of course, have its proponents, who will in turn naturally

strive to convince others of the virtues of their projected systems. Under the rules of the game, as I understand them, it would not be wise for the proponents of a proposed system to draw attention to the merits of other possible systems, for the latter may be used against them in higher courts. In other words, there is a pressure to surpress alternatives. Secondly, once plans have been drawn up and submitted to higher-echelon agencies, it is difficult to change them since changes might well be regarded as a sign of weakness in plan and uncertainty of will. Third, when and if the development program is started, the rules as they exist reward a strategy of getting the program underway with sufficient steam that it will be terribly difficult to stop. Economists can iterate and reiterate that past investments should not be considered in making future decisions, but they will be.

One can say, of course, that those who obey these unwritten rules of the game act irresponsibly. To do so indicates a willingness to judge them that implies the game itself is poorly understood: no individual in the organization is more responsible for the kinds of rules of the game that result in such behavior than is an individual in a corporation whose rules result in other kinds of strange behavior.

Some argue that the only way to get around these problems is to set up a centralized system for both procurement and research and development. But I myself would not want to see such a solution adopted. Without attempting to go into the reasons, let me only say that one thing that weighs heavily in my judgment is the experience of the British Ministry of Supply. Though the Ministry did very well during World War II—when there apparently was not time to get things really well organized—in the postwar period what the Ministry did to improve efficiency in the small was far overshadowed by the conservative influence it had on military research and development as a whole.

To date, very little work has been done by social scientists on the crucial problem of getting better rules of the game. But there is no problem facing the Defense Department that is more important—or more challenging—than removing these and other obstacles to a more effective set of R&D policies.

THE INTERACTION OF GOVERNMENT AND CONTRACTOR ORGANIZATIONS IN WEAPONS ACQUISITIONS

Paul W. Cherington

AT THE PRESENT TIME, the basic pattern in the United States for the acquisition of military supplies, weapons, and space systems is for the government to place major reliance upon private industry. The purpose of this paper is to examine some aspects of the relationships and interactions which are engendered by this reliance, partly for the purpose of defining the nature of these interactions and partly to comment on some of the rapid shifts which are now taking place in them.

There seems to be a good deal of misunderstanding concerning the actual nature of such relationships in various types of military acquisition; and, as a result, there is often impatience, frustration, and sometimes downright anger on the part of those who are involved in the process and of those who are interested observers of the process, such as congressmen. Without a better understanding of the fundamental nature of the several types of interactions existing between business firms and the government, many events and actions are almost inexplicable and frequently lead to the strongest suspicions that rascality, stupidity, carelessness, and deceit are the main hallmarks of the weapons-acquisition process. While there is much that should be done to improve this process, a major attack on these subsidiary symptoms is not likely to be productive of major improvement.

Military Supplies

It is important to distinguish at the outset the several levels of acquisition. The services buy in every year a substantial volume of supplies—petroleum, food, clothing, hardware, and spare parts. In large part this class of material is either "standardized" or can be rigidly described by military specifications, drawings, etc. The prescribed way of acquiring this material is by advertised bid, award of a fixed-price contract to the lowest acceptable bidder, inspection of the end product to assure conformance to specifications, and usually some form of penalty for late delivery. Although there are many special features of this type of military procurement, it is, nevertheless, close to the kind of arms-length, buyer-seller relationship that characterizes normal business. Given the focus of this conference, we may pass quickly over this class of procurement. It is sufficient merely to say that the special features surrounding government procurement of routine items have been gradually added to the process either to preclude collusion between representatives of the buyer and seller or to prevent the seller from "taking" the government. These special features have added a certain rigidity and excessive formality to the process, but they have not funda-mentally altered the essentially "market" nature of the rela-tionship. A public scandal involving the discovery of horse-shoes in casks of "beef" is likely to lead to the addition of more government inspectors in every packing-house line but no basic change in the business-government relationship takes place.

Systems Production

A substantial volume of acquisition is accounted for by the quantity production of systems and equipment. These range from the relatively simple (a rifle) to the extremely complex (a missile system, airplane, or aircraft carrier). Here the type of relationship between government and "seller" is more varied. In the case of relatively simple systems or even more complex ones (tanks, for example) that are well along in the production cycle, the relationship is close to that of supplies— firm specifications, fixed price contracts, rigid inspections, advertised bids, etc. Such model changes or improvements as the government desires to make can be identified, separately priced, and kept distinct from the basic contract. Unforesee-able contingencies can often be taken care of by special features in a fixed-price contract, as, for example, an escalation provision for wage rates or material prices. This device is common in the purchase of ships.

Yet even for relatively simple systems which are bought over a relatively long period, there begins to be a change in the straight market buyer-seller relationship as usually described. The shift is brought about primarily because of the length of time during which the relationship persists and arises from "learning" on the part of the manufacturer. Because his workers learn the best ways of turning out the system, because unique shop practices are developed to handle difficult problems, and because management gets to know preferred vendors and suppliers, a manufacturer tends to build himself into a position where, to all intents and purposes, he is a sole source. Competitors cannot hope to compete on a price basis unless the original manufacturer is greedy or unless the competitor is willing to "buy in"—losing money on the first contract in the hopes of making it up on subsequent contracts.

As a manufacturer moves into the fortunate position of being a *de facto* sole source, the relationship between him and the government takes on more and more the characteristics of an administered relationship rather than those of the market place. He gradually acquires a greater measure of freedom in his pricing; he is in a favorable position to suggest changes and improvements that may eventually amount to a new model or generation of the weapon, not subjected to the forces of competition. He knows, and the government knows, and both know that the other knows that the government cannot change sources without paying a higher price, risking delayed delivery, and perhaps risking deteriorated performances. The situation approaches more and more the traditional monopoly-monopolist situation and looks less and less like a free market. Fortunate indeed is the manufacturer who finds himself in this position. If he is competent and not too greedy, he can almost always bargain successfully with the government negotiators. He has enough people, he has data, and he has the knowledge. Unless pushed too hard, the government is in effect "locked in."

Countervailing powers of the buyer. This is not to say that the government is powerless in this type of situation. In the first place, the room for maneuver enjoyed by the manufacturer is restricted. In the second place, the government as a matter of policy may not let itself get too deeply committed to a particular manufacturer. It may put a second source in business in an effort to provide competition and hence simulate market forces. While this will probably be expensive for the government in the short run, it may be cheaper in the long run, and will also provide alternative sources against work stoppages or calamities at the original manufacturer's plant. Or the government may "break out" one or more subsystems or components and put these out for competitive bidding, thereafter furnishing them to the manufacturer as government-furnished equipment. Finally, the government has a formidable array of administrative devices it may employ. Auditing teams, special quality assurance inspectors, drawn-out negotiations, production specialists, calls for data, cost-finding teams, etc.—all can be deployed as needed. While there is no evidence that the government uses these devices as part of a deliberate campaign to harass a contractor who is moving into a position of *de facto* sole source, it is, on the other hand, probably natural that when they see that they are being "captured" by a contractor, various agencies of the buying service struggle to free themselves.

It should be pointed out here that business firms are often confronted with the same type of situation in which they become the "captives" of their suppliers. At least with respect to large companies, however, business usually has the alternative of "making" rather than "buying." This is an alternative that is typically not available to the government, both on the grounds of general policy and because the government does not, except in special situations, such as shipyards, have the facilities, workers, or management for manufacturing operations.

Increasing recognition is being given in the production area to the use of contractual devices to the manufacturer to make his interests and those of the government coincide more closely. The Office of the Secretary of Defense (OSD) has launched a campaign to use fixed-price contracts to the maximum extent in the production area. Where this is not feasible, it favors the use of some type of incentive contract in which the manufacturer is given a strong financial incentive to get costs down below a negotiated target. But whether fixed price or incentive contracts are used, a great deal depends on the data and knowledge available to the government negotiators and on their skill. One of the most impressive features about the purchasing departments of many large companies is that they are staffed with competent people to a depth that permits them to have an intimate knowledge of their suppliers' operations and costs. Government competence in this area is likely to be spread thin, thus leaving a considerable negotiating advantage with the contractor.

Development learning carry-over. With respect to the early production of large complex systems, it might seem that the inherent advantage which a manufacturer acquires as he moves down the learning curve would not apply. But typically he has a different kind of advantage, stemming from the fact that he was almost certainly the development contractor and has all the advantage of having designed and manufactured the prototypes and test articles. This has provided him with learning of a different type. It is currently being urged by some that development and production are, and should be, separate functions, performed by different companies or by different types of contractors (non-profit institutions or universities for development and private enterprise for production). This argument fails to recognize the essentially continuous process from development into early production, the substantial overlap and similarity between the two, and the essential learning that is transferable (and should be transferred) from development to initial production. Although advocates of this separation like to cite the successful case of Sidewinder, which was developed by NOTS (a government laboratory) and produced by industry, they tend to ignore the other weapons where the results achieved in terms of getting effective weapons at low cost do not support the desirability of having different types of contractors perform the two functions. It may be significant that, whereas the Army developed the successful Redstone and Jupiter in-house and had them produced by Chrysler, for the follow-on Pershing system, the Martin Company was brought in very early in the development cycle and has lived with the weapon through development and into production.

II

The Development Phase

For present purposes, primary attention must be directed to the development phase of the acquisition cycle. The word "development" has been widely and loosely used, but as we shall use it here it means the experimentation, testing, and integrating of a variety of components and subsystems into a new weapon system. The word denotes that the great bulk of the weapon's subsystems and components are within the art at the outset of the program, that there are few if any things yet to be discovered, although a great deal of design, applications, engineering, and testing undoubtedly remain. The development phase is bordered by quantity production for inventory, on the one hand, and by applied research (of components or subsystems) and program definition, on the other hand. The development phase does include, however, the production of test articles. And for many systems, test quantities are large and inventory quantities quite restricted.

A major difficulty with many past development efforts is that the system at which they were aimed was imperfectly defined either as to purpose (mission) or general configuration. In several instances, a considerable number of unknown or inadequately known elements of the final system were specified, calling for extensive applied research concurrently with the development effort. To the extent that these applied research areas frequently involved uncertainty and risk of failure, they made the over-all development program risky and extremely expensive. It seems to be generally agreed now that development should not be undertaken until the great bulk of applied research has been successfully completed and the feasibility of the components confirmed with considerable assurance. In this connection, the Director of Defense Research and Engineering is increasingly imposing hold-backs on development funds until feasibility has been established and the program defined.

Sharp criticisms are frequently leveled against some past programs because they were put into development without adequate definition. But in making these criticisms, it is necessary to differentiate and distinguish the urgency of the need for the system and to equate urgency with the risk of failure due to incomplete applied research or lack of program definition. If the system is urgently needed (the case of some ballistic missiles), it may well be worth the risk to initiate development before complete definition is achieved. But such an action must recognize the inherent risks, and attempts must be made to minimize such risks through an extensive concurrently applied research program.

Predevelopment relations. In terms of government-contractor relations, the development phase formally starts out like a routine procurement of military supplies—preliminary solicitation of interest in the program, invitation to bid, bidders conference, bids, selection of a limited number of winners, design and definition-study contracts, selection of a final winner. These formal steps are more complex than for the supply of breakfast food, but their main distinguishing feature is the relatively little weight given to cost or price, whereas this factor is a major feature in routine supply. Until recently almost all development contracts have been of a CPFF (cost plus fixed fee) variety so that whatever the cost figures submitted in proposals, the cost target and fee were essentially arrived at through later negotiation. In the last analysis the cost of the program was typically well above both the estimate in the proposal and, for that matter, above the negotiated target price. This overage has two sources: changes in scope and poor cost estimating.

But while the initial formal steps leading to a development contract may appear similar to those involved in routine procurement, there is considerable activity beneath the blankets that is not part of the formal process but which, in fact, is largely determinative of the outcome. In theory the several services develop requirements for new weapons independently of contractors. Actually new weapon requirements sometimes originate with contractors and in most cases are heavily influenced by ideas, data, and technological advice from contractors. In most cases failure by the contractor to participate in this prerequirement study phase virtually precludes him from winning the development contract award. If he has not participated, he is not fully aware of the government's wishes nor with the details of the technology which can meet the requirements. He is, furthermore, unaware of the various trade-offs that can be made within the system. Some of these involve trade-offs among time, cost, and performance. Some involve alternative ways of meeting specific performance characteristics that have been laid down.

The activities of contractors in this prerequirement stage have, of course, their counterpart in marketing of industrial products. Especially for new industrial goods, equipment, and processes, a good deal of marketing effort must be directed toward convincing the buyer that he has a requirement for the item. Tire companies must be persuaded that nylon cord is superior to rayon. Paper companies must be persuaded that a system of gauges and controls introduced into the production line will so improve quality or reduce wastage as to be worthwhile, etc. But compared to the informal government-business relations existing in the predevelopment stage, industrial marketers have a comparatively easy road.

In the first place, it is extremely difficult, in the case of weapons, to determine the real centers of decision-making and the true path by which decisions are finalized. Are new requirements originated by operations personnel, by the scientific-engineering development community within the service, or by an outside source? Who is really behind the new requirement, and who is against it? What programs or incipient programs are in conflict or competition? It is safe to say that of the major weapon systems in the present U.S. arsenal, each had a somewhat different origin and a different route by which it became an approved requirement and program. A large bomber was heavily influenced by the wishes and demands of the Strategic Air Command. A large missile was forced through by the scientific-engineering development community in the service over the indifference of the user-operating personnel. For a while within one service, it was virtually impossible to "sell" a new tactical weapon system. Today tactical weapons, especially those designed for warfare in primitive countries, are more fashionable.

Generalities in this area are dangerous, but it is perhaps safe to conclude that support from influential operations-user personnel is important. If, instead of support, there is active opposition, the chances of establishing a requirement are considerably diminished. In that event, there must be the strong unswerving support from the development community for the requirement. For the outside contractor interested in "selling" a new requirement, the problem is complicated by the fact that these several groups are far from unified. There are several kinds of operators-users—carrier operators, submarine operators, and anti-submarine operators. There are also several kinds of developers—missile developers, electronics, aircraft, etc., as well as numerous subspecies of each kind. Finally there is a long ladder to climb from field office or laboratory, up through intermediate commands, to service headquarters and on into the OSD level. No one, so far as is known, has plotted out all of these interests and groups in matrix form, but it would certainly require a very large piece of paper.

Nor would a matrix of government groups and interests, no matter how detailed or complete, tell the full story. For the several levels and types of groups are constantly seeking and obtaining outside support for their particular requirement or program. Air-defense advocates, for example, got major support from a series of "summer studies" conducted in the Boston area and spearheaded by MIT. Another summer study Project Nobska—gave a major impetus to underseas and anti-submarine warfare. The composition of activities such as this typically involves some combination of military, contractor, and academic personnel. Another source of outside support is the scientific advisory panel or board, usually composed of academic and contractor personnel.

Finally, in many instances the government interest groups use contractors for outside support. They are especially useful in jumping vertical channels of command. The head of a government research laboratory or office usually cannot communicate with the chief of staff directly. On the other hand, the president of Company X can and does. An exciting new development or concept can probably be passed upstream more quickly via this outside channel than by resorting to the five, six, or seven-rung ladder provided by the official organization chart.

In his attempts to inject himself effectively into this web of predevelopment maneuvers, the intelligent and competent weapons contractor inevitably drops his role of an arms-length bidder for the eventual development contract. He, and a handful of competitors, have worked on an intimate day-to-day basis with the government groups seeking the establishment of the requirement. He is intimately familiar with who is for, and who is opposed or lukewarm to, the proposed system. He knows what the major trade-offs are and the major risks in various approaches. Inevitably he enters the "competition" with a major head start over those who may receive an invitation, attend a bidders' conference, and prepare a *de novo* proposal in sixty days. The services often boast that eighty, say, companies showed an interest in ("competed for") a new system. But, in fact, nothing like this number are really potential bidders. For a major system, it is rare to have more than half a dozen serious proposals. Considering that the drawing up of a proposal (for a large system) may cost from a few hundred thousand to over a million dollars, the reason why so few decide to run the race is not difficult to understand.

Source selection for development. One of the most inscrutable aspects of the weapons-acquisition process is source selection. The requirement for the system has been established, the long list of interested firms has been screened and narrowed to a handful (almost certainly less than ten and probably four, five, or six). Now comes the moment of truth, the selection of the development contractor. Since, as we have seen, the development contractor will almost certainly be the production contractor, too, the source-selection process is determinative of a relationship which is likely to persist for a decade or more, assuming that the weapon is successfully developed and is put into the inventory in considerable quantity.

In recent years, two-stage source selections have had considerable vogue. Two "teams" or two contractors are selected from the screened group and are allowed to continue competing for an additional six-month to one-year period. But whether the selection is a "sudden death" or a two-stage process, its basic nature is the same. Here formalities are imposed, past informal relationships are not supposed to be in evidence. Each bidder drafts a "proposal" outlining his technical and management approach to the system. The word "outlining" is not, perhaps, the *mot juste*, for in fact the proposal on a large system is likely to consist of eight or ten volumes, each of which is one to two inches thick.

These proposals are typically studied, analyzed, and appraised by a special board or group especially selected for the task. While the process is under way, the group is kept in a sort of priest-like isolation. Fortunately for the selection boards, the exact weights which they give to various aspects of a proposal are usually not revealed, but most selection groups apparently use some kind of a point system, reflecting the major and minor criteria. In some cases the board or group may pay a visit to the contractor's facility to see for itself what is so glowingly described in the proposal. If it is unusually diligent, the group may interview the key personnel of each contractor whose résumés are included as an important part of the proposal. Woe unto the contractor who has included in his proposal a Cal. Tech. physicist who bluntly tells the visiting group that he has never heard of their Project X and that, in any event, he would much prefer to work on Project Y for the next three years.

There are at least two enigmas wrapped up in the mystery of the source-selection process. One is the real weight given to the past performance of the contractor; the other is how, and by whom, the so-called political factors are evaluated and given weight in the final evaluation process.

With respect to past performance, it is generally agreed that some contractors are better than others, not necessarily in all kinds of work, but in the handling of large system developments. Others have a spotty record, while still others have an almost untarnished record of failure. And while the awards of contracts for new systems developments are not wholly uncorrelated with past performance, still the correlation is far from perfect and some of the poor performers seem to stay around for an unnaturally long period of time. Peck and Scherer found that "exiting" from the industry was an extremely rare occurrence, and that over the past decade even the few firms that had left the ranks of systems developers were still active at the subcontracting or major-component level.

When queried about the weight given to past performance, government officials connected with source selection reply almost unanimously that considerable weight is given to this factor in source selection. Yet an examination of a limited number of specific instances indicates that past performance is given little weight, since there was a very small or non-existent range in the points "assigned" for this dimension to the leading contenders for the contract. Obviously if all bidders get an equal score, or nearly equal score on this dimension, its net weight is of little importance. Recently increasing attention is being given to this problem, not only by the services, but also by OSD.

The second enigma concerns the handling of the political considerations or "large policy questions" on source selection. National policy dictates that due consideration shall be given to small business in military contracts. But small business is almost never directly involved in development contracts for major systems. Similarly, national policy dictates that attention shall be given to distressed labor areas. From time to time, there are indications that this factor has dictated a greater measure of consideration for a bidder than he might have received on the strength of his proposal alone. And in a few cases, there is at least the suspicion that where a distressed labor area is in a crucial and doubtful state in an election year, this becomes a major determinant of award. For the rest, although there is often a great deal of political activity, it is extremely hard to prove that this is not essentially self-canceling. In any event, this type of consideration appears to be injected directly or indirectly by top-level service officials rather than by those immediately involved in the source selection.

Confronted with this type of environment in a contest which may well spell long life or, alternatively, extinction, the major systems contractors lavish enormous time, effort, and attention on the source-selection process. The proposal is drafted and redrafted. The best technical brains in the company are devoted to developing an imaginative yet believable technical plan. The latest fashions in management organization and control are described in detail in the management annex to the proposal. The résumés of personnel who are known to be particularly acceptable to the service are included. An ideal combination is a project technical director who is an MIT graduate, a deputy who is from Cal. Tech., and a program controller (the titles will vary) from the Harvard Business School.

When the deadline for submittal approaches, the several hundred pounds of documents are flown or hand-carried to the source selection group. If the opportunity is afforded, top officials of the company will participate in a briefing of the selection group. The strategy and tactics of the briefing are carefully worked out in advance so as to have the fullest impact and effectiveness.

During the actual selection process, it is usually regarded as poor form to attempt any *ex parte* approach to the immediate members of the selection group. But the same constraints do not apply to other military and civilian officials of the buying service nor to congressional personnel. It must be said, however, that much of this activity, both before and during the selection process, is clearly defensive in nature.

It may be noted here that while in the pre–source-selection period a good deal of day-to-day give and take goes on between government and contractor groups, the source-selection process itself is one of formalized, arms-length dealing. Some contractors find it difficult to make this rapid transition gracefully.

III

Contract Negotiation

Once the "winner" is selected, the balance of power begins to shift imperceptibly from the government to the contractor. Unless the government is willing to admit that it has selected unwisely, it is virtually tied to the selected contractor. And in the negotiation which follows selection and leads up to a definitive contract, the contractor tends increasingly to have the trump card of detailed knowledge of his organization and its costs and capabilities. Except in rare cases, the costs and prices set forth in the proposal are not the basis for the negotiation and may not even become the starting point for such negotiations. Considerable time may have elapsed between proposal costs and contracts costs. Changes may have been made in the system. It is usually to the advantage of the contractor to do the pricing *de novo,* on a higher level. For in cost-type contracts, the negotiated target is the basis for the fee. If, during the negotiation, the contractor feels that he cannot for the time being get any more from the government, he may settle for what he regards as an inadequate cost base in the expectation that funded changes in the scope of the contract (on which a fee is paid) will bridge the gap to reality.

In truth it must be admitted that in some past cases, the government and the contractor organizations have faced up to the true costs of the system for the first time in the contract negotiation. If these costs had been explicitly set forth in advance of program approval, the system might never have been launched at all, or at least not in the year in question.

The government has increasingly discovered over the years that it must enter contract negotiations well armed with data, cost estimates, and timetables. To some extent the inability of the government to negotiate closely has led to the current drive for incentive contracts even for development contracts. One recent incentive contract has been negotiated in which the major incentive to the contractor is to keep a satellite in orbit successfully for specified periods of time. Two years ago, this project would have been covered by a CPFF contract. There is considerable room for believing that artfully designed and vigorously negotiated incentive contracts will force contractors to better performance than has characterized many past systems. Yet it must be recognized that in large part the effectiveness of incentive contracts depends on the contract negotiation and the targets and criteria thereby established. And it is at least questionable whether the government will ever be able to enter into a post-award negotiation in as strong a position as the contractor. Recent trends call for the submission of an increasing amount of data and information from contractors prior to the negotiation and prior to the award. Especially where two-stage contracting has been employed, and there are still two competitors involved, such information can be especially useful for a tight negotiation.

Project Management

Once work on the development program is under way, the basic nature of weapons acquisition as an administrative, rather than a market, process becomes especially clear. Numerous technical decisions must be made concerning details and, perhaps, major components of the system. A detailed test program must be developed. Make-or-buy programs must be implemented and subcontractors chosen. Increasingly, under cost contracts, the government is playing not only a formal directive role in these decisions but a substantive directive role as well. And the reason for this increased role lies in the fact that too often in the past the contractor, when left to his own devices, has reached decisions which proved to be counter to the interests of the government. Under a cost contract, the government either had to pay or terminate the contract. And the latter alternative was used only in the most extreme cases.

The past experience of the three services in the area of project management has varied. But primarily it was in the field of large missile systems that each service developed increasingly tight project monitoring or management over its contractors. The Navy's Special Project Office exercised the closest type of control and decision-making authority over the Polaris contractors. In the Atlas program, the Air Force retained a special contractor to do the systems-engineering job; and this contractor, under general supervision of the Air Force, essentially directed the efforts of the hardware contractors. Whereas the Army Ballistic Missile Agency (and its predecessors) conducted the bulk of its own development work on its early missiles, when the Pershing system came along, it moved toward a program of reliance on industry for development but, nevertheless, maintained close surveillance over the Pershing contractors. Since the advent of Mr.

McNamara's administration of OSD, an increasing volume of contractor controls, measurements, and evaluations have been developed and imposed. Their efficacy is yet to be fully tested, but they leave no doubt that the development process is to be administered, and closely so.

Contractor reaction. Quite naturally, the reaction of the contractors to a full recognition that weapons development is an administrative process, and is to be controlled as such, has been something less than jubilant. Yet the arguments against having controls over an administered function, especially when voiced by businessmen, are scarcely credible. And the past evidence on the results of lack of control is too clear to argue against very hard. Furthermore, it is always dangerous to quarrel too vociferously with your best source of future business. As a result, although there is considerable muttering on the part of contractors, the main substantive argument that is usually heard against the increased control is to the effect that the government is duplicating what it is paying the contractors to provide—management. The risks to the contractors in this argument are so apparent that it is used sparingly. Recently the aerospace industry has retained a non-profit group to do a study of government-industry relations in weapons acquisition and, presumably, to define the optimum role of industry in the weapons-acquisition process.

Government's capability for project management. Even if it is granted that the government *should* treat the development process as one requiring extensive administrative surveillance of the on-going contractor's conduct, there remains the question of whether it has the capability of exercising this surveillance in an effective manner. The Air Force has supplemented its own capability in this area by causing the creation of a number of non-profit corporations to provide systems engineering and technical advice to its program offices. The Army has established a series of project offices designed to exercise closer control and surveillance over its larger and more important systems. These offices will continue to rely heavily on Army arsenals and laboratories for technical advice and assistance. The Navy also relies primarily on in-house talent, plus a few university-controlled laboratories. A new departure in the space area is the retention by NASA and the Air Force of profit-making hardware companies to furnish systems engineering and technical advice. These companies are thereupon precluded from being candidates for development or production contracts on the system involved.

Trends. Thus the current trends in the development phase of weapons acquisition are two-fold—first, closer administration and surveillance of contractor decisions and efforts, and, second, contractual incentives to make the contractor perform in accordance with the interests and wishes of the government. Both recognize that the weapons-acquisition process in the development phase is not a market operation but an administrative process. Although these two approaches might seem to be mutually exclusive, there is some reason to believe that they may both be employed simultaneously on a given contract, to the undoubted discomfort of the contractor.

Still another avenue open to the government, to which attention is only beginning to be given, is the greater use of evaluations of past contractor performance for the purpose of making source selections. In systems development the past is not always prologue, but it is probably a better guide to future performance than primary reliance on a proposal.

Between the greater use of administrative controls and of incentive contracts, together with the possible use of contractor past-performance evaluations as a form of competitive incentive, the relationships and interactions of business and government in the development phase of weapons acquisition is changing. The objectives of the change are clear and also clearly desirable: to obtain the development of better weapons, more cheaply and faster. Whether the means for achieving these objectives will prove effective remains to be seen. But one thing is clear—the impact on development contractors is likely to be severe.

Comment on Part V Papers

J. Stefan Dupré

ONLY RECENTLY have social scientists begun to focus their attention on the economic, political, and administrative implications of military research and development. The path-breaking studies undertaken by the RAND Corporation and the Harvard Weapons Acquisition Project have now become available and will undoubtedly contribute much toward stimulating further research and analysis, as will such events as this conference. The conceptual and practical issues raised by military research and development will surely provide fertile ground for analysis for quite some time to come. Reflecting the relatively primitive state of knowledge at present, in addition to the author's own shortcomings, this brief paper is an attempt to offer a few elementary remarks on some institutional problems of military research and development, especially as they arise in the field of government-business relations.

Perhaps the most striking thing about the process whereby technologically sophisticated weapons are procured is the extent to which it involves a juxtaposition of the traditional functions of government and industry. Through the use of cost-reimbursement contracts, the government assumes the classic entrepreneurial role of financial risk-taker. Conversely, in so far as industrial contractors, through their know-how and research capabilities, sometimes originate new weapon possibilities, they have a substantial impact on the shaping of military and strategic policies and thereby impinge upon the traditionally exclusive domain of government. Furthermore, in the absence of the automatic checks of the market mechanism, government and business jointly share administrative responsibilities for the supervision of subcontractors, the implementation of small-business policies, and the like.

In sum, the present procurement pattern for advanced weapon systems involves a complex realignment of the classic functions of the public and private spheres. It has brought about a new and peculiar partnership between business and government, a partnership whose many ramifications are still being discovered.

The strengths of this partnership deserve emphasis. As to tangible assets, the partnership has had the dual virtue of taking full advantage of the flexibility and technical capacity of industry while bypassing some of the principal disadvantages associated with government work—low pay and civil-service red tape. It has also stimulated a degree of innovation in the civilian economy and, perhaps even more important, educated business firms to the value of industrial research and the techniques for its management. At the intangible level, the partnership draws important support to the extent that it ties in with the vague but powerful American consensus over the value of free enterprise. These factors provide sturdy ground for the assertion that the partnership, at least in its broad outlines, will remain substantially unaltered so long as the demands of national security are high, and so long as it continues to meet its principal objective, that of producing a formidable array of highly advanced weapons.

Where the partnership is open to criticism is in the methods through which it reaches its goal. While the quality and range of weapons which it has placed in the hands of the user services have so far kept the free world fully competitive in the cold war, there is increasing worry over the level of costs and noticeable chafing at the length of lead times. Possibly the most contentious point of criticism is over the major question of the extent to which, in letting systems contracts, the government may commit itself to a weapon and a business firm before sufficient data exist to make informed choices among alternative technologies. The nature of the controversy over this point comes to light in the conflicting stands taken by the RAND experts, represented in this book by Burton Klein, and the Harvard Weapons Acquisition Group, whose director is Paul Cherington.

After studying a number of weapons systems, both groups discovered unquestionable evidence of significant time and cost overruns. But while the Harvard group traces most of the difficulties to the government's ability as a buyer, to techniques of industrial control and decision-making, and to business incentives, the RAND studies call into serious question the entire systems approach to the procurement of weapons.

In the managerial sense, the systems approach consists ideally in placing responsibility for the development, testing, evaluation, final assembly, and production of a weapon, with all its components, in the hands of a single prime contractor or a small team of associate contractors. As it is generally understood, the rationale for this approach is that all the steps involved overlap and hence that substantial time savings will result from integrating or telescoping the spectrum that begins with development and ends in production. As an alternative to this approach, the RAND group would emphasize the sequential development of weapon components, using multiple approaches where necessary, and postpone the integration of the components until the major problems inherent in technological novelty have been solved.

From one perspective, the differences between the RAND and the Harvard experts can be chalked up to semantic difficulties and to the fact that their evidence is based on an examination of different weapons projects. The RAND concept of "development" may well include certain steps that the Harvard group would label "applied research." There is also evidence that the systems projects studied by RAND included both more complicated weapons and more instances of failure, while the Harvard projects enjoyed higher priority and required less substantial advances in the state of the art, thereby showing the systems approach in a more favorable light. In general, however, the RAND-Harvard debate raises a question with extremely important implications for weapons development. This question concerns the rate at which new knowledge is accumulated in the development process. If this rate is such that substantial uncertainty prevails until a proposed weapon approaches the assembly stage, then there is little alternative to the systems method of financing the integrated development of the entire weapon until the final outcome, which may involve the drastic expense of scrapping the entire weapon, or the appreciable cost of painfully backtracking to redevelop malfunctioning components. On the other hand, if the rate is such that uncertainties dwindle fairly early in the development process, multiple and sequential approaches to the engineering of components offer the possibility of substantial dollar savings and reduced lead times.

The respective merits of the RAND and Harvard cases are probably not something about which informed judgments can be made at this time. But the implications of these viewpoints for public policy are enormous. The principal worry which presently concerns critics of the government-business partnership for research and development is focused on the extent to which business may have become the dominant partner to the detriment of the public interest. If the RAND appraisal is correct, then there is much room for the government to parcel out development projects among a variety of firms and non-profit institutions, thereby promoting competition at that level while gaining the knowledge that subsequently makes possible rigid assessment of production performance and fixed price contracts. Conversely, if the Harvard conclusions are right, then far less can be done to counterbalance the predominance of industry.

The extent to which business has perhaps come to dominate the weapons-acquisition process is worth close consideration, and is the subject of growing consternation, not only in the Department of Defense, but at the congressional and presidential levels as well. In the absence of the controls of the market mechanism, essentially three checks remain against business abuse. The first is the government administration involved in negotiating contracts and supervising the contractor. The second is a defense firm's incentive to keep its manpower and facilities busy and to maintain profits at a satisfactory level. The third involves the risk that poor performance will damage company reputation with the military departments. The reliability of each is open to serious question. Because of low pay and other disadvantages of public employment, the government lacks sufficient numbers of qualified personnel to offer a strong counterbalance to the trained and experienced representatives of industry. Next, a firm's internal incentive to keep its facilities busy and profits up is extremely ambiguous. When costs are reimbursed and fixed fees can be renegotiated, there are strong temptations to stretch out a project by "gold-plating," i.e., adding unnecessarily complex features and refinements to a weapon. While the use of so-called incentive, as opposed to CPFF, contracts offers a partial corrective, it is well to bear in mind that the use of incentive contracts is directly related to the government's negotiating skill. This type of contract gives the firm every temptation to negotiate inflated target costs. Finally, the reputation risks assumed by contractors do not constitute a life-and-death proposition. The national security need to maintain an industrial mobilization base, together with political and socioeconomic pressures, insure that weapons projects will be spread about without strict attention to past performance.

What remedies have been proposed to counteract these weaknesses? They range from the relatively minor to the more drastic, from the self-evident to the more complex. Perhaps the most obvious approach would be to promote a marked amelioration in the quantity and quality of government negotiating and supervisory personnel. Clearly, improving the quality of government officials is a *sine qua non* to redressing the balance between business and government. In similar vein, measures that would seek to increase non-business capacity for research and development deserve close consideration. Here, as the Budget Bureau contends in a 1962 report, not only is the strengthening of the government's intramural facilities appropriate, but the continuing support of non-profit institutions and the possible creation of a limited number of public corporations deserve attention. A more extreme suggestion would envisage the conversion of certain major weapons contractors into mixed public-private corporations. The above are by way of illustrating the institutional range of alternatives that lies open. At a more minor level, other reforms are embodied in OSD's present attempt to make greater use of incentive contracts, and by the growing affinity of the military departments for business firms or non-profit institutions which can be used as technical directors or advisors.

However, the general question of redressing the balance between government and business in military research and development hinges closely on the basic method through which weapons are procured. As long as the systems approach continues to predominate, the effectiveness of measures that would seek to counteract the present dominance of major contractors, short of such drastic steps as are envisaged in their conversion to public or semi-public corporations, will be severely limited. In so far as the systems approach involves commitments at the early stages of development, little can be done to reduce the extent of cost reimbursement contracting, which necessarily accompanies a state of technological uncertainty. Furthermore, the possibility of increasing non-business development capacity is severely limited if development remains integrated with production.

That there is much to be said in favor of the systems approach there can be no doubt. Likewise, that the government-business partnership in its present configuration has managed to work as well as it has is a tribute to the integrity of certain businessmen, the hard work of some underpaid government personnel and the effectiveness of such ever-present threats as congressional investigations, anti-trust actions, and the like. The extent to which reform is desirable is a matter of degree, not of revolution. What is needed involves increasing the attractiveness of government service, breaking away from overemphasis on the systems approach, restoring market incentives wherever possible, and promoting the growth of development capacity in government, non-profit institutions, and possibly public corporations in order to provide a yardstick for evaluating the work that will continue to be performed by business.

VI

INTERNATIONAL COLLABORATION

U.S.–EURATOM COLLABORATION: AN EXPERIMENT IN INTERNATIONAL RESEARCH AND DEVELOPMENT

Philip Mullenbach

IN RECENT MONTHS many American economists and business-men have been suddenly challenged by the prospect of an enlarged Common Market, by more intense trade competition between western Europe and the United States, and by former President Kennedy's restrained projection of a possible future "partnership" with western Europe. These events should have been no surprise. Most economists should have been sensitive to the accelerating speed with which strong political ideals looking toward unification have led to new economic institutions in that part of the Atlantic community. Euratom,[1] one of these supranational agencies, holds special interest because it is deeply involved in ramified atomic research and development.

Had one been watching Euratom, he would have seen, for example, that policy leaders in the United Kingdom had substantially concluded as early as 1958—years before in-tense negotiations on her membership in the Common Market —that full-fledged membership in Euratom was a necessity if she was to fulfill her nuclear marketing ambitions on the Continent. One would also have been aware that United State collaboration with the "Six"[2] in research and develop-ment of nuclear energy had already revealed both the prob-

---

[1] Details of the joint agreement between the United States and Euratom may be found in: Joint Comm. on Atomic Energy, *Proposed Euratom Agreements* (with associated documents and materials), 85th Cong., 2nd Sess. (1958); *Hearings on Proposed Euratom Agreements before the Joint Committee on Atomic Energy,* 85th Cong., 2nd Sess. (1958); and *Hearings on Agreements for Co-operation with Euratom before the Subcommittee on Agreements for Co-operation of the Joint Committee on Atomic Energy,* 86th Cong., 1st Sess. (1959).

[2] Euratom is a contraction of European Atomic Energy Community, consisting of the "Six"—Belgium, France, West Germany, Italy, Luxem-bourg, and the Netherlands. Euratom was formed on January 1, 1958.

lems and opportunities implied by former President Kennedy's reference to the responsibilities of future "partnership." The pace of today's science and technology is, indeed, compelling equally rapid development of new institutional arrangements — political and economic — like Euratom, the European Nuclear Energy Agency, and the International Atomic Energy Agency.

In choosing to comment on U.S.–Euratom collaboration in nuclear-power development, my intention is to emphasize three economic aspects: the respective objectives the United States and the Six have been trying, not altogether successfully, to achieve; the economic and institutional obstacles that have confronted these joint efforts; and, finally, the economic lessons the first five years' experience may suggest for the next phase of collaboration in research and development. Necessarily, this ignores the extremely important Euratom co-operation with other agencies, with other countries, and with major companies and research institutions within the Six.

OBJECTIVES

Fortunately, there has been clear understanding among the Six, on the one hand, and the United States, on the other, with respect to the major goals of Euratom and the joint program of co-operation. The original broad objective of Euratom was to take one additional step toward economic integration in western Europe, support of which has been a bipartisan aspect of American foreign policy throughout most of the postwar period.[3] Economic integration of western Europe—through the institutions of the Coal and Steel Community, the Common Market, and Euratom, and possibly still

---

[3] Max Kohnstamm, "Europe and Atoms for Power," an address to Twelfth American Assembly, in *Atoms for Power: United States Policy in Atomic Energy Development* (New York, 1957). Also, Ben T. Moore, *Euratom—The American Interest in the European Atomic Energy Community* (New York, 1958).

others to come—is accepted as the principal route to political confederation and, hopefully, a peaceful "United States of Europe." (Economists recognize that since political and institutional motivation is dominant, there is danger that economic evaluation of programs and objectives will appear academic. Yet such evaluation has become more, rather than less, pertinent. It explains why joint undertakings have proved less productive than expected, and it can make a contribution to the future direction of research and development.)

The Euratom countries and the United States had different reasons in 1958 for engaging in the joint program of research and development on nuclear power. The Six were interested in establishing an atomic-energy industry as rapidly as possible, partly because the United States, the United Kingdom, and the U.S.S.R. had already moved ahead and the Six were fearful of falling further behind in this new technology. Full and close collaboration with the United States was seen as desirable, first, to overcome national inertia by taking a large and bold approach to this new supranational institution; second, to secure American technology and "know-how" in the varied types of nuclear-power reactors being developed here; and, finally, to secure access to the supplies of enriched uranium which only the United States had in quantities sufficient for large-scale export.[4] The British technology, it may be recalled, was confined almost entirely to one type of highly capital-intensive reactor (the gas-cooled, natural uranium system), and British supplies of enriched uranium were limited. The Euratom nations, it should be emphasized, had sufficient financial resources to establish an extensive reactor development program and could secure the technology under bilateral agreements with the United States. Euratom did not need to call on U.S. help to finance the program, though Export-Import Bank lines of credit were established to finance the purchase of American equipment and materials for construction of power reactors.

The U. S. objectives in supporting the joint program were remote from those just mentioned for Euratom. In 1958, the

---

[4] *A Target for Euratom,* report submitted by Louis Armand, Franz Etzel, and Francesco Giordani at the request of the governments of Belgium, France, German Federal Republic, Italy, Luxembourg, and the Netherlands, May, 1957.

U.S. reactor development program, it should be recalled, was having difficulty getting underway. Bitter conflict between the Joint Committee on Atomic Energy and the Atomic Energy Commission had arisen over the ends and means of power-reactor development. The private- vs. public-power controversy had been aggravated as a result of actions taken by the executive office and the AEC. Estimated costs of generating nuclear power were rising instead of falling—as experience increased knowledge. Private utilities saw little merit in making investments in uneconomic machines. And the AEC, hoping that private utilities would be able to take the initiative in developing competitive nuclear power, was being compelled to provide progressively greater assistance to so-called prototype or demonstration plants. This help included research and development expenses and the waiving of rental charges on nuclear fuel leased from the government. At the same time, under the atoms-for-peace program, the AEC had pressed forward—primarily for political reasons— with numerous bilateral agreements which presupposed greater advances in power-reactor technology than had actually been achieved.[5]

In these unpropitious circumstances the joint program with Euratom appeared to offer a means of strengthening European integration and also the U.S. reactor-demonstration program—though it was not a solution to, nor a way to bypass, the numerous domestic problems that had arisen. Construction of American types of demonstration reactors in the Six would help to fill a widening gap in the domestic program. It would do so without incursion of the private- vs. public-power controversy and without involving the debilitating conflict between the Joint Committee and the AEC on domestic measures for accelerating development.[6] At the same time, American manufacturers and exporters would be

---

[5] For description of the policy controversy in the U.S. program see James L. Morrison, "Federal Support of Domestic Atomic Power Development—The Policy Issues," *Vanderbilt Law Review* (December, 1958), pp. 195–222; also, John G. Palfrey, "Atomic Energy Law in the United States," *Law and Administration, Series X, Progress in Nuclear Energy* (New York, 1959), pp. 15–46.

[6] See, for example, Harold P. Green and Alan Rosenthal, *The Joint Committee on Atomic Energy: A Study in Fusion of Government Power* (Washington, D.C., 1961).

placed in a strong position to develop—before the British
could do so—the presumably large market for nuclear equipment in the Six. There were, then, strong domestic and foreign
policy incentives for the United States to undertake heavy
commitments in support of the joint U.S.–Euratom program.

The joint program, developed in 1958 and 1959, consisted
of two closely connected parts—first, construction of several
nuclear-power reactors of different types, and, second, a joint
research and development program designed to provide "post-
construction" support of these plants. The joint power reactor
program originally contemplated construction of five prototype
reactors of so-called proven types, three to be completed by
the end of 1963 and the other two not later than the end of
1965. These were to total one million kilowatts capacity,
representing an investment of $350 million in plant and $100
million in associated research and development. However, the failure of European utilities to come forward
with proposals under the "first-round" invitation in 1959
resulted in a discouragingly slow start. As it happened,
only one reactor—the Italian SENN project which had already
gotten underway—was included by the end of 1960. Under
the "second-round" invitation, announced in September, 1961,
at least two power reactor projects are expected to be included, looking toward completion by the end of 1965. A
German project is being evaluated and a joint Belgian-French
plant has been accepted for inclusion in the joint program.
    The other part of the collaboration, the supporting ten-year
research and development program, originally was projected
on the scale of $100 million—$50 million each by Euratom
and the United States. (The joint research and development
projects are divided—the U. S. projects being undertaken with
U.S. funds in laboratories here, while the Euratom projects
are performed and funded there.) Because only one reactor

instead of five eventuated under the first-round invitation, the supporting research has been on a much smaller scale than expected. By the spring of 1962, Euratom had authorized contracts to expend $13 million and the United States had obligated only $3.7 million out of $10 million appropriated for joint research and development studies.[7] These were largely in support of the SENN project. The joint program therefore could have been described—and it was—as a "failure," considering the spacious objectives raised at the outset.

OBSTACLES

Looking back over the first five years of Euratom and the first four years of the joint U.S.–Euratom program, one has little difficulty in discerning the major obstacles to fulfilment of such a grand design. They provide point to Secretary of State Rusk's gentle understatement that "U.S.–Euratom relations have known periods of frustration" (January 11, 1962). Among the main problems confronting the joint program— and, it should be added, to some degree the first five years of Euratom—we would cite these:

Easier fuel situation. By far the most important factor was the rather sudden easing of conventional fuel shortages following the end of the 1956 Suez Crisis.[8] In brief, by the end of 1958, surplus stocks of coal and oil in western Europe had weakened one of the main economic reasons for developing competitive nuclear power with urgency. Moreover, the rich discoveries of petroleum in North Africa, now being developed "this side of Suez," loomed as the immediate alternative to coal as boiler fuel.[9] Nuclear power, it was assumed

---

[7] *Hearings on Public Works Appropriations for 1963 before a Subcommittee of the House Committee on Appropriations,* 87th Cong., 2nd Sess., 213–216 (1962). AEC testimony indicated that $9.8 million was ready for obligation or actually obligated.

[8] Organization for European Economic Cooperation, *Towards a New Energy Pattern in Europe,* report of the Energy Advisory Commission (Paris, 1960).

[9] *Oil: Recent Developments in the OEEC, 1960* (Paris, 1961).

by many policy-makers, could be left for leisurely development on a reduced scale. The eased fuel situation also raised
questions about the emphasis of development—whether short-
term or long-term objectives should dominate the choice of
reactor systems to be sponsored. Today a new aspect of this
dilemma confronts the United States and Euratom: American
water-cooled types of reactors, using enriched fuel, are believed to be on the point of becoming strictly competitive,[10]
so additional demonstration plants representing current technology are not as urgently needed as before. This is, of
course, a measure of technical success, but raises the question
whether a *joint* research and development program aimed at
short-term results may not have become obsolete. Advanced
concepts looking toward very low cost or most efficient use
of neutrons, or both, would seem now to warrant greater
emphasis. (This issue will be examined at greater length.)

Reluctant investment by utilities. As is true in the United
States, the primary initiative and responsibility for investment
in nuclear power plants rests with the managements of European electric-utility systems—whether they be privately or
publicly owned. Thus far, the experience in western Europe
has not been strikingly different from that in the United
States where, it should be noted, the proportion of public
power is much smaller. Electric utilities on both sides of
the Atlantic have been reluctant to undertake the investments
in plant necessary to achieve the pace of development originally expected. The AEC, under joint committee pressure, has
had to make progressively more generous subsidies to help
the electric utilities proceed with power reactor demonstrations. (The most recent is the provision of design costs, in
addition to research and development and waiver of fuel-use
charges.) Hindsight suggests that one of the grave miscalcu-
lations, on each side of the Atlantic, was the assumption that
electric-utility systems would be prepared to make the initial
investments in non-economic plants required for vigorous
development.[11]

---

[10] *Hearings on Public Works Appropriations for 1963*, pp. 42–43.

[11] See the testimony of former AEC Commissioner Thomas E. Murray, *Hearings on Development, Growth, and State of the Atomic Energy
Industry before the Joint Committee on Atomic Energy*, 85th Cong.,
1st Sess., Part 1 at 55 (1957).

Rising estimated costs of nuclear power. The primary reason electric-utility systems did not, and probably could not, make such investment commitments was the confusing evidence available after 1958 on the estimated costs of nuclear power and the prospects for closing the competitive gap. On the one hand, American industry and the AEC in 1957 and 1958 encouraged representatives of the Six to proceed vigorously. This was on the assumption that while the first reactors could not be competitive in western Europe, the small margin above conventional costs at the time would be a price worth paying in order to gain a fast start on a new technology. On the other hand, foreign observers and representatives of European utility systems were aware that the 1958 Geneva Conference provided rather gloomy projections of estimated nuclear power costs, particularly for the size stations suitable for western European grids (150,000 kilowatts). The easing of conventional fuel prices in 1958 and 1959 did not help nuclear power's immediate prospects—nor did the hesitant example of American managers of utility systems in undertaking no additional full-scale demonstration plants. As a consequence, the merits of building uneconomic plants seemed so dubious in the Six that the opposition of the coal industry and the reluctance of electric-utility systems to become engaged left the joint reactor program without great incentive.

Diversity of reactor types. At the time (1958 and 1959) it was not clear which reactor concepts, out of three the AEC felt were most advanced, were especially suited to western European conditions and objectives.[12] The techno-economic problem of choosing among reactor systems can only be alluded to here. In brief, Euratom representatives and utility systems seemingly had to decide whether to choose the power reactor types that were most nearly "proven" or to allow scope for more advanced, "unproven" types of longer-term interest. It was concluded that the joint program should be confined to "proven" reactors, since this was to be a "demonstration" program, not an "exploration." At least three prototype plants, including the boiling water, pressurized-water, and organic-moderated types, were expected to be built. As we have said, however, only a boiling-water reactor was

---

[12] *Hearings on Proposed Euratom Agreements,* pp. 88 ff.

covered by the joint reactor program, hence research and development contracts were confined largely to this reactor and its fuel system.

The other "proven" types of reactors are expected to be included in the second round of projects. This would seem to suggest, therefore, that the joint program has deferred the highly advanced, long-term reactors as subjects of collaboration. In doing so it is overriding the recommendations of some observers that near-term reactors be de-emphasized as economically unworthy in the new fuel situation and that the effort be shifted to systems presumably possessing greater long-term potentialities.[13] (This view assumes a degree of flexibility that the program may not have, considering its initial commitment to "proven" types.)

POLITICOECONOMIC RATIONALE

These brief comments on the obstacles to collaboration in development indicate that the central issues, or "frustrations," while essentially economic are also political or technical in character. Despite the obstacles, neither the United States nor the Euratom nations have diminished their desire to proceed with the joint program, though it is on a smaller scale. Nor have the technical problems proved any more troublesome than those appearing in the national programs of the respective countries. One of the apparent drawbacks of the joint program is the lack of challenge, since national programs have already moved well toward competitive feasibility with the reactor types being considered now. The joint program, small as it assuredly is, can do little more than supplement national programs of development. Neither the United States nor the Euratom countries have reason to rely on projects of the joint program to accomplish technical objectives that are "at the frontiers" of domestic efforts. The

---

[13] See the "McKinney Review" in *Review of the International Atomic Policies and Programs of the United States, Report to the Joint Committee on Atomic Energy*, 86th Cong. 2nd Sess., Vol. I at 73–78M (1960).

program is not intended to do so. Rather, the purpose is to share and transmit latest technology—with no strong expectation of creating new.[14]

Under these circumstances, therefore, we need to examine more carefully the underlying economic rationale of Euratom. Initially, it is desirable to dispose of certain invalid economic reasons given for Euratom to develop nuclear power. The development of nuclear-power plants in western Europe was not conceived as a "crash" alternative to Middle East oil, though some have tried to give the program that interpretation. During the height of the Suez crisis in 1956, no American or European policy-maker seriously held out the hope that nuclear power could become economically competitive soon enough (within five years) to provide a "strategic alternative" to the Middle East oil while the rich North African fields were being brought into production. But it was expected that nuclear-fueled plants might compete with oil imported from the Western Hemisphere—if access to Arabian sources were denied for any reason. (At that time, too, the importance of the Sahara discoveries was not realized.)

Second, it proved misleading for Euratom planners to have set such an extreme figure for the nuclear-power capacity that might soon be installed—15 million kilowatts by 1967, or nearly one-fifth of present capacity. There are, of course, explanations for this figure. It represented the most rapid conceivable introduction of nuclear power on the assumption that mounting energy imports would have to be stabilized not later than 1963.[15] The goal also represented one of the unfortunate by-products of excessive encouragement given to the Six in 1957. Unforeseen was the end of the fuel shortage that had prevailed in most of the postwar period and that came to a climax with the closing of the Suez Canal. Nor did the target allow for the slower pace of development in the United States. (In effect, the inconsistency of American foreign and domestic policies had come to a day of reckoning. How could we expect Euratom to pursue a vigorous demonstration program if we failed to do so at home?)

[14] See the list of ninety-two proposals for research and development work authorized by the U. S.–Euratom Joint Research and Development Board (AEC Release, E–240, July 9, 1962).

[15] *A Target for Euratom*, pp. 18–24.

Despite these questionable assumptions, there are sound long-term reasons for Euratom and the joint program to proceed with nuclear power with greater vigor than private commercial considerations alone might seem to warrant. First, there is the fairly high probability today that nuclear power in large central stations will soon (five to eight years) become an economically justifiable alternative in regions of high fuel costs, such as western Europe—as well as New England and the Pacific Coast. Indeed, the major justification for developing nuclear power is that such power plants will be commercially profitable and at the same time will provide important social and political benefits. From the point of view of the privately- or publicly-owned utility system, the economic motivation is uppermost. However, without substantial continuing governmental support and initiative here and in western Europe, it is unlikely that utility systems would be prepared to commit the resources still required to bring this major new energy source into being on a reasonable time scale—alongside coal, oil, natural gas, and water.

The second economic factor is a function of the geographical pattern of fuel prices, particularly the prices of petroleum and fuel oil used in steam generation. For whatever reason (among many one might set forth), it has long been true that energy prices in western Europe have been significantly higher than in the high-fuel-cost regions of the United States.[16] That difference, to be sure, has diminished somewhat during the last few years with the greater decline in the prices of petroleum in the Eastern Hemisphere. Agreement on the reasons for this price differential is lacking, and some observers mistakenly believe the differential does not exist any longer. Nevertheless, energy prices and the energy mix in western Europe suggest that this region provides, together with Japan, one of the most promising "demonstration platforms" for nearly full-scale nuclear-power plants.

---

[16] In particular see the cost data furnished by Euratom to Robert McKinney, indicating fuel costs before 1965 were expected to decline to 50 cents per million BTU and after 1965 to 40 cents per million BTU. These are significantly higher than fuel costs for New England and Pacific Coast steam-generating plants. See "McKinney Review," Vol. IV at 1241–42, and *Steam-Electric Plant Factors*, 1961 (Washington, D.C., 1962), Table 2.

Plants are interconnected and are large—though not as big as the 300,000-kilowatt plants planned in the United States and Great Britain. Systems are predominantly publicly owned, permitting government financing of high-cost plants. Fuel costs, as we have said, are comparatively high. Finally, for political and strategic reasons this large energy-deficient (fuel-importing) region needs an economically assured source of stably priced energy, which neither petroleum nor coal has thus far provided. For these reasons, too, competitive nuclear power would provide a ceiling on boiler-fuel prices generally—a desirable influence considering the special governmental attention given to the two chief conventional fuels (through taxation of one and subsidies for the other). These would seem to be sufficient economic reasons for introducing nuclear power in western Europe on an accelerated schedule involving a substantial measure of public assistance.

IMPLICATIONS FOR THE FUTURE

If one looks ahead, what do the lessons of this five-year experimental collaboration in development suggest for future plans and objectives? The lessons are essentially techno-economic and may be applicable only to atomic energy. They hinge, first, on the distinction between scientific research and reactor development, and, second, on the close connection that exists between the long- and short-term objectives of developing different power reactor types.

Nuclear scientists make a point of distinguishing between research and development—partly because of overlapping functions.[17] Basic research is customarily centered in educational and non-profit institutions and is aimed at new scientific knowledge, usually without consideration for its economic or other immediate effects on established institutions. In

---

[17] See, for example, Henry DeWolf Smyth, "Basic Research and Atomic Energy," Conference on the Peaceful Uses of Atomic Energy Co-sponsored by the Atomic Industrial Forums of the United States and Japan, Tokyo, May 13, 1957. He noted that science, unlike technology, is not "constantly tied to the inertia of existing industry."

contrast, development is carried on mainly by industrial and closely allied laboratories where the goal is profitable commercial application and where the prompt effects on established markets, methods, and ways of business are very important considerations. Research on nuclear energy is quite suitable to close and fruitful international collaboration. It is not as clear that reactor development can permit fruitful and close international collaboration at this stage.

Reactor development today involves sensitive questions of company "know-how," patent rights, and initial access to or position in new and expanding markets. In entering into joint reactor projects, the United States, one might say, was prepared to place in the hands of European industrial concerns the technology and "know-how" that American companies had developed under AEC contracts and could not patent or profit by exclusively themselves. These European companies, it is reported, are able to exploit this technology practically on an exclusive basis—within local custom and law, of course. Clearly there are two sides to this controversy that deserve exploration. For our purposes, however, the question of private and exclusive rights is raised merely to illustrate, not to judge, the institutional obstacles confronting international collaboration when powerful potential competitors are involved.

At the outset of collaboration with Euratom, American industry had to be persuaded that the release of "know-how" was a necessary price to pay for advancing the technology, opening the European market to U. S. suppliers, and meeting national objectives of foreign policy. The implications of this experiment for the future are numerous. If close collaboration is to occur in joint development projects, rather than in research only, then the competitive position of foreign and domestic companies needs to be considered. An equitable arrangement for keeping public information available for nonexclusive use by all on both sides would need to be established. If not, U.S. manufacturers might well be given rights to patents filed abroad.[18] As an interesting alternative, non-

---

[18] The AEC's policy with respect to such foreign patents is stated in the *Annual Report to Congress of the Atomic Energy Commission for 1961* (January, 1962), pp. 59–60.

profit research organizations might well be called on to undertake the joint research and development projects.[19]

The second "lesson"—the relation between short-term and long-term objectives of joint development—has become important as a result of the diminished urgency for nuclear power in western Europe since 1958. Presumably, the priority among the objectives of nuclear-power development should be shifted in favor of those reactor systems that hold greatest promise over the long term. Stated another way, it might seem more desirable to aim development at achieving lowest-cost nuclear power through greater laboratory effort on technology than to accomplish marginally competitive nuclear power soon with the construction of obsolescent demonstration reactors based on current technology.

In fact, however, this has not become the pertinent question, nor does the issue permit the "either-or" choice implied by the statement. The state of reactor technology is such that reactor scientists are still unable to judge with confidence whether low-cost power will ultimately be achieved by steady improvements in present converters (and "burners") now dominating the joint program or by a "leap" forward with highly advanced breeder types of reactors not now included in the joint program.[20] A balanced Euratom program calls for work on each of these lines, in light of the substantial resources that are available and the benefits to be derived. But major emphasis in the joint program should and must continue to be on the enriched uranium reactors that are approaching competitive feasibility now. The U.S. program needs these projects as additional plant demonstrations in electric-utility systems and Euratom needs them for evaluating enriched uranium systems as compared with natural uranium systems put forth by other countries. Were Euratom to drop near-term technology and demonstration plants in favor of joint laboratory efforts on highly advanced breeder reactors, the result might be several years of wasted effort.

---

[19] Most of the U.S. studies under the joint program are undertaken by industrial laboratories.

[20] A long debate has been proceeding among reactor scientists over the merits of developing "breeders" or "burners." See, for example, "Breeding—How Soon a Necessity?", *Nucleonics* (February, 1960), p. 60.

This would include the loss of important by-product benefits associated with the technology of fuel elements, chemical processing, and plant operation.

Finally, there are important non-commercial considerations —political, social, and ethical objectives—that the five-year program has revealed as being imperatives in the future. Politically, the emergence of Euratom and the Common Market, with the United Kingdom and other western European countries probably becoming full-fledged members, almost compels the United States to maintain vigorous participation in nuclear-power development there. Euratom is also providing the first real test of safeguard procedures by multilateral international inspection, that is, safeguards for detecting and preventing the diversion of nuclear materials from power reactors in unauthorized weapon applications. Euratom, too, represents the only example of large, inherently dangerous power reactors being operated under international conventions, including requisite health and safety measures with indemnification for possible reactor accidents.[21] In addition, the United States is fulfilling a moral obligation to provide a prompt return, from its great and growing resources, on the help received from several countries of western Europe in the earliest days of the atomic energy program. Europe, we may recall, gave us the basic knowledge of nuclear fission and indirectly provided supplies of natural uranium (from the Belgian Congo).

Many economists in the United States sense that the emerging economic integration of western Europe may be leading to a unique form of political unification—despite the recurring awkwardness and frustration engendered by competing national sovereignties and leaders. One relevant historical pattern of unification, not necessarily applicable in western Europe, comes from this side of the Atlantic. Hence, in judging the means and ends of collaboration with Euratom, one's criteria might well extend beyond the techno-economic considerations to include valid ethical and political objectives.

---

[21] Health and safety standards are, to be sure, established by Euratom, but regulation remains a function of each member state. Moreover, the Euratom Liability Convention cannot go into effect until adoption of a liability convention by the OECD.

SYSTEM AND FUNCTIONS OF EURATOM

Hans K. Sauer

TO BEGIN, I would like to draw your attention to some historical features of the European co-operation in the nuclear field.
We have seen several promising attempts for a multi-lateral
co-operation which I deem worth mentioning because they
are basically quite different from Euratom and cannot be
taken as a kind of preliminary stage therefore.

Since 1954, the European Atomic Energy Society (EAES)
has been in existence, which is something like a nuclear information club consisting of eight members in the beginning,
while there are now thirteen of them. In the EAES, the scientific heads of the national atomic energy authorities meet
for an exchange of scientific ideas. Although there is neither
a statue nor a budget, this informal society is still alive and
has become well known for its outstanding symposia which
are of a very high level and comprise only a few participants
at a time.

Up to 1958, two organizations were envisaged and finally
established with a political background. Euratom, compris-
ing six member states, an organization of which more will
have to be said in the following and the European Nuclear
Energy Agency. The ENEA took up its activities on February
1, 1958, one month later than Euratom; unlike Euratom,
it did not require a completely new organizational set-up,
but almost all of the nuclear-energy problems which had so
far come under the responsibility of the common secretariat
of the OEEC with its fifteen member states were now focused
on one agency. With its relatively small staff of some fifty
persons, the agency tackled a number of problems in the
fields of security control, health protection, third-party liability, trade with nuclear material, and certain fields of research
(such as in the Nuclear Data Committee). It organized tech-

nical-scientific conferences and, above all, was concerned
with the encouragement of joint enterprises for the peaceful
utilization of nuclear energy. May it suffice here to mention
three of them:

1. The Dragon project, a gas-cooled high temperature
   reactor of 20 MW (thermal) which is under construction in England.

2. The operation of the Halden reactor in Norway, a
   heavy-water boiling reactor of a similarly low power.
   These two joint enterprises have no legal personality
   of their own but are based on contracts under international law of the governments concerned or, as in some
   other countries, on public corporations as well as on
   contracts of association with the atomic energy authorities of the respective countries in which they are located
   (England and Norway) and which bear most of the
   responsibility for the organizational and administrative
   execution of these projects, whereas the research program is equally shared by all partners. Euratom participates in both projects.

3. Eurochemic, which is the oldest of the three enterprises,
   was the first international joint enterprise in the atomic
   field. It is based on a convention ratified by thirteen
   participating states. The plant, which amounts to some
   thirty million dollars, is being set up in Belgium and
   will be a center for the reprocessing of irradiated fuel
   elements. That shares are issued which are acquired by
   the participating governments and interested industry
   emphasizes the private character of this enterprise.
   Euratom does not participate in this enterprise.

Contrary to the examples of international co-operation in
the nuclear energy field which we have mentioned, Euratom
is a part of a European political will for integration. The
functional co-operation in the international field is supplemented by much more far-reaching institutional integration.
The first step toward integration had already been taken in
1951, when certain basic resources were pooled, in the form
of the European Coal and Steel Community, and was fol-

lowed early in 1958 by the European Communities for Economy and Atomic Energy.

As a historical curiosity, I would like to mention that, apart from the major political aims, some ideas and plans were fostered when Euratom was founded that soon turned out to be wrong or unfeasible and had to give way to a more realistic attitude:

1. A study which was prepared on behalf of the governments of the six member states and which has become well known as the "Report of the Three Wise Men" predicted a wide energy gap in Europe for the next ten years. In the days of the "nuclear boom" and under the impression of the Suez crisis, this gap was supposed to be bridged by 15,000 megawatts of nuclear power to be installed by 1967. It is well known that development took another turn.

2. A common electricity supply system relying on nuclear energy and having a supranational organization did not take off well, owing to the private character of energy supply companies in countries such as Belgium and the Federal Republic.

3. Another action jointly discussed with Sweden, Denmark, and Switzerland and aiming at the construction of an isotope separation plant was pending for quite some time and finally had to be dropped for various reasons.

4. It was widely held that supranational co-operation in the new field of nuclear energy could be achieved smoothly because national efforts had not yet led to fixed programs with diverging tendencies; this, however, was only partly true.

The political arguments for integration were independent of these prerequisites.

ORGANIZATION

Let us turn to the organization of Euratom. The above-mentioned three European communities are all of an organizational structure similar to Euratom, combining national and federative principles and being characterized by four institutions:

1. The *Council of Ministers* consists of one representative of each of the six governments, thus being a kind of federative unit. It decides on all important problems with simple or qualified majority or, in the case of major issues, a unanimous vote is required according to the treaty.

2. The *Commission* (or "High Authority" as it is called in the case of the European Coal and Steel Community) is the main executive institution and "shall perform its duties in the general interest of the Community with complete independence" as set out in the treaty.

    The Council and the Commission are advised by the Economic and Social Committee. All of these institutions are common to the European Economic Community.

3. The *Assembly* is the parliamentary organ with consultative and control functions under the treaty.

4. The *Court of Justice* supervises the interpretation and implementation of the treaty. The Assembly and the Court of Justice are common to all three European communities.

The Scientific and Technical Committee is a consultative organ of the Commission and comprises twenty experts from science and industry who are not bound by any mandatory instructions. Since 1961, a Consultative Committee for Nuclear Research has been in existence; it was formed on the initiative of Minister Balke in the Council of Ministers. It consists of government delegates who are responsible for the national programs.

One of the Commission's duties is to draw up a *budget* both for administration and research (including investments) and submit it to the Council for approval. The funds approved are raised by the member states according to a special scale of contributions. The first five-year program (1958-62) comprised $215 million. The second program amounting to $425 million has recently been approved; to this figure, a remainder of $20 million is to be added. The number of employees amounted to 2,100 (mid-1962), 600 of whom were in the Brussels headquarters (operational budget for 1961: $9.3 million, $6 million of which are allocated to the commission).

These figures give an idea of the moment of the community with regard to national programs, a moment which differs widely in the six countries depending upon the relation between the national budget and the contribution to Euratom. Certain difficulties for which the Commission is blamed, and of which only one should be indicated in this context, are due to this fact. Apart from its own research and development work, the community is to undertake supplementary activities in the member countries which may easily lead to an undesirable shift in emphasis.

FUNCTIONS

Research and Training

Research and development are at the heart of Euratom's functional activities. Yet, unfortunately, for lack of space these activities can be described only very briefly.

Research and development are encouraged by the work done in a so-called Joint Nuclear Research Center, the national programs being supported and co-ordinated by contracts. The research center consists of separate establishments situated in various countries. It comprises four such establishments, two of which are of general competence:

1. ISPRA, situated in the north of Italy, is the biggest center and is mainly concerned with the development of the ORGEL reactor, a heavy-water-moderated, organic-cooled reactor. Apart from this, it has a considerable potential of electronic, digital, and analogue computers which are used for reactor calculations and for the problems of automatic documentation and translation.

2. The research establishment Petten in the Netherlands has a high-flux reactor and is concerned with its own

studies on metallurgy and high-temperature chemistry. Its main task is the co-ordination of the Dragon high-temperature project and that of the German group BBC/Krupp which has become known as Pebble Bed Reactor.

The two other establishments have specialized functions as their titles indicate:

3. The Central Bureau for Nuclear Measurements in Belgium.
4. The European Institute for Transuranic Elements in Germany.

The work of the Joint Nuclear Research Center is supplemented by a large number of research contracts (so far about 250) concluded for one specific object only, as well as by several contracts of association for large and long-term projects that are carried out in co-operation with national institutions. Examples of the latter include the development of fast breeders and high-temperature reactors, the operation of the Belgian high-flux reactor, fusion and plasmaphysics, and radiobiology. In addition, there is a program for the participation in power reactors and for the development of advanced reactor technology, such as nuclear superheating, fog cooling, variable moderation (spectral shift). Some 50 per cent of the total funds of the second five-year program will be spent on contracts.

It is not possible for me to deal at length with *training.* May it suffice here to say that apart from co-ordinating activities, Euratom employs students and research associates for limited periods of time. Mention should also be made of the plans aiming at the establishment of a European university.

Dissemination of Information

The treaty makes special reference to the dissemination of information. This term does not only include the publication or notification of the results of the community's own work but also the comprehensive nuclear documentation with a rate of increase of 50,000 reports per annum. It should be remembered that good documentation also means careful selection and delimitation.

It should especially be mentioned that even a rather pretentious research program for the methodology of scientific documentation is under way. Automatic documentation is the ultimate aim, but for the time being much work goes into the electronic storage of nuclear information. The Dessemination of Information division issues several periodicals, two of which are of special interest in this connection,

1. The *Transatom Bulletin.* Under agreements with the U.S., A.E.C., and the editors of *Nuclear Science Abstracts,* as well as with other countries, this publication of Euratom contains information on publications translated from Eastern languages.

2. The *Quarterly Digest,* the complete title of which is *The Joint Research and Development Quarterly Digest,* reports on the aims and results of projects which are carried out under the agreement concluded between Euratom and the United States.

Matters relating to patent law in the nuclear field give rise to particular difficulties. Let us note some of the reasons:

1. The connection with "military applications";
2. The network of bilateral and multilateral agreements, all of which provide for an exchange of experience and sometimes even for certain procedures relating to patents;
3. The outstanding role which government plays in most of the leading countries. In addition, some countries have established regulations concerning nuclear inventions.

With its distinct policy of disseminating information, Euratom endeavors at the same time to protect the commercial rights of inventors. As far as research contracts are concerned, the contractor acquires title of the patents resulting from his work and is entitled to grant licenses to interested persons outside the community. Euratom gets a free license with the right to grant sublicenses on the condition that they are only granted to persons and enterprises within the community. Patents arising from research contracts with institutions of the type such as Battelle are an exception, since they are owned by the community. Furthermore, the research contracts under the bilateral agreement Euratom/United States are treated in a different manner. In addition, there are special provisions as to the joint enterprises of the OECD in which Euratom participates, i.e., the Dragon and Halden projects.

Health Protection

The Health Protection division deals with:

1. health and safety regulations,
2. the control of radioactive waste disposal,
3. environmental radioactivity.

The so-called basic standards for the protection of workers and the general public, as required by the treaty, were established by the Council of Ministers late in 1958 after this matter had been thoroughly studied by a special committee. These norms constitute a very exhaustive series of basic standards for the maximum permissible concentration based on ICRP recommendations. They are guiding principles for national legislators and have become law in the Federal Republic of Germany. With regard to the control of radioactive waste disposal, the treaty requires all respective installations to be reported already in the planning stage, on which matter the Commission will comment within six months after consultation of experts. The control of artificial environmental radioactivity involves co-operation with ENEA and the national authorities and measuring stations in order to improve and standardize measuring methods and to compile the results obtained.

Investments

The treaty requires the Commission to publish reports on its programs at regular intervals to encourage investments in the nuclear-energy field and to facilitate their co-ordination. These programs are based on investment reports by enterprises of the member states as provided for in the treaty. The investments include new installations, replacements, and operational adjustments if they exceed certain limits. Contrary to the treaty establishing the European Coal and Steel Community, it is not provided that the Commission intervenes directly in any investment project by rendering its comment thereon; the report is merely followed by a discussion without any binding effect. Thus the liberal economic structure of the individual countries has been taken into due consideration. In general, it is not envisaged to entrust the community with an investment competency except for the setting up of joint enterprises for which, according to the treaty, a unanimous vote in the Council is required in case of Euratom's participation. Such joint enterprises may be granted a number of privileges, such as the exemption from direct taxes, duties, and other specific rates and charges. The first enterprise of such special status is the SENA (Société Nucleaire Franco-Belge des Ardennes), a pressurized-water reactor of 720 MW (thermal), similar to the Yankee Atomic Power Reactor.

Supplies

The functions of the Supply Agency are especially far-reaching owing to the shortage of nuclear fuel prevailing at the time when the treaty was established. In the meantime, however, supply has outgrown demand, as is well-known; and the Commission endeavors to avoid any impediment to industry by the stringent rules envisaged and to confine itself to such formal functions as are indispensable.

The exclusive rights of the agency—sometimes called a "barrier to industry"—of concluding all contracts concerning the supply of ores, source, and special fissionable material were owing to the present supply situation delegated to the consumers by way of a general or specific authorization. No authorization is required for supply contracts inasmuch as they do not concern exports to third countries. Such exports need the Commission's authorization.

Security Control

Security control is linked with the provisions of the treaty on the community's ownership of special fissionable material (Article VIII). Since all ores and sources material, special fissionable material as well as the technical criteria of all nuclear installations, have to be reported, the Commission is in a position to insure that they are used in accordance with the purposes reported. This then is checked by regular inspections on the spot.

It should be emphasized that the treaty itself binds only the community to use nuclear energy for peaceful purposes, while it does not, however, prohibit member states from using it for other ends. A more rigid control is exercised on contracts concluded with third countries, such as the agreement Euratom/United States under which the Commission agreed to control the peaceful utilization. In general, the right of control and ownership extends to any fissionable material but does no longer apply if the fissionable material has gone into a nuclear weapon. A well-known French expert gave a good idea of the complicated situation when saying that, according to the treaty, a U-235 atom may, to the satisfaction of the lawyers, change its nationality several times: when extracted from the ore, it may be French, for instance; when being enriched, it will become European in order to become French again in the end, when it goes into a military project.

The security system established by the treaty may rightly be claimed as the most rigid and comprehensive one in the international field; this is also reflected by the fact that the community's competency with regard to the security control was accepted by the United States, the United Kingdom, and Canada in their agreements with the community since these states waived the right of exercising the security control.

The Nuclear Common Market

The creation of a nuclear common market as provided for in Chapter IX of the treaty aims at (1) the realization of a free exchange of all nuclear products, (2) the regulation of liability and insurance matters, and (3) free movement of so-called qualified workers. The latter provision was defined by the directives of March, 1962, and ensures free access of qualified labor to working places in all member states. Owing to the shortage of such personnel, this provision will be of little practical effect, at least for the time being. The impact of the Common Market is much more felt on the products and equipment sector as specified in Annex IV of the treaty. Contrary to the general common market, the realization of which is brought about step by step, all customs duties and quantitative restrictions as between member states were already eliminated on the nuclear common market as of January 1, 1959. The adoption of a common customs tariff with regard to third countries is meant to insure a common trade policy within the community.

In July, 1961, the European Nuclear Energy Agency achieved a promising success in the important field of third-party liability for nuclear accidents, when a convention was signed by all European OEEC-countries (except for Ireland and Iceland) which, however, has not yet been ratified by the five signatory states required. The convention is supposed to harmonize principles of civil law on the international level as is analogously envisaged by the planned world-wide IAEA convention on minimum standards. In addition to this the Euratom countries have prepared an amendment to the convention to be concluded with almost all western European countries. This amendment is to guarantee government indemnification. Great Britain, Switzerland, Austria, Spain, Denmark, Norway, and possibly Sweden, too, are expected to sign this amendment. Further rules for nuclear ships were prepared at the diplomatic conferences on maritime law of London and Brussels (1960-62).

External Relations

The community was particularly successful in establishing and fostering good relations to other countries and international organizations so that there is a more or less close co-operation with IAEA, ILO, and FAO. Special forms of co-operation have developed with ENEA within the OECD that have already been mentioned. First and foremost, the community concluded agreements for closer co-operation with the leading western atomic powers in the years 1958-59. The particularly far-reaching agreement with the United States has already been discussed by Professor Mullenbach. Six months later (February 4, 1959) the agreement with the United Kingdom entered into force which differed considerably from the agreement with the United States. It is a standard agreement in the form of a skeleton agreement as it has been concluded by the United States with many countries. It does not contain any arrangements for programs but enables the conclusion of contracts in each particular case, e.g., between industrial groups. There is a similar agreement with Canada amended by a technical agreement with Atomic Energy of Canada, Ltd. (AECL), on a joint research and development program for heavy-water reactors.

Apart from the standard clauses on the exchange of information, technical personnel, equipment, etc., the agreements with Brazil and Argentina contain provisions to the effect that Euratom will help these countries in the training of personnel and the opening up of mineral resources. Beside these formal agreements, Euratom maintains close relationships to some fifteen states which have set up diplomatic missions to Euratom. Mention should also be made that bilateral agreements, which Euratom member states have concluded with third states, may remain in existence. Any new agreements require the authorization of the Commission except for certain cases (military applications).

ACCESSION OF OTHER COUNTRIES

Finally I would like to make some remarks as to the accession of other countries. At the present time, Denmark and possibly Norway are up for discussion, both of which have gained international renown for their nuclear research and development work. No difficulties should arise as to their accession.

Things are different, however, in the case of Great Britain with its great research capacity and a power reactor program which—though based on a single reactor type only—is the largest such program in the world with a fixed capacity of 5,000 megawatts (electrical) to be installed by 1958. In this context I can only refer to some of the complex problems which the participation of Great Britain will raise. The agreement with Euratom, which has been in existence since 1959, has led, it is true, to numerous contacts and co-ordination talks. The practical co-operation was tried out on the Dragon project but the stringent stipulations of the Euratom treaty and the institutional claims of the Commission confront the British government with fundamental decisions.

Particularly difficult is the area of military applications of nuclear energy in connection with security control since the interlocking with peaceful uses is stronger in the United Kingdom than it is in France. The existing long-term contracts concerning the import of nuclear fuel and ores should entail less difficulties with the Supply Agency; the same applies to stipulations of the treaty as to the exchange of information and patents. With regard to the capacity and productivity of the British industry, a future participation in the nuclear common market is of special importance and requires, in particular, an adjustment of the customs tariffs with third countries. There is no doubt that the integration into the second five-year program does need very careful preparation. (Thus, for instance, it can hardly be imagined that the British could erect reactors of U.S. design under the Euratom/United States agreement.) Finally, the accession of Britain will entail the domination of governmental nuclear policy within the area of Euratom, which would especially be felt in the Federal Republic of Germany with its private economy conception.

We may hope that the negotiations under way will in the near future be brought to a successful conclusion despite all difficulties and will contribute to strengthen and to advance the atomic energy community. The efforts of other countries to become members equally demonstrate that Euratom with its system and functions has become an internationally recognized partner of equal standing in the atomic energy community.

As Nehru said, scientists are already living in the Space Age, whereas politicians have not yet outgrown the Stone Age. I think, however, that the political aims which were the basis of the Euratom *system* came from a modern spirit. As far as the quality and efficiency of Euratom's *functions* are concerned, nothing definite can be said today.

Comment on Mullenbach and Sauer

Jaroslav G. Polach

I AM VERY MUCH IN AGREEMENT with Mr. Mullenbach's thoughtful and well-rounded inquiry into the causes of a relative failure of the United States–Euratom joint program in the field of atomic energy. Nevertheless, there still remain areas sufficiently significant to initiate a useful discussion where I would not fully subscribe to his position, although the differences between us may appear more as a shift in emphasis than in substance.

Thus, I would hesitate to apportion a major part of the blame for the failure of the United States–Euratom reactor-development program to refusal of the public utilities to be sold on nuclear power under the joint program. I would even say that electric utilities in the Euratom countries showed sound judgment when they resisted being swayed by somewhat doubtful cost analyses which were attached to the agreement and should have supposedly added "to the proof of the economic feasibility of the nuclear power stations." [1] To illustrate this point, it may suffice to mention that the United States–Euratom working group's cost estimates were based on such assumptions as, for instance, an equally long, useful life for the first generation of untried nuclear stations as for the new, technically advanced, conventional fuel-burning plants. Moreover, this first generation of the nuclear plants was supposed to provide a base load, operating at 80 per cent load factor during the whole period, estimated in some cases to stretch to thirty years.

Similarly unwarranted was an assumption of an average burnup of 10,000 $tMWd/t$. That this was a too high standard

---

[1] Joint Committee on Atomic Energy, *Proposed Euratom Agreements (with Associated Documents and Materials)*, 85th Cong., 2nd Sess., 36, 38, 39–41 (1958).

has been pointed out by the Joint Committee on Atomic Energy itself.[2]

Of course, the average burnup the *entire* core will produce is an essential element of the production and cost functions of nuclear electricity. That a failure to attain the promised average output of heat would have resulted, notwithstanding all the financial guarantees the joint program offered, in substantial losses was pointed out by Professor O. Löbl, scientific advisor to the Rhine-Westphalian Electric Company, in Stresa in 1959.[3]

I fully concur with Mr. Mullenbach's more or less implied conclusions that if there is to be competitive nuclear power in the future, some unprofitable large-scale industrial nuclear ventures must be tried now. But how the resulting risk and costs should be borne and what are the priorities in allocation of scarce nuclear resources to various programs are, however, major public policy issues. They involve also giving answers to questions concerning future profits, atomic-industry concentration, and protection of rare knowledge gained by those willing to embark upon nuclear ventures.

Turning to the joint research program, I am inclined to believe that its rather disappointing results are attributable to its rigid provisions and restriction to two "proven" reactor systems, the PWR and BWR, which, as the London *Economist* observed,[4] were considered obsolescent already at the time of the agreement. Moreover, strict orientation of the entire joint research program to nuclear electricity as outlined in *A Target for Euratom* has not been a favorable augury either. In fact, identification of Euratom with nuclear-generated electricity greatly diminished its immediate impact and was a cause of the serious lag in other fields of nuclear research, such as radioisotopes, radiation, hot plasma, etc.

---

[2] *Hearings before the Joint Committee on Atomic Energy on the Proposed Euratom Agreements and Legislation to Carry Out the Proposed Co-operative Program,* 85th Cong., 2nd Sess., Part 2 at 432–33 (1958).

[3] O. Löbl, "Cost Factors of Nuclear Energy," *Stresa Conference (The Industrial Challenge of Nuclear Energy,* Vol. III [Paris, 1960]), Part 1, pp. 57–67, esp. 63–66.

[4] *Economist* (London), March 23, 1960, p. 1038.

This was pointed out by none other than Minister Balke in *Atomwirtschaft* as early as February, 1958.[5]

It must also be kept in mind that in spite of all its supranational characteristics, Euratom does not command its own human and natural resources but is primarily dependent on the goodwill of the member states and, as is usual in the free enterprise system, concerned industries. Needless to say, it might have been expected that they would give priority to their own rather than the United States–Euratom-sponsored plans, unless the latter would have looked to them as particularly promising. Unfortunately, the joint research program closely tied to the mentioned reactor systems has not provided this kind of incentive.

Nevertheless, the United States–Euratom atomic collaboration has not been lacking. In addition to some positive achievements mentioned by Mr. Mullenbach[6] and Dr. Sauer, I should point out a close tripartite collaboration in research, characteristically outside the joint program, on ORGEL (organic, liquid-cooled reactor systems).

To close my comments to Mr. Mullenbach's paper, I would venture an opinion that if the United States–Euratom research collaboration is to develop more successfully in the future, two changes, *inter alia,* are necessary. On our side, the approach to the scope and objectives of such a joint program must be far more open-minded than it has been up to now. Euratom, at the same time, should show more willingness to commit larger resources to research in other than natural-uranium, gas-cooled reactor systems.

Insofar as Dr. Sauer's paper is concerned, I wish I could have paid to it the attention this interesting and concise paper certainly deserves. Due to unavoidable circumstances, I did not obtain a copy of the paper until shortly before the writing of this comment. Consequently my comments are directed chiefly at such parts of Dr. Sauer's analysis which caught my attention during a rather rapid reading.

---

[5] Siegfried Balke, "Euratom—Wirtschaftpolitisch gesehen," *Die Atomwirtschaft,* II (1958), 43–45.

[6] *Cf.* also C. Heidenreich, "Euratom's Activities and Future Aims," a lecture delivered to the Canadian Nuclear Association Nuclear Conference and Exhibition on Heavy Water Reactors and Radioisotopes, May 28, Ottawa, Ontario, p. 6.

One of the very good points Dr. Sauer makes and which, I believe, is worth-while stressing is the existence of a common market, we may say nuclear customs union, within Euratom. We, in the United States, have a tendency, whenever discussing European integration, to speak about *the* Common Market, believing that there is only one such arrangement and not realizing that the Euratom common market has existed since 1959, whereas that of the Economic Community will not come into force before the 1970's.

I also agree with Dr. Sauer's enumeration of the community institutions and his placing of the Assembly below the Council and the Commission. In the main, the Assembly is chiefly an advisory body. I wish only that Dr. Sauer would have mentioned—though I understand that his official position might have prevented him from doing so—that the Community member states, although unmentioned in this capacity in the treaty, are also a Euratom institution and, in effect, its most decisive policy-making organ.

I have made this point elsewhere and thus would elaborate it here only briefly. First, Euratom institutions are not agencies of a self-perpetuating federal government as we are used to knowing it. Euratom's effective work depends very much on a series of positive actions to be undertaken by the member states and their "common agreement." When it comes to the decisions of the member states, there is no majority voting and each state, in fact, has the right of a veto. Second, the Community cannot levy any taxes, and its discharge of the assigned tasks is contingent on the timely contributions of the member states. That is particularly significant in the field of our discussion on research and development. The outcome of the last year's clash between France and the Euratom Commission may serve here as an example.

In 1961, the Euratom Commission president, Etienne Hirsch, a Frenchman, argued, in addition to some other issues of contention, that Euratom is fully authorized to use its funds from the research budget for defraying the development costs of initial commercial operations. France contested it and lost when the Council applied the majority-voting principle. Yet, it was a Pyrrhic victory for Mr. Hirsch, who by the end of the year was out of the job. Moreover, the French views prevailed also in other respects, since the second five-year research program does not provide any funds for the development costs of commercial ventures.

In this context it may be useful to mention that the member states' financial quotas to the Euratom research and development budget substantially differ. Thus France and Germany are contributing 30 per cent each of the total budget; Italy, 23 per cent; Belgium, 9 per cent; the Netherlands, 6.9 per cent; and Luxembourg, 0.2 per cent.

On the other hand, Euratom total outlays on research and development in the first four years of activity, ending December 31, 1961, were territorially allocated as follows.[7] From approximately $141 million spent by Euratom, less than 9 per cent and about 11 per cent went to research conducted in France and Germany, respectively, whereas Italy and Belgium received close to about 50 per cent of all Euratom research expenses. Moreover, research ventures in the United Kingdom, Norway, and Switzerland, i.e., in the non-member countries, were allocated almost 10 per cent of the Euratom research funds. Thus the latter countries' total cash benefits surpassed that of one member country, France, and was only slightly less than that for Germany.

That, of course, raises an interesting question about the impact of a re-allocation of the costs and benefits in a supranational arena. To answer it would require, as I believe, a reformation of some of our ideas about social values, social costs, and social benefits which up to now have usually been cast within a framework of a territorial nation-state. In other words, we need a new tool of analysis to permit us to evaluate the economic impact of the supranational aspects of research undertaken within the European atomic integration.[8]

---

[7] Based on *Atomwirtschaft*, IV (1962), 201.

[8] I have suggested developing this approach in my unpublished Ph.D. dissertation, "Euratom: A Study in European Economic Integration" (American University, Washington, D.C., 1962), chap. vi.

THE MUTUAL WEAPONS
DEVELOPMENT PROGRAM

Richard U. Sherman, Jr.

FAR LESS WELL KNOWN than Euratom, and yet of potentially great significance, is a little-publicized program which started nearly ten years ago as part of the United States Military Assistance Program. Originally called the Mutual Special Weapons Program, it is now more appropriately named the Mutual Weapons Development Program or MWDP. Despite the small size of the program, as measured in dollars, it has been breaking new ground in stimulating greater specialization and co-operation by a number of NATO countries in military research and development.

In considering the steps which have been taken, and those which could be taken, to encourage greater international co-operation in military research and development, one should keep in mind that this effort, although it is paid for out of military funds, in many cases results in developments which have civilian applications. At the same time, it has long been recognized that military R&D has always leaned heavily upon civilian science for its pool of fundamental knowledge and that Europe has been historically a great reservoir of such knowledge.

Vannevar Bush pointed out as far back as 1946 that "international exchange of scientific information is of growing importance. Increasing specialization of science will make it more important than ever that scientists in this country keep continually abreast of developments abroad." [1]

The 1958 report by the Rockefeller Foundation, entitled *International Security—The Military Aspect*, concluded that "first of all, we must pool with our allies scientific and technical information and assist in mobilizing the research and development capability of NATO both in the civilian and

---

[1] Vannevar Bush, *Endless Horizons* (Washington, D.C., 1946), p. 57.

military fields. The history of science suggests that such pooling would, in the long run, be of special importance to the United States which throughout its history has drawn heavily on the intellectual resources of Europe." [2]

As pointed out by Secretary of Defense Robert S. McNamara in testifying on March 15, 1962, before the House of Representatives Committee on Foreign Affairs concerning the Foreign Assistance Act of 1962, "Most of the nations of continental Europe have developed economically to the point where they can carry their own defense burdens." [3] This represents a marked improvement since the time when the Mutual Weapons Development Program was started. Not only is the total U.S. military-assistance program shrinking year by year, but, in addition, the proportion of the program going to Europe has declined from 38 per cent in fiscal year 1960 to 21 per cent in 1962 and to only 18 per cent of the proposed program for fiscal year 1963.[4] In light of these developments, it appears appropriate to review the Mutual Weapons Development Program and ask ourselves what changes, if any, appear warranted at this time.

This paper will examine briefly the origin and purposes of the Mutual Weapons Development Program, the composition of the program, its cost, and its accomplishments. The program will be analyzed in the light of conditions and needs as they exist today and are likely to exist in the future; and where it seems appropriate, changes will be recommended.

ORIGIN AND PURPOSES OF MWDP

Just as a civilian inventor will frequently approach the Defense Department, invention in hand, and ask, "Couldn't this widget be used for some military purpose?", so the

---

[2] Rockefeller Foundation, *International Security—The Military Aspect* (New York, 1958).

[3] Statement of the Hon. Robert S. McNamara, Secretary of Defense, *Hearings on Foreign Assistance Act of 1962 before the House Committee on Foreign Affairs,* 87th Cong., 2nd Sess., Part I at 67 (1962).

[4] *Ibid.*

Mutual Weapons Development Program evolved almost by accident rather than as a carefully thought-out plan for meeting the need for greater international co-operation in military research and development. In 1953, Harold Stassen, then the director of the Foreign Operations Administration (forerunner of the present Agency for International Development), proposed an amendment to the Mutual Security Act of 1951 asking Congress for $250 million to be used to provide "special weapons" to nations eligible to receive assistance under the act. However, so little information was forthcoming as to the exact purposes for which the funds were being requested that Congress reduced the authorization to $100 million and then appropriated only $50 million for fiscal year 1953.

The ultimate intended use of the funds still remained unclear from the language of the authorization (Public Law 118, §542, 83rd Cong.). It did, however, require the President to determine that any obligation of the funds was of direct importance to the security interest of the United States and would further the policies and purposes of the Mutual Defense Assistance Act of 1949, as amended. The President was also required, prior to the transfer of special weapons to another country, to determine that adequate security safeguards existed in that country.

After the proposed amendment had become law, Governor Stassen asked Frank Nash, then Assistant Secretary of Defense for International Security Affairs, how he thought the funds could best be spent. It was obvious that $50 million would not buy much in the way of "special weapons" for NATO. Mr. Nash in turn discussed the matter with Donald Quarles, then Assistant Secretary of Defense for Research and Development, and ultimately asked him to assume responsibility for developing an appropriate program.

Consideration of the form which the program should take brought out a number of pertinent facts: (1) NATO countries, still in the process of recuperating from the effects of World War II, could re-establish and rebuild their military research and development programs more quickly with U.S. assistance.

(2) Such programs as did exist were not co-ordinated with those of other NATO countries or with the U.S. and exhibited much duplication and overlapping. (3) It was felt that the potential contribution of NATO countries to the development. of new weapons was considerable and that U.S. capabilities and military strength could be substantially increased by tapping the specialized scientific abilities of NATO countries. The further point was made that this process could lead to a reduction in the requirement for U.S. military aid in the future.[5]

The five principal objectives of the Mutual Weapons Development Program, according to the most recently published information brochure (August, 1961) by the Mutual Weapons Development Team in Paris,[6] are summarized as follows:

1. To make optimum use of this country's European allies' scientific and technical competence and to add their military inventive capabilities to those of the United States in order to stimulate advances in critical technical areas and in the development of weapons, components, and equipment in Europe designed to meet national or multi-national military requirements and which can be produced within the economic framework of the countries concerned.

2. To support European development efforts designed to meet NATO requirements for weapons or weapons systems with emphasis on multilateral participation to the maximum extent.

3. To assist European countries where appropriate in raising the level of skills and technical ability with respect to military technology so that they may make significant contributions to the collective defense as well as to their own.

4. To provide a mechanism for the exchange of classified scientific and technical information and technical assistance,

---

[5] Harold M. Wakefield, "An Analysis of the Mutual Weapons Development Program" (Thesis No. 136, Industrial College of the Armed Forces, Washington, D.C., 1960), pp. 4–6.

[6] Mutual Weapons Development Team, *Mutual Weapons Development Program Information Brochure* (Paris, 1961), p. 1.

including personnel, to improve the military technological capability of the allies.

5. To secure for the United States the benefits derived from MWDP, such as information on new scientific principles and facts and their applications to weapons technology, and the right of the United States to use or produce for its armed forces any item, information, or technique developed under the program.

COMPOSITION OF THE PROGRAM

Three principal types of projects make up the Mutual Weapons Development Program as it has evolved over the past nine years. In addition, technical assistance may be provided as a part of, or in addition to, the U.S. commitments contained in individual project agreements. The three types of projects eligible for U.S. technical and/or financial assistance are:[7]

1. Research and development projects: projects relating to (A) research into areas of military interest; (B) development of weapons systems, items of military equipment, or components thereof; and (C) operations research and analysis designed to improve objectives of military research and development programs.

2. Technical center projects: projects relating to the establishment of international research and development centers, including laboratories and educational facilities, for the study of technical military problems.

3. Data exchange agreements: project agreements which provide for the mutual exchange of classified technical information on selected items and well-defined areas between the United States and its allies at the project officer level. In contrast to the foregoing two categories of projects,

---

[7] *Ibid.*, p. 2.

no U.S. financial assistance is involved in data exchange agreements.

"Technical assistance" includes advice, technical visits, information, test equipment, sample components, test assistance, use of U.S. test facilities and installations, and provision of special technical training in U.S. institutions.

Participation in MWDP is extended only to those friendly countries which have executed basic MWDP bilateral agreements with the United States containing the general conditions governing the mutual co-operation in military research and development. The basic bilateral agreement forms the basis for later individual project agreements. The basic agreement is negotiated government to government through diplomatic channels, whereas individual project agreements are negotiated and signed by the U. S. Department of Defense and the defense ministry of the country concerned.

To date, ten NATO nations have signed basic bilateral agreements with the U. S. under the program. These are: Belgium, Denmark, France, the Federal Republic of Germany, Greece, Italy, Norway, the Netherlands, Turkey, and the United Kingdom. An eleventh country, Australia, has signed a data exchange agreement with the United States.[8]

Each individual project agreement sets forth the technical details and financial provisions of the project, obligates funds, and serves as the contractual instrument governing payment of the U.S. share in support of the project. Although projects are usually bilateral, the participating country must agree to make any item developed under the program available to the other countries of the free world. In addition, the United States "strongly encourages" multilateral R&D projects when the item concerned can be applied to meet broad, or multinational, requirements.[9]

Research and Development Projects

In 1954, when the Mutual Weapons Development Program was getting under way, research and development projects

---

[8] *Ibid.,* p. 3.
[9] *Ibid.,* p. 3.

constituted the total effort. At that time, primary emphasis was placed on development, particularly on accelerating the development of weapons already well advanced. In subsequent years, the program has been broadened to cover the entire spectrum from basic investigations to the fabrication of hardware for test and evaluation.

No less than fourteen separate criteria are itemized in the MWDP information brochure as "the major criteria used by U.S. reviewing authorities in selecting research and development projects for recommended financial support under MWDP."[10] In the first place, the proposed project should support one or more of the five objectives of the program stated in the foregoing section on origin and purposes of MWDP. "A research project should be concerned with a principle, process, technique or component, the successful completion of which would have a definite application of contributing to future development of an improved military weapon, weapon system, equipment, material, or component." The next two criteria apply specifically to development projects and provide (1) that the project be directed toward the fulfilment of an operational requirement or a target objective based on planned military operations, and (2) that it "be concerned with a new weapon, component, or equipment of advanced design that shows marked technical improvement over existing equipment . . . and shows promise of materially increasing the effectiveness of forces raised for the mutual defense."

Several criteria pertain to funding, and are designed to give assurance that U.S. financial support will be in addition to, not in place of, expenditures by the country of origin, that the participating country's share will be no less than 50 per cent of the total expenditures during the period of U.S. support, and that U.S. funds will not be expended for permanent-type construction not peculiar to the research project and having a capital value to the country for purposes other than the project itself.

---

[10] *Ibid.*, p. 7.

"Unnecessary duplication of effort on the same problem in different countries" is to be avoided, and the project should not detract from efforts on any similar project being made under the sponsorship of the NATO Armaments Committee for multilateral co-operation in research, development, and production of weapons. And, finally, the country of origin must agree to certain conditions having to do with making available to the U.S. government and to other friendly countries all of the technical and production data resulting from the research project.

It is difficult to measure the accomplishments of the MWDP. Money costs are a poor yardstick and number of R&D projects completed lumps major and minor projects together, some of which cover entire weapons systems while others are concerned with some small component. A few examples of completed R&D projects that resulted in a new weapon, however, will indicate the wide range of scientific investigation and the extent to which different participating countries have contributed from their specialized knowledge and abilities.

Perhaps the best-known army development resulting from the program is the French antitank guided missile, SS-11. The missile is small, can be launched by one man from a jeep or a helicopter and guided to the target by moving a small joy stick which transmits orders to the missile in flight through a fine wire trailed by the bird. The SS-11 is an improved version of the SS-10 which had been developed earlier by French scientists. MWDP funds from the U.S. are credited with making possible the development of the improved longer-range model, which was then chosen by the U.S. Army in preference to the Dart, a U.S. developed weapon with a similar purpose.[11]

One of the earliest MWDP projects resulted in the development of the Norwegian Terne III, an antisubmarine system for use on small ships. This system is largely automatic and provides for detection of enemy submarines; computation of

11 Lt. Col. George W. McIntyre, "The Mutual Weapons Development Program," *Military Review* (November, 1960), p. 50.

range, depth, and direction; and the aiming of a rocket launcher equipped with rocket-propelled depth charges. The Terne is currently being evaluated by the U.S. and Norwegian navies.[12]

Also in the antisubmarine category is the French-designed Atlantique, a patrol aircraft of which prototypes are now being tested. The Netherlands, Belgium, and the Federal Republic of Germany also participated in this multilateral R&D project.[13]

Italy has made contributions in the specialized field of mountain warfare and also played a leading role in the development of the Fiat G-91, a very light jet fighter, for close support of ground troops. France and Italy both submitted competitive plane designs, and Britain received financial support for the development of a compact jet engine. The plane is now being added to the air forces of West Germany, Italy, Turkey, and Greece.

Technical Centers

Three international research and development centers funded initially under the MWDP have been established to date: [14]

1. The SHAPE Air Defense Technical Center was the first such center and was established by the fiscal year 1955 MWDP. It is located at The Hague and has the mission of providing technical advice and assistance to SHAPE on air defense problems of western Europe. The center is operated by the military R&D agency of the Netherlands, RVO-TNO, under contract with the Mutual Weapons Development Team, and is staffed with scientists from various NATO countries.

2. The Training Center for Experimental Aerodynamics was established jointly with Belgium by the fiscal year 1957 MWDP, and is located at Rhode–St. Genese, Belgium.

---

[12] *Ibid.,* p. 501.

[13] Interview with Chauncey O. Rowe, Office of International Programs, Office of the Director of Defense Research and Engineering, August 21, 1962.

[14] U. S. Department of Defense, undated booklet entitled *Mutual Weapons Development Program,* pp. 8–9.

The center trains NATO students in advanced experimental aerodynamics with the aid of sonic and supersonic wind tunnels, laboratories, classrooms, and shops.

3. The SACLANT Antisubmarine Warfare Research Center at La Spezia, Italy, resulted from the fiscal year 1959 MWDP. This center has the responsibility of providing technical advice and assistance to SACLANT in the field of antisubmarine warfare. Initially Italy provided the facilities and certain services and the United States provided supporting funds.

It is anticipated that eventually all of the technical centers will be funded by NATO or by some other multilateral arrangement, at which time the U.S. will terminate its MWDP contract and assume the role of a participant. The centers must meet the needs and requirements of a joint allied military command. Their unique strength rests in the participation by interested countries through the employment of scientists from those countries and through the pooling of all technical information available to the participating countries in the research area.

Data-Exchange Agreements

The most recent phase of the Mutual Weapons Development Program is the data-exchange program, which was started in December, 1957. Its purpose is to promote mutual co-operation between the United States and its allies in order to reduce wasteful duplication in military research and development. A data-exchange agreement, or project, is intended to cover a specific and carefully defined segment of research and development rather than a broad, general area, and is designed to facilitate the exchange of classified technical information between the U.S. government and a participating government on a project officer to project officer basis.

The first data-exchange agreements were signed during fiscal year 1959. In that year, 170 agreements were signed. Several hundred have been signed up to the present time, and an additional large group is in various stages of negotiation.[15]

---

[15] Wakefield, *op. cit.*, pp. 15–16.

ADMINISTRATION AND COST OF THE PROGRAM

The Mutual Weapons Development Program is administered by the Director of Defense Research and Engineering in the Department of Defense through his Office of International Programs, in co-ordination with the Assistant Secretary of Defense for International Security Affairs. The program is implemented primarily by the Mutual Weapons Development Team (MWDT), located in Paris, France, as a part of the Office of the Defense Advisor to the U.S. ambassador to NATO. The team attempts to maintain close co-ordination with the NATO science advisor, the NATO Advisory Group for Aeronautical Research, and with the Army, Navy, and Air Force agencies located in Europe who sponsor research effort throughout Europe, principally in educational institutions.[16]

A comprehensive system of selection and evaluation of proposed projects is carried out by (1) the director, MWDT, with the assistance of the technical staffs of the three military services in the field, (2) the U.S. element of SHAPE, (3) the technical agencies of the military departments in the U.S., (4) the technical staffs of the Director of Defense Research and Engineering, (5) the MWDP Advisory Group (composed of outstanding civilian scientists), and (6) the Assistant Secretary of Defense for International Security Affairs (who is responsible for all military assistance programs). Periodic financial and technical progress reports on approved projects are required by the U.S. government.[17]

The total cost of the program to the United States as of June 30, 1962, amounted to approximately $275 million, covering some two hundred project agreements and nine years of operation.[18] U. S. financial support is slightly less than 50 per cent of the joint MWDP expenditures, but is only

---

[16] U. S. Department of Defense, *op. cit.*, pp. 2–3.

[17] McIntyre, *op. cit.*, p. 49.

[18] Chauncey O. Rowe, *op. cit.*

about 36 per cent of total expenditures, since in most cases the allied governments had expended funds on the project prior to its adoption under the program.[19]

England and France have received the largest amounts of financial support under the program, followed at a considerably lower level by the Netherlands and Italy. Very few dollars have flowed to the Federal Republic of Germany under MWDP despite the excellent scientific and technical talent in that country; this situation may reflect a greater capability than other European countries to finance and carry out its own R&D programs plus the fact that Germany was not eligible to participate in MWDP until 1957.[26]

CONCLUSIONS

Dr. Theodore von Karman, chairman of NATO's Advisory Group for Aeronautical R&D, wrote in the *NATO Journal*[21] a year ago: "There are two extreme philosophies under which research and development could be organized within the North Atlantic Treaty Organization. One thought is to integrate the talents and facilities of those countries and then to agree on a common program which is kept under continual review by a joint council and supervised by a unified research and development command. The other is to allow every country to work according to its own program and utilize the results for the common good after the process of research and development is terminated. It is evident that neither of these extreme methods can lead to the highest degree of success."

Dr. von Karman goes on to point out one serious obstacle to total integration of R&D programs—proprietary interest on the part of inventors—and a "comparable reticence" on the

---

19 U. S. Department of Defense, *op. cit.*, p. 4.

20 Wakefield, *op. cit.*, p. 26.

21 Dr. Theodore von Karman, "How to Improve Scientific Co-operation in NATO," *NATO Journal* (September, 1961), p. 61.

part of nations toward early disclosure or sharing of new equipment and techniques. He cites as a more valid argument against complete integration "the fact that scientists and engineers of the respective nations have diversity in their training, traditions, and methods of working. Pooling them together without proper care that every group can fully develop and apply its capabilities may lead to the disappointing result that the whole is considerably smaller than the sum of its parts."

Nevertheless, as Dr. von Karman points out, "every effort must be made to put the best brains to work on the more significant programs. In instances where national capabilities excel in particular directions, ways must be evolved to stimulate accelerated development of these capabilities with the understanding that such concentration of activity will be balanced by contributions from other countries."

The Mutual Weapons Development Program has been an effort in this direction. It has had some success. It has grown, though more recently at a decreasing rate. Harold M. Wakefield, of the Department of the Air Force, after a detailed analysis of the program, stated that "it must be concluded that its efforts have played a large part in the strengthening of the forces of the free world and its preparedness for possible conflict. It certainly can be stated that its contributions are far out of proportion to the costs which have been involved."[22]

Among the principal achievements of the program may be listed:

1. It has reduced duplication in military research and development, thereby permitting more productive use of existing financial and technical resources of the U.S. and of its NATO allies.

2. It has encouraged development of new weapons systems and components particularly suited to meeting the needs of European countries, and generally more economical to produce, operate, and maintain than corresponding U.S. items.

---

[22] Wakefield, *op. cit.*, p. 32.

3. It has accelerated development and testing, thus shortening the R&D lead time and making for faster availability of new operational equipment.

4. It has fostered a broadened exchange of scientific and technical information among the NATO countries.

5. It has brought benefits to the general economies of the participating countries.

6. It has assured to the U. S. all new technical knowledge coming from agreed projects and the use, if desired, by U. S. armed forces of any item developed in the program.

The House Committee on Government Operations reported in 1958, in connection with its study of the U. S. Military Assistance Program in western Europe:[23]

> While the subcommittee is aware of several major problems standing in the way of an expansion of this program, the potential return on United States investments of this type is enormous.
>
> If only a small fraction of the billions of dollars being expended for direct military aid were converted to research and development assistance, the NATO nations would undoubtedly be in a much better position to carry a proportionately larger share of the western defense load. Reduced requirements for direct United States aid would enable this Nation to place greater emphasis on its own scientific research and development program.

Although in one sense the Mutual Weapons Development Program aggravates the present unfavorable balance of payments, it can be argued that to the extent that the program makes possible a reduction in direct aid under the Mutual Security Program, it helps to ease the drain on the dollar.

A number of criticisms could be leveled at the program as it has been conducted, not with any intent to discredit it, but rather in the hope that now might be a good time to look at it critically with a view to developing an improved program —one that would take account of fundamental changes which have taken place since the MWDP was born, virtually by accident, some nine years ago. The sheer red tape and bureaucracy involved in the program as it is now managed cannot fail

---

[23] House Committee on Government Operations, *United States Military Aid and Supply Programs in Western Europe,* 85th Cong., 2nd Sess., H. R. Rep. 1371, p. 26 (1962).

to have a restraining effect. It would seem that the detailed statements of justification required of a country at the time of submittal of a project proposal, and subsequently in progress reports, would be bound to diminish somewhat the co-operative and friendly spirit the program is designed to encourage. The tendency to approve projects which are well along in research and development, and therefore have less risk of failure, may well result in a larger number of minor improvements at the expense of a smaller number of truly significant breakthroughs in weapons technology.

Although over the years four NATO countries have been added to the six originally in the program, MWDP still lacks breadth both as to the number and geographical diversity of participating countries and as to the number of areas in which technical and scientific data are exchanged. There are many free-world countries not in the program whose addition would strengthen it. In this connection, there is a great need for more multilateral agreements; to date almost all agreements have been bilateral only. "Through multilateral arrangements a higher degree of scientific and technical co-operation can be achieved which will bring a better unity of purpose and product," according to Harold Wakefield. He also contends that there "appears to be a definite need for a stronger NATO voice in the guidance and direction of the program," that "many of the MWD projects have been carried on without clear recognition of how they relate to NATO needs and requirements."[24]

In conclusion: For all its shortcomings, the Mutual Weapons Development Program may be said to have contributed to greater international specialization and co-operation in military research and development. Such co-operation in the civilian as well as the military sphere is fundamental to the long-run peace, prosperity, and security of the free world.

---

[24] Wakefield, *op. cit.*, p. 34.

Comment on Sherman, Mullenbach, and Sauer

Foster Lee Smith

MY MISSION is to discuss all three of the preceding papers, with particular emphasis on the last.

I cannot quite agree with Professor Sherman that the Mutual Weapons Development Program evolved "almost by accident." In 1952, a matter of high concern in Washington was the prospect of growing U. S. expenditures for European military aid to support the higher NATO force goals established at the Lisbon Conference that year. Many proposals eventually to decelerate these rising costs were explored.

There existed a body of experience in international military collaboration in research, development, and production which, if applied, might help eventually to stem the rising tide. Collaboration in the "full and complete exchange of military, air and naval information" between Canada and the United States had begun in August, 1940; in the same month a British mission led by Sir Henry Tizzard to Ottawa and Washington had instituted an era of American-British-Canadian collaboration in defense research and development which continues today. The Hyde Park Agreement of 1941 had initiated a Canadian–U.S. program of mutual defense production and economic co-operation. In 1949, at Canadian urging the United States, Britain, and Canada had begun a military standardization program encompassing research and development. The Korean War had expanded all these programs.

Thus, when Mr. Quarles turned to his staff, he found active programs of international collaboration in defense research, development, and production; their application in a program of military assistance represented no great conceptual innovation, yet offered an investment opportunity which might lead to eventual reductions in direct military aid to

Europe. Accordingly, I suggest it may be appropriate to reappraise the role of accident or chance in the beginnings and evolution of the Mutual Weapons Development Program.

Professor Sherman points out that in 1953 R&D programs among the NATO countries were duplicative, overlapping, and unco-ordinated. I was hopeful he would explain that much of this could be accounted for by the understandable reluctance of sovereign nations, in a new and untested partnership, to abandon symmetry in their respective national defense forces in order to create specialized forces for a balanced NATO force structure.

I agree with Sherman that to measure the accomplishments of the Mutual Weapons Development Program is not easy. Such measurement would seem to require a fuller description than given of the context within which the program operates: explication of how the program is related to other western scientific and military undertakings, an explanation of its project procedures from government-level agreements to hardware production, evaluation of whether lessons learned from other international collaboration programs are applicable to the role of the MWDP, and how successfully pertinent lessons have been applied.

Questions to assist further research might include some of these:

1. How will the scope and focus of the program be affected by the recent disestablishment of the Mutual Weapons Development Team and assignment of the program to the Research and Development Division, Office of the U.S. Defense Representative, North Atlantic and Mediterranean Area (DefRepNAMA)?

2. Does the hardware so far derived from the program's multilateral development projects confirm or overturn the conclusion reached in the American-British-Canadian Tripartite Technical Co-operation Program that basic and applied *research* projects are most suitable for multilateral participation but that participation in weapon *development decisions* should be *bilateral* at most?

3. Does the answer to the foregoing question account for the accelerating activity and expansion of the Mutual Weapons Data Exchange Program?

4. How has the Mutual Weapons Development Program been influenced by the NATO Groups of Experts, who advise the NATO Armaments Committee, and by the NATO Standardization Working Groups, whose increasing standardization of doctrine, organization, procedures, and material is harmonizing applied research and development aims of NATO nations?

5. Are the careful limitations of Mutual Weapons Data Exchange agreements a result of security restrictions, or do they reflect the exponential increase of scientific documentation reported by Derek Price[1] and a shortage of scientists to evaluate it, as Canadian–U.S. collaboration has shown?

Answers to the foregoing questions would, I believe, aid the measurement of the program's accomplishments.

Confidence in Sherman's conclusion that the Mutual Weapons Development Program has had "some success" could be strengthened by exploration of the following questions:

1. What other programs and policy decisions have contributed to reducing duplication in international military research and development?

2. Have the weapon systems and components so far developed under the program been in service long enough to measure adequately their operating and maintenance costs against those of comparable systems developed unilaterally or bilaterally elsewhere?

3. Has the program really developed a system for shortening the innovation cycle of weaponry, or is it that the tendency of the program, reported by Sherman, to select projects well along in development provides experience not necessarily applicable to the full research-to-hardware cycle?

---

[1] Derek J. deSolla Price, *Science since Babylon* (New Haven, 1961), p. 96.

4. What are the technological and economic factors which thus far have prevented agreements with Iceland, Luxembourg, and Portugal for mutual weapons development?

5. Can the absence of Canadian participation in the program be explained by the extent of Canadian–U.S. defense scientific collaboration and that Canada has been a donor, instead of a donee, of foreign aid?

As to Professor Sherman's view that the program as managed is restrained by the "red tape and bureaucracy involved," I first note that his conclusion is not supported by descriptions of program processes and organizational relationships which would permit the reader to form his own judgment. Second, I suggest that restraints on the program should be evaluated in light of the program's role in accommodating the larger objectives, organizations, and processes of military assistance, U.S. defense development programs, and NATO.

Sherman's generalized conclusion that more multilateral agreements are needed is worthy of a closer look. If it is meant that such multilateral agreements should provide for multilateral participation in applied research projects, for bilateral participation in development projects, or for multilateral financial support of single-source or standardized production, your discussant strongly agrees. However, if the major goal of an agreement is prompt development of effective weapons or reactors, a pact providing for multilateral participation in development decisions may provide more lessons in bargaining theory than advanced hardware. There is considerable experience available in this and other programs which indicates that timely development of weapons required by several users may be achieved more reliably by unilateral or, at most, bilateral project participation, since the addition of a third party to a bilateral arrangement multiplies the bargaining combinations six-fold. Accordingly, the referenced assertion by Wakefield that through multilateral arrangements the higher degree of co-operation achievable will bring a better unity of purpose and product at best provides inadequate guidance and, at the other extreme, confronts logic and experience.

The Mutual Weapons Development Program has been an important constituent of the United States Military Assistance Program. Professor Sherman's summary of the decline of MAP appropriations and the more rapid decline of their application to European defense reflects the effective coupling of U.S. economic assistance and military aid with the self-discipline and hard work of our allies. The ultimate triumph of military assistance will be in its extinguishment upon the creation of economic and military conditions which remove its reason for being. The research and training institutions founded by the MWDP and its Mutual Weapons Data-Exchange Program, whose growth continues to accelerate, have become important members of the NATO defense research and development structure; they are earning their own keep and are no longer wards of the Military Assistance Program. Projects begun by the Mutual Weapons Development Program have helped catalyze research and development in at least ten European nations and have put weapons in the hands of NATO forces. For its first eight yers, NATO was diligently occupied in building forces-in-being. In the last five years, it has devoted increasing energy and resources to longer-range scientific and defense development activities and has now developed mechanisms, with the important assistance of the MWDP, to continue and exploit work begun by this program.

From all three papers some similarities between Euratom and MWDP appear: In the beginning, neither program had as its only objective, or criteria for success, the most economical development of equipment. Second, economic lessons to be derived from both undertakings should be approached with some caution since neither endeavor is competitive or profit-maximizing in the usual sense; both have other, more important, goals. Third, their choices among alternatives are made in the face of great uncertainties in an era of rapid scientific and economic change. Fourth, both programs demonstrate the difficulties in balancing long-term and short-run development objectives. As long as development cycles remain large multiples of budget cycles, joint endeavors such as Euratom and the MWDP may be expected to hedge great risks with an insurance strategy of expending significant effort on projects which will produce earlier, if less dramatic, advances. Fifth, both programs are confronted squarely with problems on patent rights in which the balance between public interest and private incentive is difficult to strike. Finally, both programs are important warps in the fabric of "interdependence among free nations which promises one day to bind together a new Atlantic partnership."[2]

---

[2] *Department of State Bulletin*, XLVII, No. 1204 (July 13, 1962), 131–33. A report of an address made by the President at Independence Hall, Philadelphia, July 4, 1962.

VII

THE EMERGENT NATIONS

ECONOMICS OF TECHNOLOGY FOR LESS-DEVELOPED AREAS

Richard A. Tybout

A VARIETY of issues in public policy have focussed attention on economic development in the last two decades. East-West rivalries combined with the burgeoning political power of masses long suppressed by Malthusian subsistence have produced a new awareness of an old economic problem. The result has been a substantial growth in academic as well as political interest in the problems of less-developed areas.

Since technological change played a crucial role in the economic development of the Western world, it is natural to expect that technology will be a crucial variable in economic progress of the new nations. Moses Abramovitz, introducing a discussion of capital for underdeveloped countries, stated the point: "It is probably safe to say that only the discovery and exploitation of new knowledge rivals capital formation as a cause of economic progress."[1] Yet our knowledge of technological change is, to say the least, no rival for our knowledge of capital formation.

There is no shortage of interest in both subjects on the part of the emergent nations, but there is considerable difference in the value of the advice we can offer. Perhaps we are on newer ground (if that is possible) in dealing with the emergent nations than in any other part of the economics of technology. At the same time, the operational significance of the subject assumes first-line importance.

FACTOR PROPORTIONS

It is customary to note the great difference in relative amounts of capital and labor available in advanced and primi-

---

[1] "Economics of Growth," in B. Haley (ed.), *A Survey of Contemporary Economics* (Homewood, Ill., 1952) II, 146.

tive societies. To simplify the matter somewhat, today's advanced nations are beset with a potential surfeit of investable funds in the form of Keynesian excess saving. The have-not nations are beset with the opposite problem of overpopulation and deficient sources of capital. The contrast has been made with precision and due recognition of the complications of post-Keynesian economic theory by William Fellner, who observes as a conclusion:

> One disadvantage of basing economic development in primitive countries on Western knowledge is that Western technological progress seems to have adjusted to Western resource positions which, of course, are different from the resource positions of primitive countries. Thus, the present problem of primitive countries frequently is to choose between a backward capital-saving technology and an innovated Western labor-saving technology.[2]

Fellner's observations were made as obiter dicta in the context of a different, though related, analysis. Nevertheless, they furnish an adequate starting point for the present discussion. The new nations are faced with technologies that have been developed for a different economic environment than that in which they seek to bring economic progress. What problems of adjustment are involved in using these technologies? What are the implications of such adjustments for the social order? And what are the implications for future technological change?

With reasonable assumptions as to the rate of growth of per capita product in underdeveloped countries, it can be shown that for those now starting to gain economically (many are not yet starting) a time period of one or two centuries may be necessary to reach the level of per capita product currently prevailing in the United States; if, in fact, this level is ever reached.[3] About half as much time would be needed to reach

---

[2] "Does the Market Direct the Relative Factor-Saving Effects of Technological Progress?", National Bureau of Economic Research, *The Rate and Direction of Inventive Activity: Economic and Social Factors* (Princeton, N.J., 1962), pp. 187–88.

[3] The calculation assumes a 2.25 per cent annual compounding of per capita gross national product as a high rate of growth and 1.25 per cent as a low rate of growth. For numerical values and other considerations in making the calculations, see P. N. Rosenstein-Rodan, "International Aid for Underdeveloped Countries," *Review of Economics and Statistics*, Vol. XLIII (May, 1961).

the level of per capita gross national product of western Europe. If periods of time of the order of magnitude of a century are involved, it is clear that a good deal of change in social structure and technologies is possible.

CAPITAL EFFICIENCY

The history of economic development in the Western world offers limited prospect for progress without extensive capital investment. The evidence is that today's advanced economies typically experienced increases in over-all capital output ratios from times of earliest record through periods varying up to a century in length as economic development proceeded.[4] Where development has been in progress for a sufficient length of time, there has been a tendency for the capital output ratio to go through a maximum. In the United States, this is usually considered to have taken place in the second and third decades of the twentieth century.

Two causes of the over-all change are relevant for less-developed countries. First, there is a shift in product-mix as development proceeds. A number of capital-intensive industries are required at early stages of economic development. These include, especially, public utilities and transportation, generally classed as social overhead services, and such manufacturing industries as machinery and metal products.[5] Since these industries are likely to be built early in the progress of development, available technologies will not be much different from those which exist today.

The second cause of the downward movement of capital/output ratios is the only one that has been effective in the United States. Capital/output ratios in eighteen of twenty-two major American industries increased from 1880 to about

[4] S. K. Kuznets, "Quantitative Aspects of the Economic Growth of Nations: VI, Long-Term Trends in Capital Formation Proportions," *Economic Development and Cultural Change*, Vol. IX (July, 1961).

[5] Details can be found in H. B. Chenery, "Patterns of Industrial Growth," *American Economic Review*, Vol. L (September, 1960).

1920 and have since declined. Peak capital/output ratios were reached in the different industries over periods of time one or two decades apart, but the evidence is sufficiently strong to substantiate the general pattern of change despite certain weaknesses in the data.[6]

The next question is whether improved capital productivity is the result of increased scale of plant. The evidence on this point is indirect, though nonetheless conclusive. Capital/output ratios decline continuously with the size of firm in each of twelve of the twenty-two industries and decline to the next-to-the-smallest class of firm ($100,000 to $1,000,000 asset size) in fifteen of the twenty-two cases. The structure of capital/output relationships with size was not affected by the over-all decline of industry-wide capital/output ratios.[7] The difficulty with these results is that they apply to total assets classes of firms rather than plants. It is necessary to proceed on the hypothesis that smaller firms by and large operate smaller plants. I believe this hypothesis is valid enough to infer greater capital efficiency in smaller plants.

So interpreted, the above facts suggest that improved capital efficiency in recent decades has not been the result of increased size of plant but that technological progress has been responsible. Capital productivity has gone over a hump, to the advantage of late-coming nations who may be interested in introducing modern technologies now. In many industries, capital/output ratios were, in 1953, half or less what they were at their peak some decades previous.[8] The quantitative significance of this last fact is the greater in the face of known increases in concentration of industry in recent decades, which would give more weight to the larger, less-capital-efficient firms.

There are two other respects in which the decrease of capital/output ratios with size appears to be favorable for the emergent nations. First, forced-draft economic development results in the creation of interdependencies. Economic

---

[6] Daniel Creamer, Sergei Dobrovolsky, and Israel Borenstein, *Capital in Manufacturing and Mining* (Princeton, 1960), chap. v.

[7] *Ibid.*

[8] *Ibid.*

development must take cognizance of the input-output relationships among industries in the sense that where domestic
sources of supply or markets for intermediate industrial products are concerned, the capacity constructed in one industry
is limited by capacity in existence or soon to be constructed
in other industries. One way to achieve balance with limited
investment capital is to build relatively small facilities in a
number of related industries.

Second, because of specialization in capital equipment,
American manufacturing typically employs less capital-intensive methods of production in smaller plants. It is thus a
reasonable inference that the decrease in capital/output ratios
at the small end of the size scale results from less intensive
use of capital. Any evidence that manufacturing capital can
be used in labor-intensive applications is promising, but must
be examined more closely with special concern for the distinction between skilled and unskilled labor, as will be noted
below.

The possibilities of increasing the marginal productivity of
capital by using it in combination with greater amounts of
unskilled labor are best known in agriculture and construction. If labor is sufficiently cheap, the best use of capital may
be to buy shovels rather than a bulldozer. To take another
example, there is reputed to be a dam in India half of which
was built with heavy construction equipment, while the other
half was built by women carrying small baskets of concrete
on their heads. The two halves are identical in appearance
and performance, but obviously not identical in factor proportions used for construction.

Similar flexibility of combining proportions is not found in
many industrial technologies. All too often, a choice must be
made between technologies which result in fixed proportions
of capital and labor, impeding short-run adjustments of work
force and sometimes resulting in structural unemployment.[9]
Arrow, Chenery, and associates have recently published a
statistical study of labor-capital proportions in selected in-

[9] R. S. Echaus, "Factor Proportions in Underdeveloped Areas,"
American Economic Review, Vol. XLV (September, 1955).

dustries for a cross-section of countries in all stages of economic development. One of the main conclusions of their study is that the elasticity of substitution between capital and labor in manufacturing is typically less than unity.[10] The significance of this finding is to confirm at the aggregative level a general tendency for labor to substitute imperfectly for capital in manufacturing.

SKILLED LABOR

The difficulties inherent in imperfect substitutability of labor for capital are compounded by shortages of skilled labor. Skilled labor is usually required for modern technologies, especially in maintenance but also often in operation. Lack of education, low standards of public health, malnutrition, and absenteeism contribute to the problem. Specific training for industrial jobs can fill the need in part and is properly regarded as a capital investment. For the rest, general social change is required. General education and public health likewise require investments. Moreover, there is the fact that industrial plants usually require a supporting urban community, with housing for the labor force and various utility and other services for the plant itself. Underdeveloped countries are rural, almost by definition (as follows from reliance on primary industry). In some cases, such as India and China, urban communities with facilities of a sort and urban unemployment exist. The situation facilitates the installation of industry, but hardly provides all of the community services needed for industrial plants and an efficient labor force. Other underdeveloped countries must create more urban facilities from the ground up.

---

[10] K. J. Arrow, H. B. Chenery, B.S. Minhas, and R. M. Solow, "Capital-Labor Substitution and Economic Efficiency," *Review of Economics and Statistics*, Vol. XLIII (August, 1961). As the authors note, this result is in conflict with the Cobb-Douglas production function, which implies an elasticity of unity.

A further difficulty arises from the tendency to import social institutions as well as technologies from the advanced nations. Social-security legislation, minimum-wage standards, and restrictions on work practices through labor organizations are often encountered. Galenson and Leibenstein cite the case of Mexican textile manufacturing where low productivity is attributed in large measure to "present contract legislation for the industry, which stipulates the number of workers to be employed in relation to the capacity of the mills, and establishes an inflexible basis for the proportion between production and wages."[11] Several other examples in the same vein are supplied, including the prevalence of make-work devices where productivity improvements threaten jobs.[12]

One solution is to go all the way to automated technologies. Higgins cites the example of a fully automated refinery in Bombay and a completely automatic water-filtration plant for the city of Djakarta.[13] Where automated technologies are available and permit sufficiently high capital productivity, the way to avoid high labor costs is to adopt automation. There is, of course, no general presumption that unskilled labor has no utility in manufacturing, but only that where industrial skills are involved, the less-developed countries are dealing with a factor input even more expensive than capital. Similar reasoning leads Kuznets to favor the more nearly automatic machinery of American manufacturing, which requires low levels of industrial skills, to the less capital-intensive technologies of some European countries.[14] In some cases, labor-intensive and capital-intensive technologies may exist side by

---

[11] Walter Galenson and Harvey Leibenstein, "Investment Criteria, Productivity, and Economic Development," *Quarterly Journal of Economics*, LXIX (August, 1955), 360. Galenson and Leibenstein supply the quoted passage from United Nations, Department of Economic Affairs, *Labor Productivity of the Cotton Textile Industry in Five Latin-American Countries* (New York, 1951).

[12] *Ibid.* See also examples given by C. P. Kindleberger, *Economic Development* (New York, 1958), p. 173.

[13] Benjamin Higgins, *Economic Development* (New York, 1959), pp. 672–73.

[14] S. Kuznets, "Toward a Theory of Economic Growth," in R. Lekachman (ed.), *National Policy for Economic Welfare at Home and Abroad* (New York, 1955), p. 98.

side with no implication of economic contradictions. Automatic devices for metal cutting in one department are not necessarily inconsistent with labor-intensive methods for metal conveying in another department of the same plant. The first use relatively scarce skilled labor. The second employ abundant unskilled labor.

Insofar as the use of automatic technologies is concerned, a paradox seems evident: the underdeveloped countries with the greatest share of human suffering seem likely to experience the adverse effects of automation feared by American unionism. Norbert Wiener introduced his landmark work on cybernetics with the observation that the second industrial revolution—by which he meant the substitution of electronic controls for man's nervous system—would mean that "the average human being of mediocre attainments or less [would have] nothing to sell that is worth anyone's money to buy."[15] If automation results in sufficient increases of capital productivity, it is conceivable that the emergent nations may never reach the point of devoting a major percentage of their labor force to manufacturing industry.

Traditional economic development with first-industrial-revolution technologies has been marked by a shift of the labor force out of the primary industries, agriculture and mining, into manufacturing. In late stages of economic development, the shift is out of manufacturing into the service trades and government.[16] Now, the pattern might well be shifted somewhat for the new nations. Entering Wiener's second industrial revolution with no backlog of industrial skills, their comparative advantage may well fall in the more easily automated industries. Accordingly, there is the long-term prospect that they will short-circuit manufacturing in some degree and concentrate instead on service areas. Whether such a result will be gainful and humanly satisfying is another question.

---

[15] *Cybernetics* (New York, 1948), p. 38.

[16] Empirical confirmation of this pattern and related details on the structural aspects of economic development can be found in H. B. Chenery, "Patterns of Industrial Growth," *op. cit.*

There is a possible corroboration of this tendency in the existing pattern of international trade. Professor Leontief has drawn our attention to the fact that the United States tends to export products that require less capital and more labor than do the products imported.[17] That is to say, American comparative advantage is not with the more capital-intensive products, as might be expected. We are heavy importers of lumber, paper, chemicals, and nonferrous metals. We are strong exporters of machinery of all kinds, agricultural machinery, electrical machinery, transportation equipment, and so on. Leontief suggested an explanation of this result that has since become known as the Leontief Paradox: that American advantage in relatively labor-intensive exports results from greater relative efficiency and despite the relative scarcity of American labor.[18] The explanation sounds familiar. It is, in fact, the other side of our preceding observations on labor skills in underdeveloped areas.

Automation had not proceeded very far at the time Professor Leontief wrote (1953), and hence his results do not reflect its impact. (Nor would trade patterns today.) Moreover, it is true that automation will impinge on jobs requiring industrial skills. Otherwise it would not work to the advantage of nations without such skills. But just as the first industrial revolution passed by some trades such as carpentry and skilled apparel fitting, certain other trades may well require skills not suitable for programming and hence survive the second industrial revolution. In this event, comparative advantage would remain with those skills, and it would be entirely consistent to find the emergent nations specializing in basic industrial products and those finished goods that can be produced by automated processes, while today's advanced nations retain comparative advantage in the remaining skilled areas.

17 W. W. Leontief, "Domestic Production and Foreign Trade: The American Capital Position Re-examined," *Proceedings of the American Philosophical Society*, Vol. XCVII (1953).

18 *Ibid.* Arrow, Chenery, *et. al., op. cit.*, question the Leontief Paradox but do not conclusively refute it, nor are they able to explain his results on any other basis that would be consistent with their analysis.

COTTAGE INDUSTRY

We began by noting the possibility that the emergent nations have an immediate choice between modern technologies that may not be best suited to their resources and primitive technologies. The latter do, in fact, fit the resource structure of the new nations and might therefore be expected to play a part in economic development well into the future.

Mahatma Ghandi's views on the importance of hand-woven textiles for the economic future of India are well-known. The necessary skills are, of course, already existent. A considerable opportunity for saving capital is apparent in figures cited by a distinguished Indian economist: capital investment runs $20,000 per person employed in the steel industry; about $2,000 to $2,500 in consumer-goods factories, but only $120 to $140 per artisan family in cottage industry.[19] Thus, capital-saving can be expected from two sources: the use of labor-intensive technologies (cottage industry) and the absence of concomitant investment in labor training.

Further capital saving results from the location of production facilities in (rural) communities that are already established. The question is not so much whether social overheads (utility services, public education, and other public services) could be more efficiently provided at a given per capita level in an urban as compared with a rural community, but rather how much *more* social overhead investment would be required to support an increase in industry. The costs are greatest where population relocation from rural to urban areas is required. Over the long run, economic development does, in fact, envisage such a relocation of population. But for the immediate future in any investment program, consideration must be given to the fact that most of the people in

_____

[19] C. P. C. Mahalanobis, as reported in C. P. Kindleberger, *op. cit.*, p. 179.

the least-developed countries are now living in rural communities. Somehow or other, they are housed and obtain
drinking water and what public services there might be. Perhaps higher standards of public service are desired, but it
should be remembered that an influx of population to urban
areas requires that housing and all social overheads be provided from new investments. Continuing residence in rural
communities means that improvements can be built on pre-
existing investments and are more readily postponable when
necessary.

Spontaneous migration from rural to urban poverty is not
unknown in underdeveloped countries. Institutional difficulties inhibit the integration of migrants into the urban
community. In a rural community, the provision of housing
and drinking water is undertaken by individuals in a simpler
organizational pattern that gives maximum opportunity for
self-employment. Seasonal work in agriculture affords opportunities for idle time occupations. The more complex economic
organization of urban areas often does not. Casual urban
labor cannot directly undertake provision for elementary biological needs, but must work through often imperfectly functioning labor markets of the sort previously described.

The opportunity to integrate productive activities with seasonal agriculture in the rural sector is not limited to the provision of housing and rural overheads. Cottage industry and
small-scale manufacturing can similarly be integrated with
agricultural demands on the rural labor force. Considerable
emphasis will need to continue on agricultural production for
the early decades of economic development. The possibilities
of high marginal capital productivity in labor-intensive agriculture have been noted. To these we now add the possibilities
of using capital efficiently in labor-intensive local manufacturing.

The relatively greater abundance of labor skills for handicraft production, the comparative dearth of skilled labor of
machine-age trades, and the capital demands required to establish a level of health, education, training, and industrial
competence in an urban environment combine to restrain

central manufacturing and to sustain local production in the early decades of economic development.

The result is that labor-intensive technology leads to high marginal efficiency of capital in cottage industry. Simultaneously the most modern technologies lead to high marginal efficiency of capital in automated processes. These two appear entirely compatible, omitting in the middle western-style skilled-labor manufacturing.

PLANNING TECHNOLOGICAL CHANGE

The most conspicuous avenues for new developments of science and technology are in agriculture and other extractive industries. In these fields, it is mainly a matter of adapting existing knowledge of weed killers, fertilizers, and implements to the climate, terrain, and crops at hand. Similarly minor adaptations are implied in utilizing existing science for the exploitation of minerals, forests, and fisheries. Over the longer term, there is some prospect for improvements in desalinization of water and perhaps for weather controls. Since many of the new nations have large arid regions, these developments could redound to their comparative advantage.

It is difficult to suggest analogous avenues for the development of industrial technologies that would increase productivity and at the same time lead to more suitable combining proportions of capital and labor (skilled and unskilled) for the new nations. Our previous conclusion favoring automated over skilled-labor technologies recognizes the social capital required for the latter in the form of education and training. Perhaps this is a case where social adaptation to technology will be more important than adaptation of technology to society. I have in mind the creation of a technological society in underdeveloped areas that will breed high-level technological competence and labor skills as well.

The advanced nations benefit from centuries of the scientific tradition, conditioning their educational institutions and providing the basis for engineering applications. Our youth grow up in a mechanical environment. The facts of life include the know-how of power mowers, jalopies, and short-wave radios. It is this environment that produces technological progress. The new nations might well consider the use of more second-hand capital goods, if only for the training they get in trying to make them work. Second-hand transportation equipment is not expensive and is already used to a considerable extent in underdeveloped areas. The industrialization of Japan was made possible by second-hand British textile machinery.

A combination of three forces will work to determine the future pattern of technology in the emergent nations. They are capital formation, the growth of labor skills, and technological change itself. From their present positions, all three have some distance to move before they are in mutual adjustment.

RESEARCH AND DEVELOPMENT
FOR THE EMERGENT NATIONS

Kenneth E. Boulding

TO AVOID ANY POSSIBLE MISUNDERSTANDING, it should be made clear that the following paper does not purport to describe what is going on in research and development in the emergent nations, for the very good reason that the author does not know. It is rather an attempt to state the nature of the problem which is involved in the development of these countries and to try to identify the role which should be played in the process by research and development.

Economic development is a polite name for a revolutionary change in the state of mankind. This has been said many times before, but it can hardly be reiterated enough. In particular it must be stressed that we do *not* mean by economic development mere "growth" in the sense of an increase in population of the same kind of people producing more of the same kind of things. Economic development means different kinds of people producing different kinds of things from their ancestors and ancestral goods. I elsewhere call this the "second great transition" in the state of man, the first transition being, of course, the change from precivilized to civilized societies which followed upon the domestication of crops and animals and the concentration, by fair means or foul, of the resulting food surplus to feed the emerging cities. The transition through which we are now passing is at least as large and spectacular as that first transition which began some eight or ten thousand years ago—so much so that I have described the new state of man toward which we are moving as "post-civilization."

This great transition from civilized society of the classical type to post-civilized society has many facets: economic, political, social, psychological, philosophical, educational, and religious. It is indeed a change which affects every area of human life and reaches far down into the human personality. Nevertheless its base is an economic change, and it is not surprising that most of the discussion of the transition take place under the heading of economic development. The essence of both of the great transitions consists in a rise of the productivity of human labor and particularly an increase in the product per man-hour. The transition from precivilized to civilized societies depended essentially on the development of agriculture, which increased the productivity of human labor in food production to the point at which the food producer could produce a surplus of food beyond his family needs for subsistence. It was this surplus that fed the artisans, the craftsmen, the builders, the priests, the philosophers, and the soldiers who built the classical civilizations. The second great transition represents an increase in the productivity of labor even more spectacular than the first. In classical civilization that is represented, say, by ancient Rome in the time of Augustus, or by Indonesia today, it takes 75 to 80 per cent of the population to produce the food that feeds the total. In the United States today, we can produce all the food we need with 10 per cent of the population, and pretty soon it will be 5 per cent, and we still have burdensome agricultural surpluses. Not only in agriculture, but in all fields of manufacturing, the increase in the output per man-hour has likewise been spectacular. With the advent of automation, we may find that we can produce all the manufactured goods we need with 10 or 15 per cent of the population as opposed to the 30 per cent which we require today. A day is within sight in the United States when we will be able to spare some 80 per cent of the population for the tertiary industries, and we will have indeed a leisure society. Europe is following rapidly behind the United States in this development and may, indeed, at the present rate of progress, overtake the United States in another generation or two. Japan is enjoying a similar development, and so is the Soviet Union, for the great transition pays no attention to the cold war. It can be argued that socialist development, while it may be more rapid at first, has a lower ultimate ceiling than development in what might be called cybernetic capitalism. What is more important, however, is that the socialist countries, at least in the temperate zone, are participating successfully in this movement toward post-civilization; and, as a result, in spite of the great ideological gulf, the difference in technology and general modes of life between, say, the United States and the Soviet Union is much less than between either of these two countries and their neighbors to the south, which are still in the age of civilization.

I

The quantitative aspect of economic development can be expressed in a very simple formula. Let us suppose first that for any particular country we can divide the labor force into two parts: L_d, which is the number of people employed in domestic industry, and L_e, which is the number of people employed in export industries. If then P_d is the productivity of labor in domestic industries and P_e is the productivity of labor in export industries, and T is the terms of trade, that is, the quantity of imports received per unit of exports, the total real product of the society, Y, is given by the equation

$$Y = L_d P_d + L_e P_e T \, .$$

If y is the per capita income, this is given by the second equation:

$$y = \frac{L_d P_d + L_e P_e T}{L_d + L_e + L_n}$$

where L_n is the number of people not employed, that is, not in the labor force, so that the denominator of the second equation represents the total population.

What we mean by economic development is a long, persistent increase in per capita income, y, which carries it to ten or even twenty times its "civilized" level, and which may even carry it beyond this. Per capita income in the United

States today, at about $2,000, is about twenty times the per capita income of $100 which is characteristic of "classical" civilized societies; and a per capita income of $5,000 is by no means inconceivable. We now look at the second equation to see what element in the equation can result in such a steady increase in y. The answer is obvious from a mere inspection of the equation: it will have to be an increase in P_d or in P_e or in both. This does not rule out the possibility of short-run movements within the society which can increase per capita income without changes in the over-all productivity of labor. Thus, if $P_eT > P_d$, that is, if the productivity in terms of domestic products or imports is greater in the export industries than it is in the domestic industries, we can increase per capita income for a time, at any rate, by shifting the labor force from domestic industry into export industry. This is a process, however, which eventually comes to an end simply because, as it goes on, P_d is likely to rise and P_eT is likely to fall, either because of declining productivity or worsening terms of trade. Similarly, for a period a country may enjoy an increase in per capita income because its terms of trade are improving, that is, T is increasing. This also, however, is a process which cannot go on forever and which is quite likely to be reversed after a time, and it cannot be relied on to produce that long and persistent increase in per capita income, y, which is the essence of economic development.

There is no escape from the conclusion, therefore, that it is only by a large and persistent increase in the productivity of labor in both the domestic and the export industries that economic development in the sense in which we have been using the term can be achieved.

The next question is obvious: what are the factors in the structure of the society which lead to a long, persistent increase in the productivity of labor? I have said hardly anything so far which is not either in or just below the surface of Adam Smith's *Wealth of Nations*, and Adam Smith has some sage words to say on the causes of increasing productivity likewise:

This great increase in the quantity of work which, in consequence of the division of labour, the same number of people are capable of performing, is owing to three different circumstances; first, to the increase of dexterity in every particular workman; secondly, to the saving of the time which is commonly lost in passing from one species of work to another; and lastly, to the invention of a great number of machines which facilitate and abridge labour, and enable one man to do the work of many.[1]

It is important to observe that all three of the causes which Adam Smith mentioned are aspects of the learning process in man. By dexterity, we mean essentially the diminution in the time of performing any particular act which results from constant repetition. This involves a learning process mainly in the lower nervous system, and it has, of course, a fairly well-defined upper limit which is generally reached fairly early in the life of the specialized laborer. A man with a machete acquires, for instance, a skill in the cutting of sugar cane which is far beyond the capability of the amateur, but he usually acquires his maximum skill in his teens. His productivity does not rise thereafter, and indeed declines in later life.

Adam Smith's second cause, the time lost in going from one task to another, is seldom mentioned nowadays. Nevertheless, it also represents an interesting application of the learning problem. When we take up a task newly, even though we may have done it many times before, a certain process of relearning has to go on before we hit our stride. This process is economized if we can devote a substantial period of time to the same task. The professor who must go from teaching to research to conferences and back to teaching again, and who longs for a solid slab of time in which he can do any one thing, may testify to the acuity of Adam Smith's observation. Nevertheless, this also is a learning process the horizon of which is reached very quickly. If we try to concentrate the task too much, we fall into monotony, which may even impair dexterity; and in a good many assembly-line processes it has been found advantageous to

---

[1] Adam Smith, *Wealth of Nations* (London, 1926), p. 7.

vary the task when it has become too monotonous and too concentrated.

Adam Smith mentions only incidentally in connection with his second cause the problem of intensity of application to a task. He observes that when the task is changed frequently, "a man commonly saunters a little in turning his hand from one sort of employment to another." Sauntering is certainly a major problem in a good many emergent nations, and it is a habit of life which the tropical sun, especially, makes extremely agreeable. The psychological origins of the orientation of the person toward achievement rather than toward sauntering through life is a problem of great subtlety and complexity. As David McClelland has pointed out, the division of labor is merely part of this problem, for even though the division of labor itself, by making tasks simple and well-defined, may help to encourage the achievement motive, the division of labor is by no means a sufficient explanation of the differences we find in different societies. This problem extends to cover the Weberian thesis regarding the relation of the Protestant ethic to the origin of capitalism and indirectly to the achievement motive, and also raises very interesting questions regarding the various substitutes for the Protestant ethic which have been found in other cultures. Even the elimination of sauntering, however, and the development of a society of eager beavers is a learning process that likewise has a limited horizon from the point of view of economic development. Hard work might increase the product two or three times in a society dedicated to the delicate social arts of laziness, but it is inconceivable that hard work alone should increase the product by twenty times.

It is when we come to Adam Smith's third cause, therefore, that we find the key to continued development with high horizons. Adam Smith observes that even the division of labor itself is likely to promote invention, and he quotes the delightful and possibly apocryphal story of the boy who tied the string on the handle of the valve to another part of the machine. He goes on, however—and the temptation to quote from him is irresistible—

All the improvements of machinery, however, have by no means been inventions of those who had occasion to use the machines. Many improvements have been made by the ingenuity of the makers of the machines, when to make them became the business of a peculiar trade; and some by that of those who are called philosophers or men of speculation, whose trade it is not to do anything, but to observe everything; and who, upon that account, are often capable of combining together the powers of the most distant and dissimilar objects. In the progress of society, philosophy or speculation becomes, like every other employment, the principal or sole trade and occupation of a particular class of citizens.[2]

Now we feel that old Adam has put his finger on the heart of the matter. It is as we develop a specialized class of people engaged in research and development and, one would like to add, education, that we find at last a learning process whose horizon seems to be almost unlimited, and the rate of economic development toward these broad horizons would seem to be determined mainly by the proportion of specialized resources which the society is prepared to devote to this end, modified, of course, by the efficiency with which these resources are used. Adam Smith goes on to observe, incidentally, that the division of labor even within the sciences themselves enhances the productivity of this activity. "Each individual becomes more expert in his own peculiar branch, more work is done upon the whole, and the quantity of science is considerably increased by it."[3]

It is interesting that in these early chapters Adam Smith hardly mentions the accumulation of capital as a force in increasing the wealth of nations. He does so later on, in Book II: "As the accumulation of stock must, in the nature of things, be previous to the division of labour, so labour can be more and more subdivided in proportion only as stock is previously more and more accumulated."[4] It is clear, however, that he does not regard capital accumulation as the most essential element in economic development, but rather as a

---

[2] *Ibid.*, pp. 9–10.
[3] *Ibid.*, p. 10.
[4] *Ibid.*, pp. 241–42.

prerequisite and a co-operator with that process of division of labor and human learning by which productivity is mainly increased. In this he shows a sound instinct. The statistical studies by Moses Abramovitch of the growth of the United States economy, for instance, show convincingly that the mere increase of capital makes a relatively small contribution to economic development, and that the increase in productivity on which economic development rests is mainly the result of changes in the structure and form of capital and in the structure of human skills and knowledge rather than mere accumulation as such. Economic development is not the mere piling up of old things; it is the making of new things which were not made before in ways that were not done before. The learning process is therefore absolutely crucial to it. It is a process which has its parallel in nature in the structuring of living bodies by the genetic material, and the teaching-learning relationship is central to it. We can indeed think of material capital as frozen knowledge, for it would never come into existence were there not images of it in the minds of men; and the more complex these images, the more complex and productive are the material capital structures which these images produce. The mere piling up of stocks of wheat, for instance, is not in itself economic development. It is only as these stocks are used to feed people who think, plan, design, and construct new material forms of capital that these stocks become part of the living, ongoing, developing fabric of society.

This structural process, then, which is the foundation of continued economic development, has three aspects: research, education, and development. Research is the acquisition of knowledge which nobody knew before. Education is the dissemination of this knowledge among the population. It is hard to measure the amount of knowledge in any particular head, but the notion of the per capita amount of knowledge in a society is at least qualitatively admissible. Without education, of course, research does very little to increase the per capita knowledge of a society, as it remains in the head of the original discoverer. Education includes not only formal education in schools; it also includes the innumerable agencies and activity by which the knowledge of any person may be increased. It includes, for instance, the press and the mass media; it includes gossip and personal conversation; it includes personal observation; it includes much of what goes on in the family and in face-to-face groups; and we must regard formal education essentially as a part of this larger process. It is a part, however, which has a peculiar responsibility, which is that of supplementing and frequently correcting the informal learning processes. We can roughly distinguish two types of cultures: the one, folk culture in which the learning process in the society, the transmission of the culture from one generation to another, is accomplished largely through face-to-face groups—the family, grandmothers, and other informal institutions. At the other extreme, we have scientific culture which is transmitted mainly through formal means and through formal educational institutions. Interesting problems arise where there are contradictions and tensions between these two educational processes, and a good deal of the social and political upheaval in emerging societies can be attributed to the tension between these two competing cultures.

Development, in the narrow sense in which it is contrasted with research and education, is not, perhaps, very different from education. There are, however, processes which are distinct enough to deserve a particular name. These are the processes by which new knowledge is translated into patterns of human behavior and into human artifacts of new kinds, such as new machinery and equipment. This might be thought of as the engineering function as distinct from the function of pure science, and it is in a sense a mixture of research and education. For new knowledge to be effective, it must be implanted in a good many more heads than those of its originators, but pure theoretical knowledge must also give rise to knowledge of a practical kind. There must be know-how as well as know-what. Know-how is as much a matter of the development of organization and of teaching patterns as it is the development of new material structures.

II

I have contended that if we have enough of research, education, and development (R, E, and D), we do not need to be either Red or dead. The evidence that we have, such as, for instance, the studies of Zvi Grilches on the rate of return on investment in research in hybrid corn, and the various studies which have been made of the rate of return of investments in education, suggest that the general rate of return on R, E, and D is substantially above the rate of return of investment in material capital. When this is so in any country, we can state with a great deal of confidence that a mere quantitative increase in the absolute amount of resources devoted to R, E, and D will increase the rate of economic development, even if diverted from low-return material investment. There is a certain tendency for countries which have been influenced by European culture to regard research, education, and development as if they were frills or social services—that is, things which are nice to do for people if you can afford it. There is hardly any point of view which is so potentially disastrous. R, E, and D must be thought of as investment with a high rate of return, and it must be given top priority in any society that is ambitious for development.

The mere quantity of resources devoted to R, E, and D, however, is not necessarily an indication of the effectiveness of those resources. One of the most urgent needs of our time is research into R, E, and D itself, that is, into the social rates of return that attend different kinds of research, education, and development. If we look upon the whole developmental process as a learning process, it is obvious that some processes and some institutions teach people faster and better than others. It is obvious also that there are some things which it is more important to learn than others. A research effort which is devoted mainly to increasing man's destructive power or his capacity to get to the moon will probably have less impact on the rate of growth of human welfare than research which is more directly pointed at that end. Similarly, education which is devoted to memorizing the classics and holy books is not likely to be so useful in economic development as education in science and engineering. Likewise, in many areas development can be sadly misapplied, and there is no country in the world in which the boondoggle is unknown.

I have been arguing that when we look at the world effort in R, E, and D, we find a very profound misapplication of intellectual resources. The most acute problems of the world lie in the area of social systems. This is even true of problems of water supply and health, which we often think of as belonging exclusively to physical or to biological systems. The problem of war and peace is very clearly a problem in social systems. Yet we persist in devoting the major part of our intellectual resources, by far, to research, education, and development in physical and biological systems, with the result that the very existence of man is threatened by his incapacity at handling the social system. Peace research, for instance, which easily could have rates of return in terms of sheer disaster insurance reckoned at thousands or tens of thousands of a per cent, is almost totally neglected; and we see much the same pattern of neglect of social systems in the treatment of water resources, flood control, irrigation, agriculture, urban development, transportation, recreation, and social security.

Next to the neglect of peace research, the neglect of an adequate R, E, and D program in economic development is the most striking. Perhaps one of the most spectacular benefits from disarmament would be the release of the intellectual resources which are now tied up in plotting man's destruction or in furthering his vanity and idle curiosity in space exploration for use in solving the intractable problems of the emergent nations. With the amount of intellectual resources we presently devote to this problem, I think it is extremely likely that economic development in most of the tropical belt will be unsuccessful. We have in the making, indeed, a major human tragedy on a scale unknown to all previous history. We all know that the impact of civilization on precivilized societies has been almost without exception disastrous. In one or two cases borrowings from the more advanced societies gave the precivilized societies new resources and new vitality, such as, for instance, the introduction of the horse among the Plains Indians. In the long run, however, the impact of civilized on precivilized societies has been like that of an iron pot on a clay pot. The precivilized societies have been shattered, and they exist either in a decadent state or their members are absorbed, often unhappily, in the form of minority groups and second-class citizens, into the civilized societies which have overcome them. What we may be facing in the world of today is an even more frightful tragedy: that impact of post-civilized societies on the civilized societies. It is easy to spread some of the techniques of post-civilization to the civilized societies, for instance, movies and DDT. These innovations, however, may easily create a dynamic to which the society cannot adapt. Movies, radio, and other modern forms of communication destroy the traditional image of the world and create the "revolution of rising expectations." DDT, by controlling the mosquito, produces a dramatic diminution of mortality and creates a 3 per cent annum population increase which in itself can easily frustrate the expectations which communications have aroused. The combination of aroused expectations and the inability to fulfil these expectations may be totally disastrous, and the civilized societies of the tropical belt may easily lapse into violence, anomie, anarchy, or even apathy. This is a gloomy view which one hopes history will falsify. Whether it comes true or not, however, depends in no small measure on the amount of intellectual resources which we devote to solving the problem on a world scale. The terrible fact today is that we are devoting so little to this problem that the chance of failure is very high. It needs, I suspect, a degree of intensity and an absolute amount of R, E, and D at least equivalent to what the space programs of the two great powers now involve. Yet nothing like this seems to be forthcoming from any direction.

We need, for instance, a massive research program on the methods of population control which are appropriate to particular cultures. The fact that two countries as culturally diverse as Ireland and Japan have both had a reasonable success in population control indicates that this is something which can be adapted to widely differing cultural milieux. In some parts of the world, such as the West Indies or Ceylon, India, and China, this problem is of desperate urgency. Unchecked growth of population at present rates even for a few years may create a situation so difficult that these countries will start to go downhill. Haiti is a terrible object lesson of what can happen to a small country where independence has meant quarantine by the world, internal anarchy and anomie, unrestricted population expansion, soil erosion, and cultural erosion to the point where per capita incomes are now not much above $50 per annum.

Another large program which needs to be pushed beyond the present pioneer stage is that of the development of machinery and equipment which is appropriate to the early stages of technological advance. It is not easy to jump immediately from digging sticks to tractors. Western technology frequently cannot be imported as it stands into the emerging nations simply because the existing material and human structure of society is not ready to receive it. In the development of society, as in the development of the phenotype from the egg, there are certain stages which may have to be gone through, and there is some sense in which phylogeny recapitulates ontogeny. This is not to say that the poor countries must go through a stage of Satanic mills and cumbersome steam engines before they can emerge into the sunlight of the electronic age. It does mean, however, that for any given society there is a next step, and it is frequently quite difficult to perceive what this next step should be. It may be a long-handled hoe; it may be an atomic reactor. At this point we often have to reckon with national pride, which sometimes puts the symbols of development, such as steel mills and reactors, in front of the realities, which may be primary schools and a better breed of mule. India has experimented, apparently without too great success, with small solar furnaces, but it may be that the development of many of these countries waits on the development of a small but cheap source of small amounts of power. The problem is not completely neglected, but compared with what needs to be done the gap is a shocking one.

Another problem which cries out for attention is the study of the locus of political power in emergent nations and the problem of how to get power into the hands of those who will use it best. Development of any kind grinds to a halt when those who have the power do not have the will and those who have the will do not have the power. In the West the system of banking and finance provided an important answer to this question, for this enabled the enterprising and ambitious to attract resources away from the rentier, the aristocrat, and the defender of the status quo. In other countries bloody revolution and social disorder have tried to achieve the same end, sometimes with success, sometimes not. This is a problem which we must face and which we are not facing—which, indeed, we are not even studying adequately.

Let me conclude, therefore, by pleading for a massive intellectual effort, of at least the magnitude which we are devoting to space exploration, devoted to solving the intellectual and organizational problems which surround this great transition to the developed world society. An effort of this kind would involve the co-operation of all disciplines and all countries. On the physical and technological side, the problems of permanent high-level technology are still unsolved. Man's existing high-level technology cannot last for more than a few hundred years because it depends on the use of fossil fuels and ores which he is rapidly using up. A permanent high-level technology, however, is conceivable, based on the sea and the atmosphere as ultimate resources, and either on the sun or on nuclear fusion as the source of energy. The Haber process for the extraction of nitrogen from the air and the Dow process for extracting magnesium from the sea are signs of things to come, but we must not deceive ourselves: we are still a long way from the kinds of scientific knowledge and engineering applications which will enable us to operate a truly self-sustaining earth spaceship without using up our long accumulated geological capital. It is probable that the biological sciences will make an important or perhaps the crucial contribution to the solution of this problem, for life itself is the major antientropic process and is the one which operates with the greatest efficiency. The solution of the problem of the utilization of solar energy for high-level societies may well lie in the development of artificial low forms of life which utilize this energy more efficiently than existing forms.

Another section of the program should be devoted to the study of population and population control. This clearly calls for a giant effort on the part of biological, medical, and social scientist, for we still know very little about the human biology of fertility and sterility, and we know still less about the all-important motivational problems which are at the heart of population control. Furthermore, we do not know even to an order of magnitude what is the population which a stable high-level technology would support on earth. It might be as small as a hundred million or as large as a hundred billion. This is an area of ignorance which it should be possible to clear up in a very few years if a concentrated effort were made, and a great deal of subsequent human history is going to depend on the answer to this question. If stable high-level technology can support only a hundred million people, then the earth is in for a grotesque agony before its utopian state can be achieved. If earth can support ten billion at high levels, we have a little time to make this transition reasonably painlessly.

The third major area of research and development should be that in the dynamics of social systems. The problem of peace research and the control of organized violence falls in this section; likewise the problem of disarmament and the release of the $120 billion now wasted on the world war industry for use in the great transition. Also in this section lies the question of political power and organization and the political development of societies toward institutions which permit the orderly transfer of power from those who use it less well to those who use it better. Political development is a concept less clear than that of economic development, but it is equally important and the two clearly go hand in hand. In the economic development of a country which is politically immature, there can be disasters both for the country and for the world, as the history of Germany so dramatically shows.

Finally, I would like to see a fourth department of this great enterprise devoted to man's cultural, spiritual, and religious development. This is the most delicate and difficult of all the problems involved; it is entangled in man's deepest emotions, and the very notion of an intellectual effort devoted to this problem is repugnant to many sensitive persons. Nevertheless, there is no point in making man rich if he does not know what to do with his riches. The great transition represents an enormous increase in the power of man, but power in itself is neutral; it can be used either for good or for evil. There is in the human personality an enormous potential both for good and for evil, and the increased power which the new technology will bring man may release either the potential for good in him or the potential for evil. It can lead him toward divinity or drive him to destruction. Even though power itself, therefore, may be morally neutral, an increase in power is not, because it causes us to raise the question of the will, that is, of the ends toward which power is to be used. As long as man is impotent, it does not matter so much what his ultimate ends are as he cannot get them anyway. If these ends are evil, however, the increase of power is undesirable. It enables man to damn himself all the faster. Any intellectual effort devoted to the great transition, therefore, must raise the question of the nature of man himself and of how his nature may be changed and how the good will in him may be encouraged and the evil will discouraged. These are the great questions with which philosophy and religion have struggled for many thousands of years They do not become obsolete merely because we can put men into space.

It is an awesome thing to have been born in the twentieth century. This is perhaps the most critical century in the whole history of the planet. Never before has man's future and indeed the future of the whole planet rested in man's own hands. This is a terrible responsibility from which we may well shrink; it is a responsibility, however, from which we cannot escape. I believe that man has the capacity to rise to this challenge, and in that fact lies our hope.

Comment on Bouding

Bruno Fritsch

PROFESSOR BOULDING'S paper represents a statement full of "European thoughts." It raises many philosophical as well as economic and political questions of great importance. It is most provoking and stimulating.

I

The points which seem to me to be of great importance and with which I agree:

1. Professor Boulding is absolutely justified, it seems to me, to start from Adam Smith, since the historical analysis of the division of labor is particularly important for developing (emerging) countries.

2. To put R (Research), E (Education), and D (Development) together in the way Professor Boulding did seems to me a very promising approach.

3. There are many statements in the paper with which practically all economists and certainly some politicians will agree, e.g., if I may quote just one thought: "We persist in devoting a major part of our intellectual resources, by far, to research, education, and development

in physical and biological systems, with the result that the very existence of man is threatened by his incapacity at handling the social system."

II

I am somewhat doubtful with respect to the following points.

1. I wonder whether even this country will become a leisure society in a time as short as Professor Boulding seems to suggest. Considering the political constellation of the present time, it is not likely to happen very soon, as far as I can see.

2. Nor does the proposition of a sort of "cybernetic capitalism" seem to be the common denominator of this country and the U.S.S.R.

3. Professor Boulding states that power in itself is neutral. This statement, of course, implies a certain philosophical position. In this context it seems at least equally justifiable to state that power in itself is evil. I do not intend to solve this most difficult problem. However, I should like to point out that any proposition of this kind implies a set of valuations underlying all further conclusions with respect to the character of the further development of our technological capabilities.

III

Finally, there are problems in Professor Boulding's paper which raise some very important questions.

If we speak of R&D (or in Professor Boulding's formulation of R, E, and D) for emerging nations, we have to observe that we argue, so to speak, in terms of the first and/or second derivatives. Let me explain what I mean. We are more or less well informed about the structure of the relationship between capital formation and output. It is usually this level on which our recommendations are based, both with respect to our own economic policy and the policies recommended for emerging countries.

In connection with this relationship (capital formation and output), where problems of production theory are the subject of analysis, we may consider the effects of research on capital formation as not yet fully explored. Professor Tybout's remark in his paper seems to refer to this situation, when he states: "Yet our knowledge of technological change is, to say the least, no rival for our knowledge of capital formation." It is this relationship which may be thought of as the "first derivative" of the well-known and well-explored functional relationship between capital formation and output.

Although many questions within this "first derivative area" are not yet answered, we are now beginning to explore the determinants of research itself, that is to say, research on research and development. This even more difficult area may be referred to as the "area of second derivatives." We have to admit that our knowledge of this area is very poor and, it seems to me, that not a single question may be said to be answered satisfactorily. Yet the most fundamental methodological and philosophical problems that influence our analysis of the first two areas arise in this very field of "second derivatives."

To speak of R&D for the emerging countries implies bypassing some of our experience and knowledge of the first and, more recently, also of the second derivatives, i.e., of results obtained from studies on the interrelationship between research and technological change with its influence on capital formation. We are not yet in a position to make any practical statements for these countries.

This suggests considering our relation toward the emerging countries as a *mutual* learning process rather than a one-sided relation between capital-receiving and capital-providing countries. Thus we may discover—and actually we already have discovered—by the implementation of certain technolo-

gies in emerging countries, the relationship between sociological environments and technologies which are of importance
for us as well as for the emerging countries. On the other
hand, this mutual learning process implies on the side of the
developing countries at least some idea of the burdens of
capital formation and of economic development, burdens
which these countries have to recognize as intrinsically connected with the very nature of capital formation and economic growth.

It thus becomes evident that we are not at all in the position of a policy-maker trying to devise some feasible development policy. We are rather, together with the emerging
nations, subject to the problems arising within the pattern
of this mutual learning process; that is, the "strategy of economic development" is not a one-way route, it works both
ways inasmuch as we ourselves are involved in it.

There are many chances for us involved in this mutual
process of learning. For example:

1. We recognize the particularity of our time preference
function and hence the relativity of our decisions. The ques·
tion is whether we should first go to the moon and then
devote our energies to solving problems of water resources,
flood control, irrigation, urban development, transportation,
social security, reshaping of the traditional pattern of international division of labor, the most likely effects of the
economic development of emerging countries, and so on—
all these questions become evident as alternatives and are
subject to rational decision-making on the basis of this
mutual learning process.

2. We may become aware that we cannot do everything
at once and that we have to set up our list of priorities
*consistent with the list of priorities applying to the emerg-
ing countries.*

3. We may become more aware of the disguised in-
consistencies both within individual development plans and
within the interaction of these plans.

4. Future patterns of international labor division become
objects of a rational decision process based on the setting-
up of priorities in negotiation with the emerging countries.

These are chances for the future. But as long as these questions—I could refer to many more—are not yet recognized as problems common to both the developed and the emerging countries, we are liable to spend all our efforts and capital in vain. It is for these problems that the paper of Professor Boulding provides us with a most valuable conception.

Comment on Part VII Papers

Harold J. Barnett

I

LET US WRITE the familiar static, aggregate national production function thus: $O = f(R, L, C; A, B, \ldots Z)$, where O is output (for example, real GNP); R, L, and C (natural resources, labor, and capital, respectively) are inputs; and A, $B \ldots Z$ are present parameters applicable to the emergent nations. The economic development concern of both authors is increase in O per capita. The authors do not explicitly introduce time into the function, but sometimes variables and parameters are assumed to experience change in value due to the passage of time or other influences. What are the authors' conclusions?

Professor Tybout summarizes with a statement that the strategic influence in economic development is change in the technology parameter. And then he says, "A combination of three forces will work to determine the future pattern of technology in the emergent nations. They are capital formation, the growth of labor skills and technological change itself."

Professor Boulding also focuses on change in the technology parameter, he says. For him, however, unlike Professor Tybout, it is primarily determined by outlays on research, education, and development—R, E, & D. Research, Professor Boulding defines as intellectual inquiry which produces new knowledge; education is dissemination of this knowledge; and development is incorporation of the knowledge into economic structures. R, E, & D, he says, is the limiting factor in economic development. As would be expected, this calls for more investment in R, E, & D and for research on R&D to make such outlays efficient. Less obviously, Professor Boulding believes that the particular research area which should be thus emphasized is that of social systems. This involves research on peace; on cultural, spiritual, and religious values, and the nature of man; and on such economic development influences as the population dilemma, technology appropriate for backward areas, and political power and processes.

My first comment is that each paper is implicitly an important critical discussion of the other. Both Professors Boulding and Tybout are concerned with identifying the strategic influences in economic development of the emergent nations. If the two papers are taken as general discussion, then I think the authors could easily resolve the differences I have demonstrated. Each could agree that the other's contribution usefully supplemented and extended his own. They might say that they had addressed different aspects of the question, or had approached it on different levels, or had different time horizons. If, however, they view their respective contributions as focussed and rigorous economic constructions on modern lines, or if they view them as the policy prescriptions of political economists, in the older tradition of our discipline, then there are important differences between them, which may or may not be reconcilable. I think that their attempt at reconciliation, whether or not it were successful, would be very useful in improving the definitions of some of their terms, in explicitly introducing time and the time horizons, and in specifying interdependencies and relationships.

II

I should like briefly to discuss priorities. If economists do not emphasize that funds for economic development of emergent nations are so woefully short as to require the most stringent economic programming, I don't know who will. If I infer correctly the authors' priorities, I disagree with them.

The peoples and leaders of the emergent nations are understandably anxious and clamorous for economic development. And we in the high income nations, for world political reasons no less than humanitarian ones, also feel anxiety and urgency. But it seems to me quite possible that the anxiety is inimical to perspective and good judgment, and may be inducing shortrun, visible expedients in place of longer lead-time R, E, and D investments which should have priority.

With a longer view, I think investment in literacy of the young should have rather near an absolute priority on the entire volume of gift funds available from the U.S. and other advanced nations. To transform the individual labor factor from an ignorant and superstitious body that can learn only from personal experience or from vocal instruction into one that can read and figure is to seed enormous, self-generating capital growth, given only the availability also of technical and other primers. In "one swoop," we raise the population's basic ability to the levels of the advanced nations a few generations back. But the "one swoop" would require several decades and, I would guess, virtually all the international gift funds available, as well as much of the indigenous savings now earmarked for investment in goods. Of course, it is proper and to be expected that profit-seeking foreign investment will not invest in literacy but rather in refineries and mills to which they can hold title and earn returns in the short and intermediate term. International gift funds, it seems to me, should be invested in children's literacy to maximize economic, political, and other social advance in a longer period. The reasons for the low state of technical economic performance in emergent nations are to be found in the present quality of people and in their social relations and institutions, and in the inadequate allocation of investment funds to improving these.[1]

Continuing on priorities, I think the second most important use of gift funds would be in the provision by the advanced nations of birth control literature and devices without cost. I do not believe the Malthusian proposition of increasing natural resource scarcity due to population pressure. But I

---

[1] I discuss this at slightly greater length in "Research and Development, Economic Growth, and National Security," in *Annals of the American Academy of Political and Social Science*, CCCXXVII (January, 1960), 36 ff.

do believe that the flow of children from a high birth rate presses upon scarce capital in the underdeveloped countries. And a society which can spare itself the degradation of having children in excess of the number which can be well treated is a society of improved ethos and other quality. I would give high priority to assisting the people in these countries to limit family size, if they want this help.[2]

III

I have two unconnected thoughts, one stimulated by the Tybout paper, the other by the Boulding one, which I would like to leave with you in closing.

First, the U.S. is in an embarrassing position. Apparently we will continue to have, even in our Keynesian-revised society, unemployed labor and other resources capable of several tens of billion dollars of output per year; we deeply desire to provide greater economic assistance to the emergent nations; and we do not know how to translate our unutilized capacity into such foreign aid. In many cases the obstacle of displacing exports would not seem to be involved. I hope that in our lifetime someone may contribute to this macro-world problem as usefully as Keynes did for macro-national problems.

Second, I am concerned (and, I hope, confused) by what I seem to observe on political aspects of economic development in the emergent nations. Effort at rapid economic development in the emergent nations places strains upon their political structures and processes. Democratic governments in these countries experience constant hazard of being overthrown and replaced by strongarm groups. These societies, which most need political acumen and democratic tradition in order to achieve stability, are primitives in political processes.

---

[2] See H. J. Barnett, "Population and World Politics," *World Politics*, XII (July, 1960), 640 ff., or Barnett and Morse, *Scarcity and Growth* (Baltimore, Md., 1963), 250 ff.

Totalitarian governments are far less vulnerable, since they exercise strenuous police restrictions and chop the heads off dissidents. And even when overthrown, the change seems to be of one totalitarian control group for another. I don't know the answer to this question either.

INDEXES

INDEX TO AUTHORS CITED

Abramovitz, Moses, 409
Allport, F. H., 217 n
Ames, Edward, 132–35
Ammann, O. H., 113–16, 117, 120, 124
Anthony, R. N., 153 n
Archimedes, 35
Armand, Louis, 355 n
Arrow, Kenneth J., 11 n, 263 n, 265 n, 300, 414 n, 417 n
Ashby, W. R., 209, 217 n

Bacon, Francis, 23, 54
Bahrdt, Hans P., 34–50, 51–54, 59–60, 174, 217 n
Baker, A. H., 121, 124
Balke, Siegfried, 371, 383
Banks, S. R., 119, 124
Barnett, Harold J., 443–47
Bavelas, A., 191, 217 n
Beer, John J., 27 n, 28–29
Blank, D. M., 97 n
Boulding, Kenneth E., 422–37, 438–47
Brown, D. J., 154 n
Brozen, Yale, 74–75, 78 n, 83–100, 128–30, 134–35
Busch, A., 39 n
Bush, C. P., 153 n
Bush, Vannevar, 386
Butterfield, H., 23, 24 n

Carson, Rachael, 267
Cartwright, D., 217 n

Chamberlin, Edward H., 69 n, 70
Chenery, H. B., 411 n, 416 n
Cherington, Paul W., 327–43, 344–47
Colbert, 25, 56
Coleman, J. S., 150, 217 n
Creamer, Daniel, 412 n
Cross, Hardy, 125

Dana, Allston, 113, 120, 125
Deutsch, M., 216, 217 n
Dupré, J. Stefan, 344–49

Eaton, J. W., 153 n, 155 n
Echaus, R. S., 413
Eisenhower, Dwight D., 13
Eisner, H., 217 n
Enke, S., 275 n, 278 n

Fellner, William, 410
Festinger, L., 191, 217 n
Fischer, A. W., 109, 125
Frankland, J. M., 122, 125
Fritsch, Bruno, 258–67, 438–42

Galenson, Walter, 415
Ghandi, Mahatma, 418

Gillispie, Charles C., 24, 26–27
Glover, J. D., 78 n
Granger, A. T., 110, 125
Green, Harold P., 356 n
Griliches, Zvi, 148–50, 302 n, 431
Gustafson, W. Eric, 81–82

Haire, M., 217 n
Hall, Rupert, 23 n, 24
Hannenberg, Richard C., 219–44,
    247–48
Hardesty, S., 109, 125
Hare, P. A., 217 n
Harsanyi, J. C., 266
Heidenreich, C., 383 n
Higgins, Benjamin, 415 n
Hitch, C. J., 275 n
Hofstätter, P. R., 217 n
Hooke, Robert, 25
Humboldt, Wilhelm von, 27

Johnston, S., 122, 125
Juda, A., 168 n
Junck, R., 217 n

Kant, 36, 268
Kaplan, A. D. H., 78 n
Karman, Theodore von, 397–98
Karol, J., 122, 125
Karsteht, U., 35 n
Kelley, H. H., 191, 217 n
Kepler, 36
Kindleberger, C. P., 415 n, 418 n
Klein, Burton H., 309–26, 344–47
Knight, Frank H., 72
Kohnstamm, Max, 354 n
Krauch, H., 174, 217 n, 258–67
Kuznets, S. K., 411 n, 415 n

Langenhagen, D., 139, 146 n
Leibenstein, Harvey, 415

Leibniz, 25, 36
Leontief, W. W., 417
Liebig, Justus von, 28, 51
Lilienthal, David, 78 n
Lindsay, G., 218 n

McCullough, C. B., 109, 125
McIntyre, Lt. Col. George W.,
    393 n, 396 n
McKinney, Robert, 363 n
McNamara, Robert S., 387
Mahalanobis, C. P. C., 418 n
Mansfield, Edwin, 128, 136–47,
    148–50
March, J. G., 218 n
Markham, Jesse W., 5 n, 67–80,
    81–82, 267 n
Marschak, J., 185, 218 n
Marx, Karl, 47
Matussek, Paul, 153–73, 245–46
Melon, J., 103–4, 108, 126
Mendelsohn, Everett, 51–58
Merrill, Robert S., 7 n, 101–27,
    130–31, 132–34
Merz, John T., 26 n
Meyer, Ernest von, 51
Mills, C. Wright, 13
Minasian, Jora R., 77, 150 n, 289
Moisseiff, L. S., 104–7, 110, 126
Moore, Ben T., 354
Morrison, James L., 356 n
Mullenbach, Philip, 353–67,
    381–83
Murray, Thomas E., 359 n

Nash, Frank, 388
Nelles, M., 274 n
Nelson, Richard R., 4 n, 288–306
Newton, Isaac, 29, 53
Nutter, Warren, 89 n, 90, 128

Ott, E., 156 n

Palfrey, John G., 356 n
Pauly-Wissowa, 35 n

Pepinsky, Harold B., 245–48
Pestrecov, 130 n
Pigou, A. C., 258 n
Popper, K. R., 272
Portas, John, 119, 126
Plessner, H., 45
Price, Derek J. deSolla, 403
Pugsley, A. G., 122, 126

Quarles, Donald, 388, 401

Raven, B. H., 216, 218 n
Rittel, Horst, 174–218, 246–47
Rosenstein-Rodan, P. N., 410
Rothschuh, K. E., 218 n
Rowe, Chauncey O., 394 n, 396 n
Rubenstein, Albert H., 219–44,
    247–48
Ruttan, V., 302 n
Ryan, B., 150 n

Samuelson, Paul A., 263 n
Sauer, Hans K., 368–80, 383–85
Scherer, Frederic M., 128–31
Schmookler, Jacob, 6 n, 19–33, 54–
    58, 59–63, 73, 79 n, 84, 88 n,
    147 n
Schumpeter, Joseph A., 4, 5, 9, 77,
    83, 87–90, 129, 140–42
Shepard, H. A., 218 n
Sherman, Richard U., Jr., 292 n,
    386–400
Siegel, Irving H., 268–87
Simon, Herbert A., 130, 218 n
Snow, C. P., 276
Solo, R., 95 n
Solomon, H., 201, 218 n
Spengler, Joseph J., 7 n
Smith, Adam, 84 n, 425–28

Smith, Foster Lee, 401–6
Smyth, Henry D., 364 n
Stassen, Harold, 388
Steinman, D. B., 108, 109, 110,
    112, 121, 126–27
Stigler, George J., 71 n, 97 n, 99 n
Striner, H., 292 n
Szilard, L., 186

Terleckyj, N., 289
Thomson, Thomas, 51 n
Thrall, R. M., 218 n
Tocqueville, Alexis de, 30–31
Tybout, Richard A., 3–15, 258–67,
    409–21, 440, 443–48

Usher, Abbot P., 7 n

Vesalius, 52
Villard, H., 83, 90
Von Kann, General Clifton, 309–10

Waddell, J. A. L., 112, 127
Wakefield, Harold M., 389 n, 390 n,
    391 n, 392 n, 395 n, 397 n, 398,
    400
Weinberg, A. M., 276 n
Weischedel, W., 38 n
Wessman, H. E., 122, 125, 127
Wiener, Norbert, 416
Windelband, W., 35 n
Woodruff, G. B., 122, 127
Worley, James S., 9 n, 128
Wren, Christopher, 25

Young, Allyn, 84 n

SUBJECT INDEX

Academic disciplines, separation of, 37, 39

Allocation: criteria for, social, 293–95; mechanisms for, 296–300; of research resources, 275, 288–92

Associations, industrial, for dissemination of knowledge, 256

Associative process in problem-solving, 209–10

Authoritarianism in research and development, 43–44, 169–70, 183

Automation, 416–17, 420

Balance of payments, 255, 399

Berlin, University of, 38–39

Birth control, 434, 445

Bronx-Whitestone Bridge, 117

Brooklyn Bridge, 104–6

Business concerns, private: as defense contractors, 327–43; diffusion of innovation by, 144–45; expenditures on research and development, 84–100, 137–39; influence of, 12; innovation and growth of, 142–43; innovation, timing, 143–44

By-product science, 255–56, 291–92

Capital, secondhand, in emergent nations, 421

Capital accumulation and economic development, 428, 441

Capital efficiency and economic development, 411–14

Capital intensive industries, 411–12

Capital/output ratios, 411–12

Capital-saving technologies, 418

Chemical industry, 97, 129

Civilian sector, problems of science in, 252–56

Clinics for technology, 257

Coal, bituminous, industry, 141–42

Collective goods, 262

Communication in group work, 183–86, 196–97, 199–200, 210–15

Compulsive personality, 158–62

Contractor system: and contract negotiation, 339–43; and countervailing power, 329–31; development phase, 332–39; for military procurement, 327–29

Co-operative in relation to hierarchy and team, 185; criteria for, 187–88

Cost-plus-fixed-fee contracting, 252, 340

Cost-reimbursement contracts, 344–49

Costs, private and social, 258–67

Cottage industry, 418–20

Countervailing power in military contracting, 329–31, 335–36, 339–41, 342–43

Cournot model, 69–70

Creativity of scientists, 153–73

Criteria, social, for allocation of research resources, 293–95

Deflection theory, 102–4, 130, 132; economic significance of, 107, 110, 111; extensions of, 110–11; and stiffening-truss proportions, 112–13, 123; use of, 104–10, 119–20

Demand, economic, 99; and development of basic science, 19; and research and development, 134; uncertainties of, 318–19

Depressive personality, 162–64

Diffusion: of innovations, 144–45; of knowledge, 103–23, 132–33

Dissemination: industrial associations for, 256; of information, in Euratom, 373–75; as a part of education, 429–30; of technical knowledge, 252–53

Division of labor: in group work, 198–200; historic, in research and development, 34–50; international, 441; and search process, 194–97; and specialization in research and development, 175, 178, 190–92; theory of, 186 ff.

Drug industry, 129

Economic development: and literacy, 445; quantitative aspects of, 424–30; R, E, and D for, 431–32; as a revolutionary change, 422–24; and technological change, 409–21; technologies for, 434–43

Education for technology, 252, 257; for economic development, 420–21, 445; formal *vs.* informal, 429–30; as a part of economic development, 429 ff.

Elastic theory, 103, 105; use of, 108–9, 119

Electrical equipment industry, 94, 97

Electrical utilities and Euratom, 359

Emergent nations, 409–47

Empiricism, 52–54

Engineering design as a source of technological change, 101–24, 133

England, science in eighteenth and nineteenth centuries in, 29–31, 44–54

Entropy measure of potential results, 205

Euratom, 353–85; accession of other countries, 379–80; financial quotas in, 385; functions of, 372–79 (dissemination of information, 373–75; external relations, 378–79; health protection, 375; investments, 375–76; security control, 376–77; supplies,

376); organization of, 370–72; systems and functions of, 368–80; U.S.–Euratom collaboration, 353–67 (first program, 357–58; future of, 364–67; objectives of, 354–57; obstacles to, 358–61)

European Atomic Energy Society, 368

European Coal and Steel Community, 375

European Common Market, 254, 353–56

European Communities for Economy and Atomic Energy, 370

European Nuclear Energy Agency, 368

Expert consensus, unreliability of, 313–17

Factor proportions and technological change, 409–11, 412–14

Firms, size of, 78–80; innovation and growth of, 140–42, 142–43; *see also* Business concerns

Flexibility in military research, 324–25

Florianopolis Bridge, 109, 119

France, science in eighteenth and nineteenth centuries in, 26–27, 56

General equilibrium model, 261

George Washington Bridge, 113–14, 117, 120

Germany: lessons from the history of, 436–37; science in eighteenth and nineteenth centuries in, 27–29, 38–40; science in twentieth century in, 43–50

Grants for research, 303

Greek science, 22–23

Group dynamics in research organizations, 189, 190–92

Group size, optimum, 204–8

Guild tradition, 48

Harvard group, 344–47

Hierarchy, dual, 177; in research and development organizations, 174–218
Hysteric personality, 164–67

Idea-flow: and idea acceptance, 228–33; and interaction of individuals, 243–44; model for, 219–23; and patterns of consultation, 236–44; questionnaire survey of, 223–29, 233–39; within organizations, 219–44
Incentive contracts, 340
Incentives: defense contractors', 347; general, 256; market, 298–300; military buyers and sellers, 325–26
Income, per capita, and economic development, 424–25
Industrial laboratories, project selection in, 219–44
Industrial research and development, 67–150; as affected by federal science, 251 ff.
Industrial structure (concentration): and innovation, 140–42; and research and development, 67–69, 78–80, 87–89
Innovation: diffusion of, 144–45; and growth of firms, 142–43; and science, 251–57; timing of, 143–44
Innovators, size of, 140–42
Instrument industry, 92, 130
Intellectual resources, misapplication of, 432
International collaboration: military, 386–406; in research and development, 353–406
International rivalry in research and development, 254–55, 272–73
International trade, patterns of, as affected by technological change, 417

Know-how, 421, 430
Knowledge: as a commodity, 263–64, 297; dissemination of, 252–56; as a public good, 296–300

Labor: and economic development, 414–17, 419–20; productivity in economic development, 425–27

Laplacian imputation of values, 281
Learning process: in defense contracting, 331–39; in economic development, 420–21, 428–30, 440
Leisure society, 423–24
Lisbon Conference, 401
Literacy and economic development, 445

Malthusian subsistence, 409, 445
Manhattan Bridge, 104–6
Manpower: skilled, 414–17; technological, 257, 285–86, 289
Market incentives, 298–300
Medieval handicraft tradition, 40, 42
Migration, rural to urban, in less-developed areas, 419
Military assistance, U.S., 387, 401, 405
Military development, 332–39; pre-development, 333–36; source selection for, 336–37
Military research: allocations for, 294–95; by-products in civilian sector, 255–56, 291–92; contrasted with civilian research, 253, 256; as focus of federal support, 278–81; weapons systems approach, 346–47
Military research and development, 308–49; and basic science, 320–22; changes in product during, 311–12; procurement cost estimates, accuracy of, 317–18; suggestions for policy improvement, 322–26, 348–49; see also: Contractor system
Military supplies, 327–28
"Mixed economy," 268
Motivation as an area for social research, 436
Mutual Security Program, 399
Mutual Weapons Development Program, 386–400, 401–6; achievements of, 398–99; administration and cost of, 396–97; Canadian participation, lack of, 401, 404; composition of, 390 ff.; data exchange agreements, 395; objectives of, 389–90; origin and pur-

poses of, 387–90; projects in, 390–91; research and development in, 391–94; suggestions for further research on, 402–4; technical centers, 394–95

National goals in science and innovation, 251–57

National Science Foundation, *v*, 21, 22, 57, 92 n

New products and research and development, 94

NATO, 386, 388–89; Advisory Group for Aeronautical Research and Development, 397; Armaments Committee, 393; participants in Mutual Weapons Development Program, 391; research and development in, 389, 402

Nuclear Common Market, 377–78

Nuclear power and European energy needs, 363–64

Nuclear power costs and Euratom, 360–61

Ohio State Conference on Economics of Research and Development, 3

Oligopolistic industries, 129

Oligopoly: and research and development, 75–78, 81–82; theory of, 67–72

Organization, internal, of research and development, 153–248

Parallel research and development as a strategy, 322

Patent controversy, 79–80

Patents, 129, 263–64, 303; in relation to Euratom, 365

Personality of scientists, 153–73; compulsive, 158–62; depressive, 162–64; hysteric, 164–67; schizoid, 168–72

Petroleum-refining industry, 141

Philadelphia-Camden Bridge, 106, 113

Philosophy, 39

Political power, locus of, in emergent nations, 435, 446–47

Population control, 434, 445

"Post-civilization," 422–24, 433

Precivilization, 422–24, 433

Prestige and hierarchy, 177

Private costs, 258–67

Problem-solving in groups, 200–208; and associative processes, 209–10

Productivity in military and civilian sectors contrasted, 291

Project management in military contracting, 341–43

Project selection in industrial laboratories, 219–44; and planning horizons, 227–29, 232–33, 236

Psychological problems of teamwork, 153 ff.

Public policy: and allocation of research and development resources, 288–306; and industrial concentration, 78–80, 138; and invention, 267; and market allocations, 296–300; and military, 322–26; and national goals in science, 251–57, 268–87; suggestions for improvement of, 255–57, 284–87, 300–306

R, E, and D (research, education, and development), 431–32, 438–39, 443–45

Radiation Laboratory, 313

RAND Corporation, 311

RAND group, 344–47

Research and development: authoritarianism in, 43–44, 169–70; differences among industries, 83–100; and the emergent nations, 409–37; expenditures on, 5, 137–39; independent organizations, 89–90; international collaboration in, 353–406; and inventive output, 139–40; and military affairs, 309–49; in Mutual Weapons Development Program, 391–94, 397; and new products, 94; and oligopoly, 75–78, 81–82; organization of, internal, 153–248; and patents, 79; public policy for, 251–306; and size of firm, 78; sources of funds, 67, 84–86, 137; and uncertainty, 72–74

Rigid theory, 103, 113
Rigidity in suspension bridges, 116–18, 123
Rockefeller Foundation, 386
Rubber industry, 95

Scale of production, 412–14
Schizoid personality, 168–72
Science, basic: in America, history of, 30–32; in ancient Greece, 22–23; in antiquity, 34–36; and catastrophe, 19–33; division of labor in, historic, 34–50; eighteenth century, 24; in England, eighteenth and nineteenth centuries, 29–31; external and financial support of, 7, 20, 57, 60–62; in France, eighteenth and nineteenth centuries, 26–27; in Germany, eighteenth and nineteenth centuries, 27–29, 38–40; history of, 19–63; humanistic animus for, 23–24; international, 13, 59; in Middle Ages, 36–37; and military progress, 320–22; as a social institution, 51; and utilitarianism, 19–33
Science base, 84–87, 92; and economic demand, 19; in relation to research and development, 97, 133–34
Scientists: liberal, 57; motivation of, 7, 20; and national goals, 252–53, 256; personality and creativity of, 153–73; seventeenth and eighteenth centuries, 24
Search process in research and development, 192–200
Shell Development, 7
"Side-looking radar," 313–14
Social institutions, imported by emergent nations, 415
Social costs, 258–67
Social systems as areas for research, 432–37
Specialization and economic development, 426–30; in scientific organizations, 178
Spillover of federal science to the civilian sector, 255–56, 291–92
Spiritual nature of man, as a research topic, 437
"Springer," 47

Steel industry, 141–42
SACLANT Antisubmarine Warfare Research Center, 395
SHAPE Air Defense Technical Center, 394
Suspension-bridge stiffening trusses, 101–24

Tax credits: for research, 303; and research organizations, 89
Teamwork in research and development organizations, 174–218
Technological change: and factor proportions, 409–11; planning of, 420–21; in the Western World, 409
Technology, automated, in less-developed areas, 415–17; economics of, for less-developed areas, 409–21; and international trade, 417; permanent high-level, 435–36
Telephone industry, 88
Textile industry, 96
Training Center for Experimental Aerodynamics, 394
Truss design, 103–23; economic significance of, 107, 110, 111, 113–16, 118, 123
Trusses, flexible, 113–16; adequacy of, 118, 120; economic significance of, 113–16

Uncertainties: of demand, military, 318–20; of research costs, 259; of research results, 72–74; of research results and costs, 271–72
United States, federal government of: government-business partnership, 347; and organization for research support, 282–84, 290–91, 304–6; and research financing, 67, 84–86, 137, 251–52; and research policies, 252–57, 268–87

Welfare economics, 258, 263